Ministry of Agriculture Fisheries and Food

Reference Book *161*
Replacing Bulletin 161

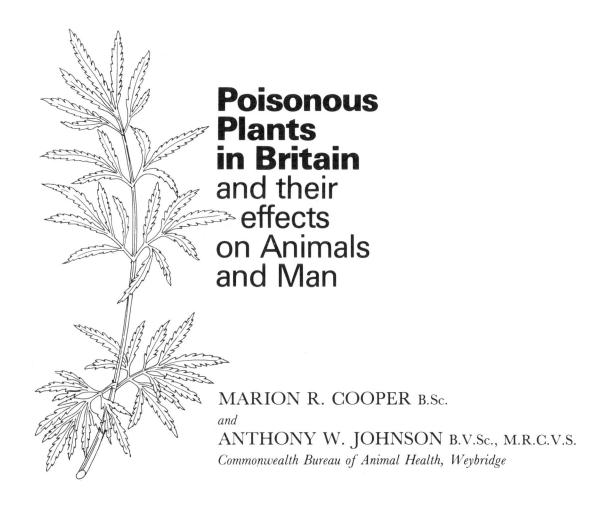

Poisonous Plants in Britain
and their effects on Animals and Man

MARION R. COOPER B.Sc.
and
ANTHONY W. JOHNSON B.V.Sc., M.R.C.V.S.
Commonwealth Bureau of Animal Health, Weybridge

London: Her Majesty's Stationery Office

ISBN 0 11 242529 1

FOREWORD

During the preparation of this book a comprehensive search of the published literature was carried out by the authors, a botanist and a veterinarian, who are on the staff of the Commonwealth Bureau of Animal Health which is responsible for documenting world veterinary literature. They consulted over 5000 relevant publications and compiled their findings to produce a book that incorporates the results of the latest studies as well as long established work. Some plants have declined in importance as a cause of poisoning, whilst recent work, as well as expanding knowledge of the subject, has contradicted or disproved some statements which have been repeated from earlier times. In addition to the main poisonous plants native to Britain, this book includes fungi, crop plants and imported feed materials. It should prove of value to the medical and veterinary professions, students, farmers and the public in general in avoiding and dealing with plant poisoning, and assist in their appreciation and understanding of the countryside.

Roy Mack FRCVS
Director
Commonwealth Bureau of Animal Health, Weybridge

CONTENTS

	Page
INTRODUCTION	1
Definition	1
History	2
Prevalence	3
Poisoning: the plant aspects	4
Poisoning: the animal aspects	6
Diagnosis	8
Treatment	9
POISONOUS PRINCIPLES	11
Alkaloids	11
Glycosides	13
Nitrates/nitrites	16
Oxalates	17
Photosensitive agents	18
Proteins, peptides and amino acids	20
Tannins	20
FUNGI	22
Larger fungi	22
Ergot	46
Mycotoxins	49
PTERIDOPHYTES	52
Horsetails	52
Ferns	53
CONIFERAE	62
PLANT FAMILIES (in alphabetical order)	63
PLANTS AFFECTING MILK	239
GLOSSARY	242
BIBLIOGRAPHY (BOOKS)	249
REFERENCES (in alphabetical order of families)	251
INDEX	297

ILLUSTRATIONS

Between pages 94 and 95
1. Ergot *Claviceps purpurea)* on barley
2. Fly Agaric *(Amanita muscaria)*
3. *Cortinarius speciosissimus*
4. *Inocybe geophylla* var *lilacina.* A common lilac variant of the whitish or pale greyish-fawn fungus
5. Death Cap *(Amanita phalloides)*
6. Grey Mottle Gill *(Panaeolus sphinctrinus)* on dung
7. Bracken *(Pteridium aquilinum)*
8. Ramsons *(Allium ursinum)*

Between pages 106 and 107
9. Cuckoo Pint *(Arum maculatum).* The orange-red berries which ripen in autumn are poisonous
10. Comfrey *(Symphytum officinale)*
11. Box *(Buxus sempervirens)*
12. Corn Cockle *(Agrostemma githago).* The small black seeds are poisonous
13. Spindle *(Euonymus europaeus)*
14. Ragwort *(Senecio jacobaea)*
15. Kale *(Brassica oleracea)*

Between pages 170 and 171
16. White Bryony *(Bryonia dioica)* (a) flowers (b) fruit
17. Black Bryony *(Tamus communis)* (a) flowers (b) fruit. The berries are red when ripe
18. Rhododendron *(Rhododendron ponticum)*
19. Sun Spurge *(Euphorbia helioscopia)*
20. Dog's Mercury *(Mercurialis perennis)*
21. Oak *(Quercus robur)*

Between pages 182 and 183

22. St. John's Wort *(Hypericum perforatum)*
23. Stinking Iris *(Iris foetidissima)*
24. Laburnum *(Laburnum anagyroides)* unripe fruits: the flowers are shown on the cover
25. Birdsfoot Trefoil *(Lotus corniculatus)*
26. Meadow Saffron *(Colchicum autumnale)*
27. Bog Asphodel *(Narthecium ossifragum)*
28. Ash *(Fraxinus excelsior)*
29. Greater Celandine *(Chelidonium majus)*

Between pages 198 and 199

30. Sheep's Sorrel *(Rumex acetosella)*
31. Monkshood *(Aconitum napellus)*
32. Wood Anemone *(Anemone nemorosa)*
33. Traveller's Joy *(Clematis vitalba)* (a) flowers (b) fruit
34. Cherry Laurel *(Prunus laurocerasus)*. The ripe berries are black
35. Deadly Nightshade *(Atropa bella-donna)*
36. Foxglove *(Digitalis purpurea)*

Between pages 214 and 215

37. Thorn Apple *(Datura stramonium)*
38. Henbane *(Hyoscyamus niger)*
39. Woody Nightshade *(Solanum dulcamara)* (a) flowers (b) fruit. Often confused with Deadly Nightshade
40. Black Nightshade *(Solanum nigrum)* (a) flowers (b) fruit. The ripe berries are black
41. Spurge Laurel *(Daphne laureola)*
42. Hemlock *(Conium maculatum)*. The similarity in appearance of many umbelliferous plants can lead to mistaken identification

Fig. 1 Hemlock *(Conium maculatum)* page 231
Fig. 2 Hemlock Water Dropwort *(Oenanthe crocata)* page 233
Fig. 3 Cowbane *(Cicuta virosa)* page 235

PREFACE

This book is the latest in a series that can be traced back to 1917 when H.C. Long published *Plants Poisonous to Live Stock,* which was followed, in 1927 by another book, *Poisonous Plants on the Farm,* by the same author. The latter was reprinted in 1934 as Ministry of Agriculture and Fisheries Bulletin No. 75, and was the forerunner of the two editions of *British Poisonous Plants,* Bulletin 161, published in 1954 and 1968 by the late A.A. Forsyth. A reprinted version of the 1968 edition appeared, with a few amendments, in 1979. These books by Long and Forsyth are similar in style and content and provided valuable information on the poisonous plants of Britain for over 65 years. The task of rewriting a book that has become, albeit in a limited field, a standard reference work, is somewhat daunting; the more so while it is in progress than before starting. It was intended originally that the present book would be a revision of Forsyth's work, but the incorporation of recent work made it necessary to make such extensive changes that the result is a completely new book, with a slightly different emphasis. The change of the title of the book from *British Poisonous Plants* to *Poisonous Plants in Britain and their Effects on Animals and Man* is indicative of the changes in content. Not only does it cover native British plants that have caused poisoning in this country, but also those that occur here, and are therefore potentially toxic, although reports of their having caused poisoning have been found only in foreign literature. Potentially toxic, imported feed components (especially seeds) are also included, although the plants of origin may never be grown in Britain. There is more emphasis on human poisoning than in former Bulletins and the section on fungi has been expanded considerably.

Despite recent advances, there is still surprisingly little known about many aspects of plant poisoning, and we can echo what W.J.T. Morton, Professor of Chemistry at the London Veterinary College, wrote in 1840

'We are, however, in want of more correct information than at present we possess ....'

The relative importance of crop plants and wild or garden plants in the context of poisoning has changed over the years, both as a result of changes in agricultural practice, particularly in the use of herbicides, which have almost eradicated some wild plants, and because there is now more publicity and consequently greater public awareness of the potential dangers of plants. It may be, however, that if the current trend away from such extensive use of agricultural chemicals, and the return to small-scale units run on 'organic' lines persists, some wild plants, including poisonous ones, may become more common, with an accompanying increase in the risk of poisoning. In general, only the more common garden plants are mentioned; house plants have not been covered. Plants having adverse effects by skin contact are mentioned incidentally, and only if they are included in the text because they are poisonous by ingestion; those listed as affecting milk are those recorded in the main text and in the editions by Forsyth.

The basic format of the book follows that of the previous Bulletins, and the practice of describing cases of poisoning has been retained, but to facilitate quick reference, the subject matter has been treated under several headings, used uniformly throughout. Technical terms have been kept to a minimum, consistent with accuracy, and a glossary is appended. The plants are arranged, for convenience, in alphabetical order of plant families and not in the more conventional taxonomic order. The references at the back of the book are grouped in the same way. The botanical names of the plants have been taken from the *Flora of the British Isles*, by Clapham, Tutin and Warburg and from *A Dictionary of Flowering Plants and Ferns* by J.C. Willis; where these two authorities differ, the name used by the Kew Gardens Herbarium has been chosen. Names of fungi and common names of plants come from a variety of sources. The descriptions given for most of the plants are included only as a guide; specialist works should be consulted for precise identification.

As it has not been possible to illustrate all of the plants, the selection includes the most important poisonous plants, some of the less well known ones, and some whose identity may be mistaken.

The subject matter has been compiled from a very wide range of veterinary, medical, botanical and biochemical publications and from computer searches of four appropriate data bases (AGRICOLA, BIOSIS, CAB and MEDLINE). Although based mainly on the most recent publications available, older sources have also been consulted to provide background material and also in the few cases where no recent information has been found. The reference material cited represents about one fifth of that read in the course of the revision, and has been chosen to give the most appropriate matter available in English. References in foreign languages have been included only where these are the best available, or where little has been written in English; many of these foreign papers have English summaries. The paucity of recent information on some of the plants is particularly applicable to their poisonous principles. Although every effort has been made to clarify the nature of these, there are still many plants in which the toxins have not been identified or whose toxicity is still attributed to substances isolated and named last century, before modern analytical techniques had been developed, and on which no further work appears to have been carried out. As would be expected, toxins that occur in commercially important crop plants and in the few plants now well recognised to cause serious problems in farm animals have received most attention.

While many plants in Britain are known to be poisonous, few are dangerously so, and cases of severe poisoning in animals or man are relatively rare. The full effects of the toxic constituents of plants are, however, difficult to assess. It may well be that plant toxins are responsible for far more deleterious effects than have yet been recognised. Indefinite characteristics, such as reduced weight gain, poor performance and mild digestive disturbances of animals could be responsible for economic losses that exceed those of the cases of poisoning severe enough to attract attention and be diagnosed.

There is still much to learn, and we share the sentiments of H.C. Long, who wrote in 1916, at the end of his preface to *Plants Poisonous to Live Stock*

'For any shortcomings I crave the indulgence of my readers, only requesting that they be friendly enough to spare a moment to call my attention thereto.'

Commonwealth Bureau of Animal Health, Marion R. Cooper
Central Veterinary Laboratory, Anthony W. Johnson
Weybridge,
Surrey.

Acknowledgements

We are pleased to acknowledge the help of many people who have made so freely available to us their knowledge, facilities and time.

We wish to thank the following librarians: G.D.R. Bridson of the Linnean Society, R. Catton of the Royal Veterinary College, S.M. Fitzgerald of the Royal Botanic Gardens, Kew, and in particular D.E. Gray of the Central Veterinary Laboratory whose excellent library and staff have provided so much of the material.

We are indebted to G.N. Volans BSc, MD, MRCP of the Guy's Hospital Poisons Unit, for information on the medical aspects, and especially to D. Lamb BSc of that Unit for her help and for making constructive comments on the text.

We should like to express our thanks to D. Reid BSc, PhD, D.N. Pegler BSc, MSc, PhD, FLS, and V.M. Spooner BSc, of the Royal Botanic Gardens, Kew, for helpful discussions and checking the section on the larger fungi; to R. Watling BSc, PhD, FRSE, DSc, of the Royal Botanic Garden, Edinburgh, for advice on hallucinogenic fungi; to P.M. Stockdale PhD, of the Commonwealth Mycological Institute, for suggesting how the section on fungi could be approached; to L. Ponsonby and the herbarium staff of the Royal Botanic Gardens, Kew, for checking some botanical names; to R.C.R. Angel BSc, also of Kew, for making available many books and references; to G.W. Cussans BSc and E.D. Williams BSc of the Weed Research Organisation for information on the current status of some weeds in Britain and to E.E. Crane MSc, PhD of the Bee Research Association for comments on toxic honey.

We have received considerable help from several colleagues at the Central Veterinary Laboratory, Weybridge. We wish to thank especially P.H. Anderson MSc, PhD, BVetMed for valuable advice on mycotoxins, L.N. Ivins BSc for his comments on bracken, G. Pepin BSc for his many helpful suggestions, particularly on ergot, and D.G. Pritchard BVetMed, BSc, MPH for information on sweet vernal grass.

All of our colleagues in the Commonwealth Bureau of Animal Health have given advice and encouragement, and in particular R. Mack FRCVS, who read and commented on the manuscript. It was at his suggestion that this work was undertaken and we are grateful to him for his cooperation throughout. M.R. Hails BSc, Dip Agric Econ, whose recent bibliography on plant poisoning in animals (with T.D. Crane BSc) was a most useful source of references, did much work on the sections dealing with some crop plants and bracken; C.D. Johnson CChem, MRSC checked the sections on poisonous principles; R. Taylor BSc helped with the revision of an assortment of plants.

We wish to thank John Harris and particularly Hugh Baillie at the Ministry of Agriculture, Fisheries and Food Publications and Displays Branch for their encouragement throughout the project and also for their patience in waiting for the manuscript. Jim Butcher's careful correction of the proofs was greatly appreciated.

We should also like to thank Susan C. Scott who has efficiently and cheerfully typed the manuscript (most of it at least twice) and produced order from the apparent chaos of some of the handwritten drafts.

Finally, thanks are due to our families and many friends and colleagues who have withstood our preoccupation with poisonous plants and its associated consumption of much of our time.

Acknowledgements of illustrations

Most of the illustrations were provided by H. C. Baillie and J. Harris, to whom we are grateful for making so many of their photographs available for our selection. For the use of the photographs of *Inocybe geophylla* var *lilacina* and *Panaeolus sphinctrinus* we thank the Royal Botanic Garden, Edinburgh; for that of *Cortinarius speciosissimus,* A.I.K. Short MB, ChB, MRCP of the Royal Infirmary, Glasgow, and for that of ergot, T.F. Preece DSc of the University of Leeds. Almost all of the plants were photographed in their natural habitat, but for permission to photograph a few plants we thank B. Halliwell of the Royal Botanic Gardens, Kew.

The photographs used on the cover of the book were taken by Hugh Baillie. We are indebted to Ken Penny for the line drawings used to illustrate three of the Umbelliferae.

INTRODUCTION

Definition

In introducing the subject of plant poisoning and poisonous plants it is necessary to define what is meant by a poisonous plant, but this is not as simple as it may first seem. Broadly speaking the plants considered here are those which, when eaten, can give rise to a departure from the normal health of man and domestic animals. It should be noted, however, that not all such plants are poisonous in all their parts or at all stages of their growth. In addition, the amounts that have to be eaten to produce an adverse effect on health, range from the relatively small (as in the case of the leaves of yew and the root of cowbane) to much greater quantities taken over prolonged periods (as in bracken and ragwort poisoning). Another factor complicating the definition of a poisonous plant is the fact that the quantity of a plant that poisons one species of animal may not affect another species; pigs, for example, thrive on amounts of acorns that produce poisoning in cattle.

Several diseases associated with plants cannot really be regarded as poisoning, e.g. the overeating of grain, nutritional deficiencies, allergies and physical injury, although some mention will be made of such conditions.

There has been little research on poisonous plants for a variety of reasons: they result in very few fatal cases of human poisoning, they are generally not serious causes of loss in farm animals, and only a relatively few individual cases are seen by medical and veterinary practitioners who may not have the facilities or time to investigate the cases in sufficient depth to be able to publish their descriptions in the scientific literature. The investigation of plant poisoning requires a specialist knowledge from a number of academic disciplines. Few investigators are competent in botany, the chemistry of poisonous principles, clinical diagnosis and pathology.

It is unlikely that the course of a natural outbreak of poisoning would be studied throughout, and it is only by feeding experiments, such as were carried out on a fairly large scale towards the end of the last century, that the full extent of clinical and pathological signs can be seen and a lethal dose of a given plant determined. Although carefully supervised feeding trials are sometimes conducted with poisonous plants, poisoning is rarely allowed to proceed so far that the experimental animals die, and little recent information of this type is available.

History

Man has always had to differentiate between those plants which are safe to eat and those which are poisonous. In early times, hunters are thought to have utilised the poisonous properties of certain plants to help catch wild animals, particularly fish, but, in addition to the realisation of the potential toxicity of plants, it was also recognised that some could be of benefit in disease conditions. These two aspects of the plant kingdom, the beneficial and also the harmful properties of plants, are described in the early medical literature of classical Greece and Rome (Hippocrates, Theophrastus, Dioscorides).

The *Materia Medica* of Dioscorides, which was completed about A.D. 60, describes over 600 plants and plant principles and was the leading pharmacological work for 16 centuries, being copied and used throughout Europe as the basis for many herbals, including the printed herbals that appeared after 1470. In Dioscorides' work and subsequent herbals, reference is made to the poisonous nature of various plants.

Botanical study based on original observations arose again in the first half of the 16th century, and works on poisonous plants began to appear in the 17th and 18th centuries. In 1775 J.F. Gmelin published a German work on poisonous plants which deals with 56 species, and by the end of the century P. Bulliard's work on French poisonous plants included 86 species, but as W. Woodville states in his *Medical Botany* (1790-1794) writers were still following the authority of Dioscorides for their knowledge of some plants. In 1814-15, however, there appeared a very influential French work on poisons by M.J.B. Orfila; an English translation of this was published in 1818. With the dog as his main experimental animal, Orfila demonstrated the toxicity of some 45 plants and isolated many of their poisonous principles. W.J.T. Morton of the London Veterinary College gave a lecture on poisoning in animals to the Veterinary Medical Association in 1836 and refers to the work of Orfila. In 1840 Morton published a Veterinary Toxicology Chart, in which he says 'We are, however, in want of more correct information than at present we possess...'. A.S. Taylor's *On Poisons in Relation to Medical Jurisprudence and Medicine* (first published in 1848) considers nearly 50 poisonous plants and fungi. More popular works were soon to follow, including *British Poisonous Plants* by C. Johnson, C.H. Johnson and J.E. Sowerby (1856) and *The Poisonous, Noxious and Suspected Plants of our Fields and Woods,* by Anne Pratt (1887).

Also in 1887 was published the first book by a veterinarian on poisonous plants *Des Plantes Vénéneuses* by Charles Cornevin, professor at the Lyons Veterinary School. This work has influenced all subsequent books on poisonous plants, including *Poisonous Plants in Field and Garden,* by G. Henslow (1901), *Veterinary Toxicology* by J.A. Nunn (1907), *Veterinary Toxicology* by G.D. Lander (1912) and *Plants Poisonous to Live Stock* by H.C.

Long (1917). In 1927, Long published *Poisonous Plants on the Farm* which was reprinted in 1934 as the Ministry of Agriculture and Fisheries Bulletin No. 75, the precursor of A.A. Forsyth's *British Poisonous Plants*.

Many of the plants now known to be poisonous were commonly recognised as such by the 18th century at the latest, as indicated by some of their names, English examples of which are cowbane, dead men's fingers, and deadly nightshade. Surprisingly two of the most important poisonous plants in Britain, bracken and ragwort, were not shown to be causes of poisoning until 1893 and 1906, respectively. The late recognition of these types of poisoning was because of their chronicity and confusion with infectious diseases whose nature was not properly understood. Other plants that were significant causes of poisoning, such as corn cockle and the Indian pea, have declined greatly in importance as the result of changes in agricultural practice.

Prevalence

Because of the difficulties in confirming a diagnosis in medical and veterinary practice, the lack of cooperation between academic disciplines and the fact that many cases of plant poisoning recover, it is impossible to obtain figures on the prevalence of plant poisoning in animals or man in Britain, although there are records available that do throw some light on their frequency. Between 1962 and 1978, some 20 000 inquiries about poisonous plants and their effects on man were received by the National Poisons Information Service at their five centres (London, Edinburgh, Cardiff, Belfast, Dublin), but only two people are known to have died from plant poisoning in this period, their deaths being due to *Amanita phalloides* and *Laburnum*. About 6-7% of the total number of inquiries at these centres concern poisonous plants.

An analysis of the numbers of post-mortem specimens examined at Veterinary Investigation Centres in Britain shows that 15-17% of all poisoning cases were due to plants. Bracken, ragwort, *Brassica* spp., oak, yew and members of the Umbelliferae family were the commonest causes of poisoning between 1975 and 1977. About 10% of the poisoning inquiries received in 1980 at the National Information Centre on Animal Toxicology at the Lyons Veterinary School in France concerned plants, but it is thought there that this represents only a small part of the true situation in France.

Poisoning: the plant aspects

Poisonous plants can be classified according to the chemical nature of their toxic constituents, but as these can be either a single substance, several similar substances or a number of substances with widely different chemical properties, a strictly chemical classification leads to considerable overlapping, with some plants placed in several chemical groups. Furthermore in many instances the poisonous principles have not been characterised. Even the presence of a known poisonous principle in a plant does not mean that consumption of that plant will produce poisoning and that it is, in fact, a poisonous plant.

It is, however, very useful to classify the plant toxins themselves into some chemical grouping and this will be considered later in more detail. Other less precise methods of classifying plant toxins can also be used. These include a classification based on the adverse effects produced in animals, e.g. digestive system disturbances, central nervous system disturbances or damage to the skin. Such a classification that could lead from clinical signs in an animal to the identification of a toxin, and hence to a diagnosis and to the plant responsible for the poisoning, would obviously be extremely useful. Such an approach, however, is too simplistic, as the signs in an animal are similar for many plant toxins and an individual toxin may evoke more than one response in the animal. An alternative method of classification is based on the ways in which toxic substances can arise in plants. Those that are present naturally, the so-called 'intrinsic' toxins, are the most commonly found. Others, such as the cyanogenic glycosides, are non-toxic in undamaged plant tissue but are rendered highly toxic (by the release of hydrocyanic acid) after the action of enzymes released when the plant is crushed. Plants or plant products may induce adverse effects when infected or contaminated with fungal pathogens that liberate mycotoxins which are ingested with the plants, (e.g. aflatoxins in grain contaminated with *Aspergillus* spp.; *Sclerotinia* spp. that cause pink rot in celery and from which furocoumarins are produced that are responsible for a photosensitisation reaction resulting in skin rashes in man). Storage can also bring about the formation or release of plant toxins, as in potatoes, where the alkaloid solanine may reach highly toxic levels in tubers exposed to light.

Poisonous substances in plants are often termed secondary plant metabolites. Any substance produced within a plant is a metabolite of that plant. For convenience they can be divided into primary metabolites, that is those involved in the essential functioning of the plant, and secondary metabolites that appear to have no such direct role and have even been described as waste products. There is no sharp division, however, between primary and secondary metabolites, and secondary metabolites are now considered to be very necessary to plants, with some functioning as defensive agents against other plants, infectious microorganisms, and

4

herbivorous insects and mammals. A considerable amount of work has been done on the ecological and plant breeding aspects of this protective role, since the increased palatability with lower concentrations of toxins, which is desirable for plants grown for animal or human food, is achieved at the expense of greater susceptibility to predation and to disease caused by invasion of plant pathogens. The reduction or elimination of toxic alkaloids from lupins, to produce the so-called 'sweet' lupin varieties, and the production of rape cultivars with low glucosinolate content are examples of plants in which alterations in the content of secondary (toxic) metabolites of the plant have increased their usefulness as feed plants but rendered them far more susceptible to insect attack; reducing the secondary metabolites is, therefore, not necessarily economic. Herbivorous insects are a potential source of major damage to plants, and a fine balance has developed between plants and the insects that feed on them. Secondary metabolites that are toxic to insects are also often toxic to other animals. Whereas some insects have developed specific mechanisms to detoxify or utilise certain otherwise dangerous secondary compounds (e.g. the predilection of cinnabar caterpillars to feed on ragwort), the large herbivorous mammals feed on many more plant species and have developed general, rather than specific detoxification mechanisms. These general mechanisms cannot detoxify all of the many kinds of plant toxins they are liable to meet, and poisoning of varying severity can result.

When the toxic effects of secondary plant metabolites are fatal or severe enough to attract attention, the cause of the deterioration in the animal can usually be traced, but it is likely that considerably greater economic loss is attributable to less obvious effects of plant toxins. They may well contribute to transient digestive disturbances in animals and a general loss of condition and performance, affecting weight gain and the quality and production of meat, milk and wool. Considered in this way, toxic secondary plant metabolites have been referred to as 'antiquality' factors.

Secondary plant metabolites, including the toxic ones, can also affect the taste and smell of plants and, consequently, their palatability. Plants of relatively low palatability will obviously not be grazed to the same extent as more palatable ones, but they may be eaten, almost exclusively in times of food shortage. At such times animals may develop a taste for a toxic plant not normally eaten and become addicted to it, still seeking it and sometimes experiencing recurrent episodes of poisoning even when other feed is available. Some animal species show preferences for particular plants that are avoided by others; a possible correlation exists between this selective feeding and the ability of the animal to detoxify potentially harmful substances in the plants.

Natural (often genetically determined) variations exist between populations of some plants and may affect their toxicity. An example of this is birdsfoot trefoil, in different populations of which either cyanogenic glycosides may be absent, or the enzyme that breaks them down to release hydrocyanic acid may be absent, or both of them may be present.

The occurrence in grazing land of non-cultivated native plants that are poisonous can be influenced by pasture management. Some poisonous plants are colonisers that increase in density with overgrazing (e.g. buttercups, docks, ragwort). As desirable forage plants decrease in density, grazing animals consume proportionately larger amounts of the toxic plants, increasing their risk of being poisoned. In addition, animals in poor physical condition from grazing poor pasture are often more susceptible to plant poisons.

Poor grazing may frequently drive animals to seek food that they would normally avoid, e.g. horses may consume acorns after a long dry summer period, or cattle and sheep consume poisonous plants such as buttercups, bracken and umbelliferous plants.

In drought conditions, some plants have a higher concentration of toxic substances, and there may be changes with season and altitude. Snow and severe winter weather can drive animals near to human habitations, which may be surrounded by protective or ornamental hedges such as rhododendron, privet, laurel or yew, all of which present an available but dangerous source of food.

Hedge cuttings and other garden waste thrown onto pasture, or fallen branches from trees are responsible for many isolated cases of poisoning.

Poisoning: the animal aspects

Different species of animals often vary in their susceptibility to individual poisonous plants. In some cases this variation can be explained by differences in the diet of animals, the anatomy of their digestive tracts, and feeding behaviour. Ruminants, such as cattle, sheep and goats have large forestomachs, where a toxic substance becomes well diluted. Its passage into the intestines, where absorption takes place, is much slower than in non-ruminants, such as man, horses, pigs, dogs and cats. Microbial action in the rumen may also destroy the poisonous principles in the plants, although the breakdown of plant material in the rumen can also be detrimental, by promoting the release of toxic constituents. It is often assumed that goats can safely eat almost anything, but this is certainly not so. Under natural conditions, the feeding pattern of the flock is determined by its leader, so that the same plants are eaten at the same site. Flock members learn to avoid the plants actively discriminated against by their leader. Goats not kept as a flock and kids separated early from their mothers show little discrimination.

The most important factors in species differences in susceptibility are probably the detoxification mechanisms specific to each species. These mechanisms can even vary within animals of the same species, e.g. some (but not all) rabbits possess an enzyme, atropinesterase, so that they are not adversely affected by deadly nightshade; goats also possess an atropinesterase that makes them less susceptible to deadly nightshade poisoning. Deer are said to be able to feed on yew and rhododendron and grey squirrels on *Amanita* mushrooms.

When a foreign compound is absorbed from the digestive tract, it may remain unchanged, break down spontaneously or undergo enzymatic metabolism. Enzymatic breakdown to a more water-soluble product than the parent compound is by far the most frequent reaction that occurs. It should be noted, however, that this enzymatic breakdown is not necessarily a detoxification, as it can result in the production of toxic substances from an initially harmless compound. Metabolic breakdown can be conveniently divided into two phases. The first phase involves oxidation, reduction or hydrolysis to primary products which may be excreted as such or linked, in the second phase, to form an easily excreted conjugated material. The many enzymes involved in these two phases differ with the species of animal, but can also be influenced by a variety of factors such as strain, age and sex of animal, season, time of day, diet, pregnancy, and amount of foreign substances absorbed.

After ingestion, poisonous plants may affect the digestive tract in a number of ways. When chewed, some plants, such as *Daphne mezereum* cause an inflammation of the mouth, but the most frequent effect of poisonous plants is an irritation of the stomach and intestines, this being shown by signs of abdominal pain and diarrhoea; a few plants causing gastroenteritis (e.g. oak) produce constipation rather than diarrhoea.

After absorption from the digestive tract the poisonous principles pass first to the liver, the major organ where enzymatic breakdown and detoxification take place. Liver damage can also occur, however, and is seen, in particular, after poisoning by plants containing pyrrolizidine alkaloids (*Senecio* spp.). When liver function is impaired, certain bile pigments, instead of being eliminated in the bile, can enter the general blood circulation and reach the capillaries in the skin where they can be activated by ultraviolet radiation so as to cause the photosensitisation syndrome. Other poisonous substances have a direct effect on the blood. Those found in rape and *Allium* spp. can break down red blood cells and cause anaemia. Excess oxalates in the blood combine with calcium to produce hypocalcaemia.

The kidneys, the organs of excretion, can be damaged by poisonous substances passing through them. For example, degenerative changes are found in them in poisoning by oak and oxalate-containing plants. In many fatal types of poisoning the immediate cause of death is heart failure, which may be the result of a direct effect on the heart muscle, or indirectly through an effect on the nerve supply of the heart. In addition to the cardiac glycosides (such as those of foxglove), taxine, the poisonous principle of yew, also has a direct effect on the heart.

Nervous signs are probably second in frequency only to digestive system signs in cases of plant poisoning; they may be characterised as being predominantly excitatory or depressive. When nervous signs are shown, it is usually not possible to find any gross or histological changes in the nervous system to account for them.

Diagnosis

Although the diagnosis of plant poisoning in animals may be fairly obvious in a few cases, such as when cattle break into a garden and are seen eating yew, it is generally not so easy. The difficulty arises for a variety of reasons: the relative infrequency of plant poisoning in comparison to infectious, metabolic and other diseases, the variety of potentially toxic plants, the sometimes long period before signs of toxicity appear, the non-specificity of these signs, and the popular tendency to ascribe any disease of obscure origin to poisoning.

To reach a diagnosis on circumstantial evidence, a great deal of information may have to be collected, particularly on the history of the patient, where it has been and the potentially toxic plants to which it has had access. In a suspected case of plant poisoning it is not uncommon to find that a number of such plants have been available to the animal, and after their identification it is important to determine how much of each plant there is growing and if any show signs of having been eaten. The presence of any predisposing factors must be considered, such as the curiosity of a young animal or a recently purchased animal in a new environment, change of pasture, shortage of feed, drought, and application of herbicides or pesticides.

The clinical signs shown by poisoned animals are usually not very helpful in making a diagnosis; either none may be observed, with the animal being found dead, or they are indefinite and not indicative of any specific disease. There are a large variety of poisonous plants and toxic principles but only a few ways in which animals can react to them: death in a short time, diarrhoea or constipation, excitement or depression, etc. Plants that can produce signs in less than a couple of hours include hemlock, hemlock water dropwort, cowbane, yew, foxglove, cherry laurel and other cyanogenic plants. Those that take 2-48 hours to produce signs include autumn crocus and nitrate-containing plants. Signs of acorn, bracken and ragwort poisoning may appear several weeks or even months after their first consumption, and at the time of appearance of signs of toxicity the animals may no longer be consuming them. Plants producing excitement and convulsions include hemlock water dropwort, cowbane, and sometimes ragwort in cattle, whereas depression is the predominant sign produced by hemlock and yew. Many poisonous plants induce diarrhoea, but there is constipation in acorn and ragwort poisoning. Haemoglobinuria occurs with annual and dog's mercury, rape and kale, and haematuria with acorns and bracken.

The changes found at post-mortem examination are also generally not specific, although careful examination of stomach contents may reveal pieces of poisonous plant, which may be identified histologically. Some plants may give a typical odour to a carcass, e.g. cyanogenic plants, *Allium* spp., hemlock. Diagnostic histological changes are found in ragwort poisoning, in which the liver has a characteristic fibrosis.

Chemical analysis is seldom of help in investigating plant poisoning, except in cases where cyanogenic plants or nitrates/nitrites are suspected. Before collecting and despatching any samples for analysis, however, verbal contact should be established with an appropriate laboratory.

Treatment

Should there be any suspicion of plant poisoning in man or animals, the doctor and veterinary surgeon, respectively, should be consulted immediately. They have the training and experience to assess the problem and decide on the appropriate course of action: whether to initiate treatment themselves, request specialist advice from a poisons centre, or refer the case to a hospital. The intention here is to outline the basic principles underlying treatment for poisoning by plants, and not to describe in detail the therapeutic measures available.

The essential first step is to make sure that there is no further access to the suspected cause of the poisoning. The two other main procedures are (1) the elimination of unabsorbed poisonous material still in the digestive tract as well as that already absorbed, and (2) the support of body functions so that they can respond to, and deal with the toxic agent(s) and the damage caused. The order in which these procedures are taken depends on the condition of the patient. If severe signs, such as convulsions, are present, then their control would have to precede measures to eliminate the poisonous substances.

Procedures to eliminate the poisonous plant from the digestive tract include the induction of vomiting, stomach lavage, manual removal of the stomach contents of ruminants, and the use of purgatives.

Vomiting can be induced quite readily in man and some animals (dog, cat and pig), and even if they have vomited already, an emetic should be given to remove any toxic material still in the stomach. The drug of choice is syrup of ipecacuanha, which is given by mouth. This has the disadvantage of not producing an immediate response, vomiting not generally occurring until at least 15 minutes after administration, but it does have the advantage over other emetics of being safe, fairly reliable and not potentiating any of the adverse effects of the toxic substances ingested. It is the emetic recommended in human poisoning, and is safe for use in children. Horses and ruminants do not vomit readily and, if they do vomit, they seldom live long after the event; emetics are not used in these species.

Stomach lavage involves the passage of a tube into the stomach, removal of its contents by gravity or suction, replacement of the contents with water or normal saline, and repetition of this removal and replacement until the washings are clear and free of the toxic material; the final replacement is with a suspension of some adsorbent material such as activated charcoal. Animals not already unconscious should be anaesthetised for stomach lavage, and a cuffed endotracheal tube inserted to prevent stomach contents entering the trachea. Human stomach lavage is an unpleasant procedure for adults, and in children should only be used when absolutely necessary; it should be remembered that berries may block the stomach tube. In ruminants the only effective way to empty the stomachs is by rumenotomy, and this has been recommended for yew poisoning in cattle. The contents of the rumen must be replaced at once, however, by warmed feed; rumen fluid aspirated from a healthy animal may be required to restore proper rumen function.

Absorption of poisonous principles from the digestive tract may be reduced by administering adsorbents, the most effective of which is activated charcoal of vegetable origin. This should be administered after vomiting and gastric lavage.

To remove poisonous material that has already reached the small intestines of animals, laxatives such as magnesium sulphate or sodium sulphate or mineral oil should be given. If the animal already has diarrhoea, the administration of a laxative may add to the risk of dehydration. Colonic lavage can be used to remove poisonous material from the large intestines.

Symptomatic therapy and supportive measures to aid the natural detoxification processes of the body are very important factors contributing to recovery. Supportive measures include control of body temperature, maintenance of respiratory and cardiovascular function, control of pain and central nervous system signs, and treatment of shock.

Specific antidotes are available for only a few types of poisoning, that is those due to cyanides, nitrates, oxalates and bracken. Atropine has been suggested as a treatment for poisoning by yew. General non-specific detoxification measures, however, can be useful, such as the intravenous administration of calcium borogluconate, or the administration of large volumes of intravenous fluids to promote renal excretion. In cases of human poisoning by some of the highly toxic larger fungi, several sophisticated methods, including forced diuresis, haemodialysis and haemoperfusion are used to assist in eliminating toxins from the body.

THE POISONOUS PRINCIPLES

Biochemically the poisonous plants may be grouped according to their toxic principles, whether these have been synthesised by the plant or selectively concentrated from the soil. These toxic principles include a vast range of compounds that have been classified traditionally as alkaloids, glycosides, saponins, nitrates, oxalates, tannins, phenols, volatile oils, photodynamic substances, minerals, etc. There is some structural overlap between these simple groups and other classifications are possible, but it must be borne in mind that little is known of the poisonous principles of many plants and that the poisonous properties of a plant may be due to more than one substance. In addition, the method used for extracting the toxic constituent from a plant may predetermine the type of poisonous principle found. In Britain most poisonous principles of plants are alkaloids or glycosides.

Alkaloids

The alkaloids are not a homogeneous group of compounds that can be defined solely on their chemical structure or pharmacological activity. The term 'alkaloid' (alkali-like) was proposed by the German pharmacist K.F.W. Meissner in 1819, after the first recorded isolation of a crystalline constituent (narcotine) from opium in 1803, although alkaloid-containing plants have been used for their medicinal or toxic properties since very early times. By 1850 a large number of alkaloids had been isolated and characterised, and now over 4000 are known, although it is estimated that they are present in less than 10% of all plant species.

In general, it is recognised that an alkaloid must be a product of plant or animal metabolism, and must contain at least one nitrogen atom that can act as a base. Two further qualifications are that it has a complex molecular structure with the nitrogen atom being part of a heterocyclic ring and that it shows pharmacological activity. As many alkaloids were isolated before their chemical structure was determined, they generally bear names derived from the Latin botanical name of their plant source, with the ending -ine (e.g. berberine from *Berberis*); a few have been named after their physiological action (e.g. emetine from *Cephaëlis ipecacuanha*).

They have been isolated from the roots, seeds, leaves or bark of some members of at least 40% of plant families, with a number of the families being particularly rich in alkaloids, e.g. Amaryllidaceae, Buxaceae,

Compositae, Euphorbiaceae, Leguminosae, Liliaceae, Papaveraceae, Ranunculaceae, and Solanaceae. Two very poisonous groups of alkaloids, however, are from the yew and the hemlock, which belong to the Taxaceae and Umbelliferae, families that are otherwise relatively poor in alkaloids. Within a given plant species the content and pattern of alkaloids frequently vary from tissue to tissue and from time to time. Climate, soil and other environmental factors can modify the alkaloid content within a genetically homogeneous group, while geographical races characterised by different alkaloid content are known within a single species.

The alkaloids are often grouped according to their chemical structure, the plants in which they occur, or their physiological action. There are a variety of structural types, and those of interest here are: piperidines (e.g. the hemlock alkaloids), tropanes (e.g. atropine), pyrrolizidines (in *Senecio* spp.), indoles (the ergot alkaloids, psilocybin, and heliosupine), isoquinolines (berberine, emetine), quinolizidines (lupinine, cytisine), steroid alkaloids (solanine, the *Buxus* group), and diterpenes (aconitine). There are still other alkaloids that do not fit neatly into such classes or whose structure has not been determined. When grouped by physiological effects, there are, in addition to those recognised principally for their poisonous effects, those with therapeutic uses, for example, as analgesics (morphine), cardiac depressants (quinidine), respiratory stimulants (lobeline), vasoconstrictors (ergometrine, ephedrine) and muscle relaxants (tubocurarine). It is rare, however, for an alkaloid to induce only one type of physiological response, and this limits their therapeutic value.

On the basis of studies carried out on the pharmacologically useful alkaloids, it has been concluded that, after consumption and absorption, the alkaloids present in plants generally undergo some metabolic transformation before being excreted. This transformation may involve only a few structural modifications produced by enzyme reactions in the liver, such as oxidation, hydrolysis or condensation with other molecules.

Structural similarities have been demonstrated between various alkaloids and the nerve transmitter substances acetylcholine, norepinephrine, dopamine and serotonin, and it is thought that many toxic alkaloids produce their effects by mimicking or blocking the action of these nerve transmitters. Some clinical features common to the acute poisoning produced by such alkaloids are excess salivation (or its absence), dilation or constriction of the pupil, vomiting, abdominal pain, diarrhoea, incoordination, convulsions and coma (as in poisoning by aconitine, atropine, the *Buxus* group, colchicine, coniine, cytisine, galegine, lupinine, solanine). Poisoning by the pyrrolizidine alkaloids is very different; it is chronic and the principal organ affected is the liver. Some alkaloids (e.g. those of *Conium maculatum*) are teratogenic, causing defects in the foetus when plants containing them are eaten by the mother.

The alkaloid-containing plants have a bitter taste and are generally not eaten, although individual animals can become addicted to them.

Treatment of poisoned animals is with drugs that counteract the central nervous system effects of the alkaloids; the poisoning, however, is often fatal, and in animals that do survive, recovery is frequently never complete.

Glycosides

The term glycoside is applied to a large group of organic substances in which a carbohydrate portion, consisting of one or more monosaccharide molecules, is combined with a non-sugar entity called an aglycone. The glycosides are easily hydrolysed by enzymes or acids to the parent sugar and the water-insoluble aglycone.

Glycosides are widely distributed in plants, and many are not toxic. The toxicity of a glycoside is determined by the aglycone, and the properties of the latter can be used to classify the toxic glycosides into cyanogenic, goitrogenic, cardiac and saponic glycosides. There are other toxic glycosides that do not fit into these groups, e.g. the coumarin glycosides such as aesculin in the horse chestnut, and those of the spurge laurel *(Daphne laureola)*, and the glycoside ranunculin, whose aglycone is a volatile, strongly irritant oil protoanemonin, which is the poisonous principle of buttercups.

Cyanogenic glycosides These are not toxic as such, but only through their release of hydrocyanic acid (HCN) which occurs when they have been broken down either after ingestion or as a result of plant cell damage before ingestion.

Trace amounts of cyanogenic glycosides are widespread in the plant kingdom, but relatively high concentrations are found only in certain plants. There is no obvious pattern in the family or genus where they occur, and even closely related species and individual plants of the same species may differ greatly in their production of these glycosides. Most cases of cyanide poisoning, however, are caused by consumption of plants of the families Rosaceae, Leguminosae and Gramineae. In general the highest concentrations are found in the leaves, but cyanogenic compounds also occur in seeds, roots and other plant tissues.

Cyanogenic plants contain an enzyme system capable of converting the cyanogenic glycoside to sugar, HCN, and an aldehyde or ketone. In the intact plant the enzyme system and the cyanogenic glycoside are separated, but on disruption of the plant cell they come together to release HCN. Maceration by the animal of the fresh plant tissue as it is ingested initiates the enzymatic breakdown of the glycoside. In man and monogastric animals, such as horse, pig, dog and cat, the acidic contents of the stomach inhibit the action of the plant enzymes, although these may be active during subsequent digestion in the duodenum. It has been suggested that the acidity of the stomach contents may not be great enough to hydrolyse cyanogenic glycosides. In ruminants (cattle, sheep and goat) the cyanogenic material remains in the rumen at neutral pH, which favours plant enzyme action, while the material is physically broken down further by rumination and the action of rumen bacteria; bacterial enzymes may also play a part in hydrolysing the glycoside. This may explain the greater susceptibility to cyanogenic plants that has been reported for ruminants. Even if a potential danger exists, the actual quantity of available HCN absorbed within a short period determines whether or not poisoning will occur.

When cyanide is absorbed it reacts readily with the trivalent iron of cytochrome oxidase in mitochondria; cellular respiration is thus inhibited and cells become deficient in oxygen; this particularly affects tissues with high oxidative metabolism (e.g. the central nervous system and cardiac muscle). As oxygen transfer to tissues is blocked, venous blood is oxygenated and becomes almost as bright red as arterial blood.

After absorption of HCN, animals do have some ability to detoxify it. A major mechanism is by combination with thiosulphate to form thiocyanate and sulphate; this is catalysed by the enzyme rhodanese which is widespread in animal tissues (particularly the liver, kidneys, thyroid, adrenals and pancreas). The thiocyanate is excreted in the urine and saliva. For poisoning to occur the body must absorb HCN more quickly than it can be detoxified. However, cyanide absorption is very rapid, and if sufficient is available (the minimum oral lethal dose is 2-4 mg/kg body weight) its toxic action is also very rapid, with death occurring from a few minutes to an hour after ingestion. The symptoms are an initial stimulation of respiration that rapidly changes to dyspnoea, excitement, gasping, prostration, convulsions, coma and death. There are no specific post-mortem lesions; the blood is bright red and stomach contents may smell of bitter almonds.

For ruminants, the recommended treatment is the intravenous injection of sodium thiosulphate at 0.5 g/kg body weight initially, and sodium nitrite at 10-20 mg/kg. The sodium thiosulphate can be repeated if symptoms reappear. The sodium nitrite promotes the formation of methaemoglobin which competes with cytochrome oxidase for the cyanide ion, whereas the thiosulphate acts as a sulphur donor for the enzyme rhodanese to enhance the conversion of cyanide to thiocyanate. For treatment of human poisoning, the nitrite-thiosulphate combination has been supplemented to good effect with oxygen and sodium pyruvate; the successful use of cobalt edetate has also been reported.

Goitrogenic glycosides These are glucosinolates (formerly termed thioglucosides) that are hydrolysed by an associated thioglucosidase enzyme whenever wet, raw plant material is crushed; they yield glucose, an acid sulphate ion and goitrogens (thiocyanate, isothiocyanate, goitrin).

Most of the plants containing glucosinolates are in the Cruciferae family, and many different glucosinolates have been isolated from wild plants of this family and also from those cultivated as fodder plants, but only one or two glucosinolates are present in relatively large amounts in a given plant species. Some of the glucosinolates have been named after the plants from which they were first isolated, e.g. sinigrin after the old name for black mustard *Sinapis* (now *Brassica*) *nigra*, but in later nomenclature the prefix gluco- is linked to the plant name, e.g. glucobrassicin.

Glucosinolates are responsible for the hot pungent flavour of several of the Cruciferae (e.g. radish and mustard) and may be found in all parts of the plant, but are often at their highest concentrations in seeds, so that animal feed mixes containing such ingredients as rapeseed meal are potentially toxic, as well as foliage.

The goitrogenic effects of these substances in animals cannot be alleviated by giving iodine, as the mechanism of the goitrogenicity is different from that involved in goitre resulting from the iodine deficiency that occurs in some hardwater areas. Plant goitrogens act by interfering with the uptake of iodine by the thyroid gland, limiting the formation of the iodine-containing precursors of thyroxine, the production of which is therefore decreased. The size and mass of the thyroid glands increase, presumably so that thyroxine production can be increased. The thyroid gland, thus enlarged, is recognised clinically and pathologically as goitre. Although work in experimental animals has indicated a direct correlation between increased thryoid gland size and the consumption of glucosinolates, the development of goitre, particularly in man, solely as a result of eating plants containing these substances has not been demonstrated conclusively. It seems reasonable to assume, however, that the effects of dietary deficiency of iodine can be exacerbated by eating large quantities of plant material containing goitrogens. The possible depression of thyroid gland activity and the development of goitre as a result of drinking milk from cows fed on large amounts of glucosinolate-containing plants has also been postulated, but is open to question.

Thiocyanate ions may also be present in plants of families other than the Cruciferae as a result of the breakdown of cyanogenic glycosides. Goitrogens of undetermined chemical structure have been reported in other plants but little is known about them.

Cardiac glycosides
On hydrolysis, these yield aglycones that have a steroid structure and a highly specific action on the heart, increasing contractility of heart muscle and slowing the heart rate. The sugar portion of the glycoside has no physiological activity of its own but often greatly enhances the cardiac activity of the aglycone. The best known members of this group are the digitalis glycosides present in the foxglove *(Digitalis purpurea);* these have long been used in medicine to strengthen the action of a weakened heart.

Over 400 cardiac glycosides have been isolated and, in addition to those in foxgloves, they are also found in Britain, in the spindle tree *(Euonymus europaeus)*, lily of the valley *(Convallaria majalis)* and *Helleborus* spp. Besides the cardiac effects, the cardiac glycosides can also produce gastroenteritis and diarrhoea; many of the other signs are a direct result of the inability of the heart to circulate blood. Signs of poisoning usually develop 4-12 hours after ingestion of the plants and, if lethal quantities are eaten, death occurs in 12-24 hours. With sublethal quantities the clinical signs many persist for 2-3 days. The only effective treatment is elimination of the plant from the digestive tract; rumenotomy may be necessary.

Saponins These are water-soluble plant constituents that are distinguished by their capacity to form a soapy foam even at low concentrations, and by their bitter taste and ability to haemolyse red blood cells. They are glycosides with a non-sugar aglycone portion which is termed a sapogenin. Saponins are classified according to the chemical nature of the sapogenin into two major groups: steroidal and triterpenoid saponins.

Saponins are widely distributed in the plant kingdom and are found in various forage legumes such as lucerne *(Medicago sativa)* and clover *(Trifolium repens)*, as well as in other plants in Britain such as birdsfoot trefoil *(Lotus corniculatus)*, beech and horse chestnut. Saponins can occur in all parts of plants, although their concentration is affected by variety and stage of growth. Saponins are more poisonous by injection than by ingestion, and are generally harmless to mammals when ingested, although large quantities can be irritant and cause vomiting and diarrhoea. They are, however, highly toxic to fish and snails. The saponins of lucerne can inhibit the growth of chicks and depress egg production.

Nitrates/Nitrites

Plants absorb nitrates from the soil and generally convert them rapidly into other nitrogenous compounds. Under certain conditions, however, some plants may accumulate quite high concentrations of nitrates. Nitrates are not very toxic, but they are readily converted by bacteria in the alimentary tract into the much more toxic nitrites.

Several factors can increase the accumulation of nitrates by plants and these include drought, shade, the use of herbicides and, in particular, application of nitrogenous fertilisers. In Britain the plants most likely to accumulate nitrates are beet, mangels, turnips, swedes, rape and kale.

Nitrites pass easily from the gastrointestinal tract into the blood, where they combine with haemoglobin in the red blood cells to form methaemoglobin, a compound that is incapable of taking up and transporting oxygen. Consequently the clinical signs of nitrite poisoning are those of oxygen deficiency and include weakness, depression, a rapid weak pulse, and a fall in blood pressure, while breathing becomes quicker and laboured. The visible mucous membranes become purplish and dark in colour; examination of the vaginal mucous membranes of cows can be used to assess the nitrate status of their feed. There may be muscular tremors and recumbency. Death from asphyxia can occur within a few hours of eating nitrate-rich plants, although it is more usual for a few days to elapse before signs of poisoning appear. During this period the digestive tract bacteria become adapted to nitrates, which they break down more quickly. Pregnant animals may abort, even in the absence of clinical signs of poisoning. High nitrate feeds have also been associated with infertility, and with vitamin A deficiency in cattle, nitrates destroying the vitamin A content of hay and silage. Post-mortem examination frequently shows small haemorrhages on the heart and in other internal organs. The blood is often a dark reddish-brown. Most cases of nitrite poisoning have been reported in cattle, although sheep, horses and pigs may also be affected.

Treatment for affected animals is the intravenous injection of a 2-4% aqueous solution of the dye methylene blue at 4.4 mg/kg body weight. This can be repeated if clinical signs recur. Experimental work has indicated that tungsten (as sodium tungstate) given orally to cattle inhibits the formation of nitrites from nitrates in the rumen.

Oxalates

Oxalic acid and its salts, the oxalates, occur naturally in nearly all forms of living matter, but some members of certain plant families (e.g. Chenopodiaceae, Geraniaceae and Polygonaceae) can contain relatively large and potentially toxic amounts, mainly as the soluble sodium or potassium salts and the insoluble calcium salts.

While the oxalate content of plants is principally a species characteristic, wide variations can occur within the same species, depending upon the age of the plant, the season, the climate and the type of soil. Anatomical variations also occur, the highest concentrations commonly occurring in the leaves and the lowest in the roots. The oxalate content of many plants tends to increase as the plants mature, an example being the leaves of rhubarb. Other plants show a rapid rise in oxalate content during the early stages of growth, followed by a decrease as the plants mature, examples being *Atriplex,* mangels and sugar beet leaves and sugar beet roots. To be potentially dangerous the plants must contain 10% or more oxalic acid on a dry weight basis.

Under natural conditions the plants with a high oxalate content are readily eaten by livestock, but if large amounts of such plants are eaten over a short period, acute poisoning can occur. When oxalates are ingested by ruminants, they may be broken down by the rumen microorganisms, they may combine with free calcium in the digestive tract to form insoluble calcium oxalate that is excreted in the faeces, or they can be absorbed into the blood stream. What actually happens to the oxalates depends upon a variety of factors, including the amount and the chemical form of the oxalates, their rate of ingestion, the previous grazing history of the animal, the amount of calcium in the diet, and the nutritional status of the animal. Ruminants can become adapted to a high oxalate intake by developing a ruminal flora that can break down and utilise oxalates. Horses and pigs can also become adapted by developing a similar type of flora in their large intestines. Hungry or undernourished animals are less tolerant of oxalates, as they absorb a higher proportion of those present. Oxalate poisoning occurs principally when hungry cattle or sheep are allowed to graze heavy growths of plants with a high oxalate content.

Such plants are toxic because of the chemical reaction of the oxalates after absorption. Their primary adverse effect is hypocalcaemia that results from the combination of the oxalates with calcium in the blood stream. The calcium oxalate produced is deposited in various tissues, and especially in the kidneys.

Signs of acute poisoning in cattle and sheep include rapid and laboured breathing, depression, weakness, staggering gait, recumbency, coma and death. There is a fall in the blood calcium concentration. Gross lesions are usually confined to haemorrhages and oedema of the rumen wall, with the abomasum sometimes being affected. Histologically, calcium oxalate crystals may be found in the tubules of the kidneys and in the rumen wall. A chronic form of poisoning with kidney damage has been reported in sheep grazing *Oxalis* in Australia.

Calcium borogluconate given intravenously to correct the hypocalcaemia is the recommended treatment. It produces a rapid improvement but does not always prevent death, as other factors may also be involved in fatal cases: kidney damage with associated uraemia, and interference with energy metabolism.

Photosensitive agents and photosensitisation

Some plants contain substances that can make non-pigmented or slightly pigmented skin hypersensitive to the ultraviolet radiation in sunlight. After ingestion, these substances are absorbed unchanged into the circulating blood and thus reach the skin, where they may be excited by ultraviolet rays and then induce chemical changes that lead to cell damage. Some of these photosensitive substances, the furocoumarins, do not require ingestion of the plant to produce hypersensitivity to sunlight; this can arise just by contact of the plant with the skin.

The body responds to the resulting cell damage by itchiness, redness, heat, oedema and swelling of the affected skin. Blisters may develop and break, giving rise to scabs and secondary infections; skin necrosis may occur. Animals with photosensitive substances in their skin are said to be in a state of photosensitivity, whereas the reaction that occurs in photosensitive animals after exposure to sunlight is called photosensitisation. The severity of the clinical signs of photosensitisation is determined by the amount of photosensitive substance in the skin, the intensity of the ultraviolet radiation and the duration of exposure.

In addition to the primary photosensitivity in which the photosensitive agent remains unchanged during its transfer from the plant to the skin, there is a secondary or hepatogenous photosensitivity in which the photosensitive substance is a normal breakdown product of digestion, usually eliminated by the liver. One such substance, phylloerythrin, is formed in the digestive tract of ruminants during the microbial degradation of chlorophyll, and, after absorption, is transported to the liver, where it is excreted in the bile. Any liver damage affecting bile excretion, however, can lead to the accumulation of phylloerythrin in the blood and thus in the skin, where it can be excited by ultraviolet rays. The liver damage leading to this secondary photosensitivity can result from disease, hepatotoxic drugs, industrial or agricultural chemicals, mycotoxins (produced by fungi infecting plant material) as well as from plant toxins themselves.

In Britain there are two plants which can produce primary photosensitivity when eaten by animals: St. John's wort *(Hypericum perforatum)* and buckwheat *(Fagopyrum esculentum)*. Primary photosensitivity in man is produced by contact with giant hogweed *(Heracleum mantegazzianum),* and has also occurred in people handling vegetables of the Umbelliferae family, such as parsnips, carrots and celery. In at least some of these the furocoumarins responsible result from the presence of fungal pathogens on the plants (e.g. *Sclerotinia* spp. on celery). The consumption of cooked or raw fat hen *(Chenopodium album)* can also result in photosensitisation in man.

The photosensitisation occurring with bog asphodel *(Narthecium ossifragum)* in sheep is of the hepatogenous type as is also that occurring with ingestion of mycotoxins in dead plant material.

Treatment of photosensitisation includes removal of the animals from the plant involved in the photosensitisation, protection from sunlight, and symptomatic measures.

Proteins, peptides and amino acids

In addition to the alkaloids and cyanogenic glycosides, there are some other nitrogen-containing organic compounds that are responsible for poisoning caused by plants. The toxic amino acids of plants do not usually produce such spectacular signs of poisoning as some of the peptides and proteins. Cases of poisoning produced by the lathyrogenic amino acids found mainly in the seeds of *Lathyrus* species have been reported in Britain, but only very rarely and not recently. Cyclic polypeptides, known as amatoxins, are the poisonous principles of the most toxic mushroom in Britain, *Amanita phalloides*. The poisonous blue-green algae *(Microcystis)* that form blooms on still or sluggish freshwater also contain poisonous cyclic polypeptides, but poisoning by such algae has only been suspected and not confirmed in Britain. Viscotoxins, the poisonous principles of mistletoe are also polypeptides.

Complex proteins of plant origin that have caused poisoning in Britain include ricin (said to be the most toxic naturally occurring compound) from *Ricinus communis*. Other plant proteins are haemagglutinins from kidney beans *(Phaseolus vulgaris)* and soya beans *(Glycine max),* and the enzyme thiaminase from bracken and horsetails.

Certain individuals may show a more or less violent local or generalised reaction (allergy) after ingestion or contact with a particular plant protein that does not have any adverse effect on most other individuals. Unlike the effects of other toxic principles, the intensity of the reaction does not depend on the quantity of the toxin but on the sensitivity of the affected individual. These allergens are not toxic constituents in the strict sense, their toxic action being the result of an altered response in those that ingest or otherwise come in contact with them.

Tannins

These are complex phenolic polymers which vary in chemical structure and biological activity. They produce an astringent reaction in the mouth and have the ability to tan leather. On the basis of their chemical structure they can be classified into two main groups: the hydrolysable tannins, which are glycosides, and the condensed tannins. The latter are the more widely distributed in plants, but pass through the digestive tract unchanged and are generally not toxic, although large quantities can give rise to gastroenteritis. The condensed tannins have also been reported to cause growth depression in chicks.

In Britain it is only the oak that is considered to produce tannin poisoning, the acorns and leaves containing hydrolysable tannins of relatively low molecular weight. These tannins are broken down in the digestive tract of cattle and sheep, the breakdown products including gallic acid and pyrogallol which are absorbed and thought to be responsible for the toxicity, although their mode of action is not known.

FUNGI

This section is a general account of the poisonous fungi found in Britain. It is not intended to give comprehensive coverage of all aspects of the subject, and does not include mycological and toxicological details of interest only to the specialist. More information can be found in the many books available, some of which are listed in the reference section. However, as it is customary to classify fungi as plants, they have been included: the larger fungi for their direct toxic effects mainly in man; ergot and some mould fungi, which, under certain conditions, produce potent toxins (mycotoxins) in growing plants or plant products stored for use as animal bedding or food for animals and man.

LARGER FUNGI

Most cases of poisoning by these fungi occur in man; there are very few reports of such poisoning in animals. Few of the fungi found in Britain are dangerously poisonous, but several can cause illness or discomfort. It cannot be emphasised too strongly that a fungus, whose identity is not properly known, should never be eaten. For identification of the larger fungi, reference should be made to the many books now available, giving written descriptions and excellent illustrations. In addition, spore characteristics (mainly colour) can be useful in distinguishing between similar fungi; spores for examination are obtained by preparing a 'spore print'. This is made by placing the cap of a gill fungus (stalk removed) or the fruiting body of a pore fungus on to a piece of clean white paper and leaving for several hours, during which time spores released from the fungus will be deposited on the paper. Placing other fruiting bodies on black (or dark) paper will enable white or pale coloured spores to be seen.

Contrary to popular belief, there are no characteristics which separate edible from poisonous species, and even recognised edible species may cause poisoning if eaten when old and damp. The names 'mushroom' and 'toadstool' should not be taken to imply any distinction in edibility. Both are common names for the fruiting bodies of some of the larger fungi, the vegetative part of which consists of fine threads (hyphae) which grow in the soil or on rotting plant material. It is inadvisable to eat fungi raw or undercooked as some are poisonous in that state although rendered harmless by adequate cooking. In Britain the only fungus collected and eaten in any quantity is the field mushroom *(Agaricus campestris)*. There is, however, a growing trend in collecting potential food plants, including fungi, in the wild, a practice which is much more common in some Continental countries. There is great variation among individuals in their response to the potentially toxic effects of fungi, and also variation in the toxicity of the fungi themselves, depending on several factors including their growing conditions and state of maturity.

The poisonous larger fungi have been grouped according to the type of toxic reactions they produce or the toxins they contain, rather than taxonomically. The groups generally recognised are those giving rise to: cytolytic poisoning (cellular degeneration of body tissues); neurological and psychotropic poisoning (involving the central nervous system); muscarine poisoning; gastrointestinal poisoning; and poisoning in the presence of alcohol. By this classification, some fungi within the same genus may be dealt with in different groups, e.g. *Amanita phalloides* under cytolytic poisoning, and *Amanita muscaria* under psychotropic poisoning.

CYTOLYTIC POISONING

Amanita spp

Unless positively identified, all members of the genus *Amanita* should be considered potentially poisonous. Although some species are harmless, a few can cause fatal poisoning, while others are poisonous when raw although edible when cooked.

Death Cap *Amanita phalloides* (photo 5)

Death cap is responsible for more cases of severe poisoning and death in man than any other fungus. The fruit bodies appear in late summer and autumn and are most common in or at the edges of beech and oak woods. At first, the fungus is enclosed in a white skin, the universal veil, which is ruptured during growth, occasionally leaving evanescent patches on the cap, but a residual cup, the volva, sheathing the wide base of the stalk. The fully expanded cap is convex or flat, easily peeled, and up to 12 cm across. It is variable in colour, usually yellowish to olive-green and faintly streaked radially with darker fibrils, particularly near the centre. The flesh of the cap is white, except just beneath the skin, where it is tinged yellow or green. The stem is smooth and white, up to 12 cm high and 2 cm thick, solid when young but hollow when old. Near the top it has an irregularly torn white ring, the remains of a membrane which joined the edge of the cap to the stem when young. The gills are crowded together, white at first, then cream-coloured (never pink or brown as in the edible field mushroom) and the spores are white. The whole fungus has a rather sweet, foetid smell when mature.

A closely related species, sometimes confused with the edible field mushroom *(Agaricus campestris),* is the destroying angel *(Amanita virosa).* It is far less common in Britain than *Amanita phalloides.* The fungus has a more slender, shaggy stem, a rather conical cap and is uniformly white, as is another species, the fool's mushroom or deadly agaric *(Amanita verna)* which is rare in Britain. Both fungi are highly poisonous. The specific name of *Amanita verna* is misleading as it is also an autumnal fungus.

Many excellent descriptions of the toxic effects of these fungi can be found in medical and mycological literature.[1] [2]

Poisonous principles The first poisonous component isolated from *Amanita phalloides* was originally called phallin, but later renamed phallolysin. It is now known to be a protein although still frequently referred to as a glycoside. Phallolysin can cause severe damage to red blood cells (haemolysis); it is destroyed rapidly by heating. It was thought for many years that haemolysis could result from eating the uncooked fungus, but it has now been demonstrated in laboratory animals that phallolysin is active only when given by injection, and not orally.[3] [4]

The main toxic components of these fungi are two closely related groups of compounds, the amatoxins (which are cyclic octapeptides of which there are at least six, including amanitin) and the phallotoxins (which are cyclic heptapeptides of which there are at least five, including phalloidin). It was thought for many years that the phallotoxins were mainly responsible for the early, acute, gastrointestinal symptoms and the more potent amatoxins for the later liver and kidney damage. However, this was not confirmed by experimental work in dogs in which amatoxin, but not phallotoxin, caused gastrointestinal symptoms.[5] It has been established recently[3] that the phallotoxins are inactive when taken orally and therefore are not normally involved in human poisoning (although they are potent toxins when given by other routes). Thus, the amatoxins appear to be the only components involved in poisoning by this highly toxic group of fungi. Amatoxins interfere with the activity of the nucleic acid enzyme, RNA polymerase B, thereby inhibiting protein synthesis.[3] The toxic reaction is accompanied by destruction of cells, particularly in the liver. An antitoxin has also been isolated from some of these fungi and was named antamanide as it was thought to act against amatoxin. In fact it acts only against the phallotoxins and, like them, is not active orally.[3] For human beings, half a fruit body or less of *Amanita phalloides* is sufficient to kill an adult. Poisoning by *Amanita phalloides,* and other fungi, is less common in Britain than in some other European countries where it is more usual to gather and eat wild mushrooms. Cases do occur in this country, however, 11 incidents having been reported (including one fatality) to one poisons centre between 1973 and 1981.[6]

Human poisoning

In man three stages can be recognised in the course of amatoxin poisoning. The first symptoms, which develop 6-24 hours after eating the fungi, include dry mouth, nausea, vomiting, abdominal pain and diarrhoea (often with blood). These symptoms, which usually last about 24 hours and may be very violent, are followed by a latent period of well-being that may last for up to three days, although severe disturbances to enzymes, particularly in the liver, take place at this stage. This is followed by the most serious phase of intoxication, during which severe kidney and liver damage caused by the toxins may result directly in death from failure of one or both of these organs, or indirectly by heart failure. In this final stage, when there may or may not be a recurrence of the gastrointestinal symptoms, the pulse is weak and rapid, the skin cold and clammy, the visible mucous membranes bluish-purple (cyanosis), and jaundice develops. There are also nervous symptoms including muscle twitching, restlessness, delirium, hallucinations and convulsions. Coma usually precedes death which occurs in 50-90% of untreated cases, depending on the susceptibility of the individual, the toxicity of the fungi and the quantity eaten.

It is strongly advised that, in cases of mushroom poisoning, the fungus eaten be identified whenever possible, but particularly if amatoxin poisoning is suspected, as the success of any treatment depends on its being started as soon as possible. Many far less toxic fungi also cause gastrointestinal disturbances, followed by recovery and this may be confused with the initial and second stages of amatoxin poisoning. Treatment started in the final stage will be ineffective as damage to the liver and kidney is, by then, almost always irreversible.

Treatment

There is no specific antidote for amatoxin poisoning. All suspected cases should receive rapid medical attention and admission to hospital. The treatment given is determined largely by the preferences of individual hospitals and most use a combination of methods. Emetics should be given (if vomiting has not already occurred) and stomach lavage performed in all cases admitted within 36 hours of ingestion. In addition many give activated charcoal orally, to adsorb residual toxins in the stomach. Aspiration of duodenal contents should be carried out to prevent further absorption of the toxin. There has been considerable success with forced diuresis,[7] haemodialysis or charcoal haemoperfusion.[8] Injections of prednisolone,[9] thioctic acid,[10] [11] [12] cytochrome C,[13] penicillin[14] or other antibiotics (in large doses) or silymarin[3] [14] (a mixture of flavones from the milk-thistle *Silybum marianum*) are used, separately or in combination.[14] Silymarin is active against phalloidin, but appears to protect against

25

amanitin as well.[15] (The anti-phalloidin serum used by some hospitals in Europe is unlikely to be of any use, since phalloidin taken orally does not produce poisoning.) There is considerable variation in the claims for success of the various treatments, but a reduction in fatalities to 25% or below is often achieved. Patients that survive may remain ill for at least 30 days, and exertion during recovery may result in a serious relapse.[16]

A much simpler method of treatment,[17] that has attracted attention recently, involves oral administration of common antidiarrhoeal agents (nifuroxide and dihydrostreptomycin), followed by intravenous injections of vitamin C and a diet consisting solely of cooked, mashed carrots. There has been considerable scepticism of this regimen, as it has no known theoretical basis. However, it has been successful on more than one occasion when the originator of the method deliberately ingested more than the recognised lethal quantity of *Amanita phalloides*.[18] The method is also used successfully in at least one French hospital.[19] To be effective, the treatment must be started as soon as gastrointestinal symptoms appear.

Poisoning in animals *Amanita* is also toxic for some animals. Mice, rats and, more recently, dogs[20] have been used as experimental models, but poisoning of animals by these fungi under natural conditions seems rare. Losses in a herd of cattle in the USA in the 1940s[21] were thought to have been due to ingestion of *Amanita verna,* of which an unusually large number were present in the woods that formed part of their grazing area. The chief symptom was painful defaecation, the faeces being highly irritant and causing ulceration of the rectum, anus and surrounding areas. In fatal cases the animals died in convulsions, and post-mortem examination revealed severe gastrointestinal inflammation, enlargement and haemorrhage of the liver, pale kidneys, distension of the bladder with urine, and haemorrhages of the heart.

More recently poisoning by *Amanita phalloides* was recorded in two Saanen goats,[22] one of which died after four days, with remnants of the fungi in its stomach. The symptoms included restlessness, frequent urination, irritation and blistering around the anus, thirst, abdominal pain, jaundice and somnolence. Post-mortem examination revealed degeneration of the liver, intestinal haemorrhages and red-coloured urine in the bladder. The second goat recovered in three weeks, having been given only symptomatic treatment.

Some fungi of other genera also contain toxic cyclopeptides, especially amatoxins. These include species of *Conocybe,*[23] *Galerina*[24] and *Lepiota*[25 26] (especially *Lepiota* spp. with pink, red, orange or rust-brown spores). As some other species of these genera are edible, correct identification is highly important.

Cortinarius spp (photo 3)

This genus includes a large number of species, with many variations in shape, size and colour which form the basis of subdivisions into smaller groups. Features common to most *Cortinarius* species are brown spores which, at maturity, give a rusty brown colour to the gills, and a cobweb-like partial veil (cortina) which extends from the edge of the cap to the stem, covering the gills when young, but tearing during growth and sometimes leaving a girdle that adheres closely to the stem. The universal veil, when present, is distinct from the cortina. It adheres to the surface of the cap forming silky, cobweb-like fibrils or a slimy, glutinous layer, especially when wet, and in some species it forms a distinct ring or series of partial rings on the lower part of the stem. Several *Cortinarius* species are edible, but others, seen comparatively rarely in Britain, are highly toxic. These include three orange coloured fungi, *Cortinarius speciosissimus,* found occasionally in coniferous woods in Scotland, and *Cortinarius orellanus* and *Cortinarius orellanoides,* found in deciduous woods further south. A full description of *Cortinarius speciosissimus* and details of its distribution in Scotland have recently been given;[27] reports indicate that it may be more widely distributed than was previously thought.

Poisonous principle A toxin, whose action was demonstrated experimentally on dogs and cats, was isolated in the 1950s from *Cortinarius orellanus* and named orellanin(e). This has been described variously as a homogeneous substance or a mixture of toxic and non-toxic fractions.[28] There is general agreement, however, that the toxins are cyclopeptides with a bipyridyl structure.

Poisoning Human poisoning by *Cortinarius* was reported first in Poland in the 1950s,[29] under the generic name *Dermocybe*. Since then there have been reports from other European countries including Switzerland[30] and Italy,[31] involving *Cortinarius orellanus*. The first case of human poisoning by *Cortinarius speciosissimus* was reported in Finland,[32] but more recently poisoning by this species was recognised in Britain[27 33] when three adults ate this fungus, collected in northern Scotland.

A latent period of 2-17 days is characteristic of *Cortinarius* poisoning. Nausea and vomiting are usually the first symptoms and are followed by sweating, shivering and stiffness, pain in the limbs and abdomen, constipation (or diarrhoea), severe thirst, urine reduced initially, then increased in volume and frequency as kidney function deteriorates.[31 33 34] There may be disturbance of liver function, and nervous system involvement with sleepiness and convulsions,[34] but the kidneys are the main organs affected. Despite treatment, including haemodialysis, kidney transplantation may be required (as in two of the cases in Scotland)[27 33] or the poisoning may be fatal.

Cortinarius speciosissimus has also caused poisoning in animals, severe kidney damage being found in four sheep that died after eating the fungus while grazing in Norway.[35] When three lambs were fed the fungus experimentally, two had disturbed kidney function after a single administration of fresh fungi and the third, given the dried fungus daily for 13 days, developed severe kidney damage and died.[35]

The effect of *Cortinarius* on other animals is not known, but it would be prudent to consider the fungus toxic and not allow access to it.

False Morel *Gyromitra esculenta*

Other common name: Turban Fungus

This fungus grows in coniferous woods in spring. It has an irregular, convoluted, dark chestnut-brown cap (up to 10 cm high and 15 cm wide) with brain-like grooves and ridges. The thick stem is up to 6 cm high, pale flesh-coloured or grey, somewhat grooved and hollow. False morel is sometimes confused with the edible morel *(Morchella esculenta)*.

Poisonous principles
A compound named helvellic acid (from the old generic name *Helvella*) was isolated from this fungus in the 1880s and said to be the active toxin. It was stated later that this substance could damage red blood cells (haemolysis) if the fungi were eaten raw, but that as it was destroyed by heat and soluble in water, the fungi were harmless when cooked. Helvellic acid is now recognised as a mixture of harmless fatty acids and not responsible for any of the poisonous properties of *Gyromitra*.

The toxic principles are N-methyl-N-formylhydrazones of low molecular weight aldehydes. The first to be isolated was gyromitrin, the hydrazone of acetaldehyde. Another substance, also called helvellic acid, isolated in the 1930s, was probably a crude product containing gyromitrin. Hydrolysis of gyromitrin liberates monomethylhydrazine which is usually stated to be the *Gyromitra* toxin. The toxicology of monomethylhydrazine (and related compounds) has been studied extensively because of their use as rocket propellants and fuel for space craft.

Poisoning
False morel is said to be safe to eat if dried or boiled in water for at least 10 minutes (and the water discarded), but is best avoided altogether. It was formerly grown commercially (350 000 kg in Poland in 1930), but sale of the fungus is now prohibited in some European countries, because of the danger of poisoning if inadequately cooked, and because workers in the canning industry and cooks have been poisoned by exposure to the volatile

toxins during preparation of the fungi.[36] Irritation of the skin and eyes can result from handling (usually large quantities) of the fungi. The apparent differences in the susceptibility of individuals, and of the same individual at different times, can be explained by the very narrow margin between the amount of toxin that has no effect, and a lethal dose.[37]

Many experiments have been done on gyromitrin poisoning in laboratory animals[38 39 40] in which liver and kidney damage often occurs. There have been reports of birth defects and carcinogenic effects in rodents,[41] but neither of these has been suspected in man.

There have been several reports of poisoning in human beings after eating the false morel.[37] A survey of cases of *Gyromitra* poisoning in Europe from 1783-1965[42] revealed a mortality rate of 14.5%. Symptoms usually appear 6-8 hours after ingestion, but have been reported after 2-12 hours. Nausea, persistent vomiting, abdominal pain, muscular cramps and watery diarrhoea (sometimes with blood) occur initially, followed by lassitude, incoordination, dizziness and jaundice. In severe cases, difficult breathing, rapid feeble pulse, convulsions and coma occur, and death may follow in 2-5 days. Post-mortem examination reveals inflammation of the kidneys, enlargement of the spleen and fatty degeneration of the enlarged liver.

Treatment is symptomatic, but all suspected cases should be referred to hospital as stomach lavage, correction of fluid and electrolyte imbalance and other measures may be required.

Lepiota spp

This genus contains several edible species, including the excellent parasol mushroom *(Lepiota procera)* although even this can have adverse effects in some individuals; palpitations, flushing of the skin and shivering were recorded after eating one specimen.[6] Recovery occurred within a few hours.

The edibility of some of the smaller members of the genus (with caps up to 5 cm across) is suspect. Some species (particularly those with pink, red, orange or rust brown pigments) contain toxic cyclopeptides (mainly amatoxins) similar to those found in some species of *Amanita*.

Common features of *Lepiota* are the mealy or scaly surface of the cap, which is convex when young, the dissimilar flesh of the stalk and cap which separate readily, and the white or pale gills which do not join the stalk. Many species have a well defined ring or ring zone on the stalk. The spores are usually white.

Lepiota cristata, which has a white cap with tiny, flat brown scales, emits an odour of radish when bruised, is unpleasant to taste and is considered by some to be poisonous.

29

PSYCHOTROPIC POISONING

Within this group are two distinct types of poisoning: that due to ibotenic acid as in *Amanita muscaria*, and that due to psilocybin, a hallucinogen present in *Psilocybe* and some other genera.

IBOTENIC ACID This is found in toxicologically significant quantities in some British species of *Amanita*.

Fly Agaric *Amanita muscaria* (photo 2)

This attractive fungus, often illustrated in children's books, is found commonly from summer to late autumn on poor soils, usually under birch trees but occasionally with pine. It is characterised by a bright red convex or saucer-shaped cap, up to 15 cm across, dotted with white wart-like portions of the skin (universal veil) with which the young fruiting body is covered. The flesh is white except just beneath the skin, where it is yellowish. The stem is firm and white, hollow when old and up to 20 cm high. It tapers towards the top, where a torn white ring hangs as the remains of the membrane which, in young specimens, attaches the edge of the incurved cap to the stem. The base of the stem is bulbous and a few scaly fragments of the volva remain on it as irregular rings. The gills are white or cream and crowded together. They reach the stem but are not attached to it. The spores are white.

Panther Cap *Amanita pantherina*

Other common name: False Blusher

This fungus is smaller than, but resembles the fly agaric *(Amanita muscaria)* except in the colour of the cap, which is dull brown, often with an olive green tinge and dotted with crowded white warts. It may be mistaken for the true blusher, *Amanita rubescens*, which is edible, although damage to red blood cells (haemolysis) can result if it is eaten raw or undercooked. The two fungi can be distinguished by bruising the flesh, when that of the true blusher will become tinged pinkish-red, while that of the false blusher will remain white.

Poisonous principles The early isolation, in 1879, of a poisonous compound, muscarine, from *Amanita muscaria* has resulted in confusion over the active toxic constituents of this fungus and of *Amanita pantherina,* which induces the same type of poisoning reaction. Muscarine is highly toxic, but is not present in these species in sufficient quantities for it to be pharmacologically active. It is, however, present in higher concentrations and is actively toxic in several species of *Clitocybe* and *Inocybe.* This confusion can have serious consequences if atropine, a specific antidote for muscarine, is given in cases of poisoning by *Amanita muscaria* or *Amanita pantherina,* the activity of whose chief toxic constituent, ibotenic acid, is potentiated by atropine.

Ibotenic acid and related compounds, including muscazine and muscimol are isoxazole derivatives, associated primarily with the toxicity of *Amanita muscaria* and *Amanita pantherina* but they have also been reported in other species of *Amanita* and other fungi, including *Panaeolus campanulatus.*[43] The presence of muscimol, (a more potent toxin than ibotenic acid), as a natural constituent of these fungi is difficult to establish,[44] as ibotenic acid readily undergoes decarboxylation to muscimol. There is considerable variation in the ibotenic acid content of different specimens of the fungi. The toxins produce psychotropic effects for which the fungi are sometimes eaten deliberately. This practice cannot be recommended because severe reactions, including coma, occur in some individuals, although full recovery can be expected and it seems inappropriate to classify these fungi as deadly. Although the reaction induced by eating these fungi is generally attributed to ibotenic acid (and its derivatives) and described as hallucinogenic, this has not received universal acceptance. It is considered by some that the only orally active principles in fungi capable of producing true hallucinations are psilocybin and psilocin. These compounds occur in species of *Psilocybe, Panaeolus* and others, but no reports of their presence in fly agaric or panther cap have been found.

Poisoning Poisoning of dogs by *Amanita muscaria*[45] and of dogs[46] and cats[47] by *Amanita pantherina* has been reported. The symptoms were similar to those described in human beings, but, in addition, paralysis of the limbs occurred in the dogs. The convulsions experienced by some of the animals and the severity of the reaction, which was fatal in some cases, may have resulted from their being treated misguidedly with atropine sulphate.

The first symptoms of poisoning by these fungi are drowsiness, dizziness and mental confusion that may or may not be associated with digestive disturbances. Depending on the individual and the amount of fungus eaten there may be excitability, feelings of well-being and inebriation, delirium and illusions of colour and false visual images (rather than true hallucinations).[48] Incoordination and muscular twitching are frequent symptoms and drowsiness leading to deep sleep or even coma are characteristic. Headache and respiratory difficulty may also occur.[49] It is usual for symptoms of ibotenic acid poisoning to develop within $1\frac{1}{2}$ hours of ingestion and last for 4-8 hours[50] (sometimes longer).

Treatment should include emesis or stomach lavage as long as the patient is not 'hallucinating'. Sedation using diazepam or chlorpromazine and other symptomatic measures may be required.

PSILOCYBIN Hallucinogenic fungi occur in several genera and have many common names including magic mushrooms, happy mushrooms, laughing mushrooms, blue legs and sillys. These names are not specific and are often applied to different fungi within the group, related only by their containing hallucinogenic substances (usually psilocybin, a tryptamine derivative). In general the fungi have small caps and slender stems. Those known definitely to contain psilocybin belong to the genera *Psilocybe*, *Panaeolus*, *Panaeolina*, *Stropharia*, *Gymnopilus* and *Conocybe*, but there may well be others.

Gymnopilus spp

Several fungi previously classified as *Pholiota* have now been transferred to this genus, e.g. *Gymnopilus junonius* was known formerly as *Pholiota spectabilis*.

Species of *Gymnopilus* grow, often in tufts, at the base of tree trunks, on stumps or fallen branches and twigs and are very common in autumn. They all have golden yellow or tan coloured caps from 3-12 cm across, according to the species. The caps are covered with thin radiating fibrils, are sometimes slightly scaly and may have a central boss. The gills and stems are of a similar colour to, or paler than, the caps and may be thick and somewhat fibrous and bear a membranous ring (as in *Gymnopilus junonius*) or more slender and without a ring. The spores are rusty brown.

Fungi in this genus may be confused with the edible honey fungus (*Armillaria mellea*), which also grows in tufts at the base of trunks and is tan coloured or pale brown. *Armillaria* can be distinguished by the gills, which tend to run down the stem, and the thick whitish or pale yellow ring.

Panaeolus subbalteatus

This fungus often grows on freshly manured soil in gardens in tufts of two to four fruiting bodies which have caps 2-4 cm in diameter. These are convex at first but the edges often become slightly upturned at maturity. They are dark brown when moist, but paler when dry. The crowded gills are mottled dark brown, and touch but do not grow down the stem, which is slender, paler than the cap and up to 8 cm high. The spores are dark greenish black. Other species of this genus, including the grey mottle gill *(Panaeolus sphinctrinus)* (photo 6) may also be hallucinogenic.

Brown Hay Cap *Panaeolina foenisecii*

Other common name: Mower's Mushroom

This small fungus, formerly included in the genus *Psilocybe,* has a moist, bell-shaped or convex cap 1-2 cm across. It is dull brown, with a slightly reddish tinge, and dries to clay-coloured from the apex outwards, often leaving the margin darker and water-soaked. The gills are pale brown at first and finally mottled dark brown. The brownish stalk is slender and fragile and up to 8 cm high. The spores are dull brown and ornamented.

Psilocybe spp

Reclassification of some of the fungi formerly in this genus has resulted in relatively few species being retained. In general species of *Psilocybe* have small caps and slender stems and grow on soil, dung or plant remains.

Liberty Cap *Psilocybe semilanceata*

This fungus is common on grassland and heaths throughout Britain. It grows in groups but not from a common tuft. The buff or clay-coloured caps are up to 15 mm wide (but usually less), conical with a sharp apical point, an incurved margin and a moist, separable covering. The gills are purplish or black with a white edge. The stems are slender, up to 8 cm high, paler than the cap and often rather wavy. The spores are dark or purplish brown.

Dung Roundhead *Stropharia semiglobata*

This fungus is very common in Britain and grows throughout the year, on dung or dung-enriched soil, sometimes singly, but more often in groups. The smooth, domed caps, 1-4 cm in diameter, are pale yellow or ochre and tend to be sticky and shiny. The broad, crowded gills are purplish, becoming brownish black as the spores mature. The slender stems are up to 10 cm high, smooth and hollow, whitish or paler yellow than the cap and have a ring, or darker ring-like zone, below which they are slimy. The spores are dark brown.

Poisonous principles Fresh specimens of fungi that contain psilocybin (or its hydrolysis product, the closely related substance psilocin) tend to stain blue or blue-green, if bruised[51] particularly at the base of the stalk. The blue colour results from enzyme action in the presence of tryptamine derivatives, but its intensity is not necessarily related to the concentration of hallucinogens present. (The blueing of some species of *Boletus* involves an entirely different chemical process.)

The active principle of most of these fungi is the hallucinogen, psilocybin, an indole, sometimes referred to as an alkaloid, and usually designated as 4-phosphoryloxy-N, N-dimethyl tryptamine. Psilocin, an even more potent hallucinogenic agent, may occur in varying amounts in the fungi, but is also produced by hydrolysis of psilocybin after ingestion. Both psilocybin and psilocin have an effect similar to that of the drug LSD (lysergic acid diethylamide), and were listed as controlled drugs in the Misuse of Drugs Act, 1971. However, at present there is no legislation against possessing or growing the fungi, and 'harvesting kits' or 'growth kits' and several booklets for potential users can be bought.[52]

Poisoning In recent years there has been a dramatic increase in several countries in the use off these fungi as hallucinogens, although this property has been known and exploited for many centuries, particularly by Mexican Indians who eat them to induce trances in religious and magic rituals. The earliest recorded poisoning by hallucinogenic fungi in this country was described in 1803; a poor London family was indiscreet enough to eat a quantity found in St. James' Green.[53] The fungi involved were named as '*Agaricus semiglobatus*' and '*Agaricus glutinosus*'. From careful study of the written descriptions and illustrations of these fungi it is reasonable to assume that they were *Stropharia semiglobata* and *Psilocybe semilanceata*, respectively;[53] it was undoubtedly *Psilocybe semilanceata* that caused the poisoning. The fungi were mistaken for edible mushrooms and eaten by a man and his four children, all of whom had physical and mental reactions.

The deliberate use of 'magic mushrooms' to stimulate psychic perception is now fairly widespread, particularly among young people in Britain, where the highest incidence is apparently in northern England

34

and central Scotland. The desired effects are often accompanied by undesirable ones, as in the case of two young men who consumed 30-60 liberty caps *(Psilocybe semilanceata)*. They experienced confusion, agitation, tremors, paranoia, palpitations, visual disturbances and respiratory difficulties.[54] Poisoning by these fungi is rarely serious, spontaneous recovery usually occurring within 6-18 hours. They are not thought to be addictive and their recreational use appears to be relatively harmless except for the risk of premature mental and physical ageing after prolonged periods of regular use, recognised in Mexico. The increased risk of accident to hallucinating individuals and the cost of treating the growing number of cases admitted to hospitals is causing concern.[52] [55] Mistaken identification can also be a problem,[55] either when highly toxic fungi are eaten instead of magic mushrooms, or when magic mushrooms are eaten instead of edible species, as occurred in an accidental case of poisoning of two individuals who ate *Gymnopilus validipes* which they assumed to be the edible honey fungus *(Armillaria mellea).*[56]

No indolyl compounds related to psilocybin have been found in *Gymnopilus,* whose hallucinogenic principle has not been identified with certainty. A yellow constituent, bisnorgangonin, has been isolated and may be involved in the toxic reaction.

Hallucinations can result from eating the fungi raw or cooked or from drinking the liquor in which they have been stewed. Within less than an hour of ingestion, psilocybin (chiefly converted to psilocin) is distributed throughout the body. The psychic effects are correlated with the concentration of the toxins in the brain, but their mode of action has not been elucidated fully. Adverse physical reactions do not always occur, but may include rapid pulse, dilated pupils, restlessness, nausea, difficult breathing and headache. Varying degrees of delirium, sometimes with uncontrollable laughter are experienced, and visual aberrations of speed, light and colour are experienced.[54] [57] Hallucinations, accompanied by a feeling of well-being, then visual aberrations occurred in three young men, each of whom had eaten 20-30 specimens of *Panaeolina foenisecii.*[58] Stiffness and a sensation of swelling of the limbs has also been reported.[55] Occasionally there is acute panic and frightening mental disorientation. As few as four specimens of fungi have produced hallucinations[54] but it is not uncommon for up to 100 to be eaten at a time.[57]

A rather different type of poisoning, with a more prolonged reaction, was experienced in Scotland by two adults who ate 5-9 cooked specimens of *Panaeolus subbalteatus* with their breakfast.[59] Within 10 minutes one became cold and unsteady, and both suffered nausea and difficulty in coordinating physical and mental activities for several days. After nine days, sharpening of the senses was reported in one case.

Apart from observation to prevent abnormal or dangerous behaviour during hallucinations, treatment is not usually necessary, as the toxins are largely eliminated from the body (in urine) within about four hours, and symptoms rarely persist for more than twelve hours. Stomach lavage should not be used during hallucinations, as this could be very distressing. Treatment should consist of rest, continuous observation and reassurance. Sedation, using chlorpromazine, may be given but is not usually necessary.

MUSCARINE POISONING

The fungi mainly associated with muscarine poisoning are species of *Clitocybe* and *Inocybe*.

Clitocybe spp

This genus contains many large, medium-sized and small fungi that have fleshy caps, often with a somewhat wavy outline. The poisonous species are mainly top-shaped or funnel-shaped and have smooth, whitish, pallid or greyish brown caps. The gills of most species run down the stem to some extent and are whitish or greyish in colour. The spores are white.

Many *Clitocybe* species are poisonous or suspect and all are best avoided. The most poisonous are *Clitocybe rivulosa* and *Clitocybe dealbata*. These two species both grow in short grass or pasture and are similar in appearance, having a pale greyish-yellow cap, covered, at first, with a white silky bloom and sometimes becoming tinged pink at maturity. *Clitocybe dealbata* often grows in complete or partial rings and may be confused with the true fairy ring fungus *(Marasmius oreades)* which is edible. The latter is buff, pale tan or ochre in colour.

Inocybe spp (photo 4)

This group of small or medium-sized fungi is characterised by the cap which is convex, with a central boss. Its upper surface is covered with radiating fibrils or scales; the gills are clay-coloured. The spores are yellowish or light brown.

In young specimens, a delicate cobweb-like veil connects the edge of the cap to the stem, covering the gills.

All *Inocybe* species are best avoided because many are similar in appearance and some are poisonous. *Inocybe fastigiata*, which has a brownish-yellow cap that often splits at the edge, and yellow gills, is dangerously poisonous, as is *Inocybe patouillardii*, a somewhat atypical species found on calcareous soils. The latter appears early, either in late summer or early autumn, is white when young, but tinged yellowish-brown as it matures and may eventually become wholly bright red. It develops a characteristic pinkish-red colouration when bruised or cracked.

Inocybe geophylla is one of the most common *Inocybe* species in Britain. It is found on damp soil, often growing in woods, and is poisonous. The fungus has a white stalk and cap which, when expanded, has a prominent central boss. There is a lilac form (var *lilacina*).

Poisonous principles   The main toxicologically active constituent of several species of *Clitocybe* and *Inocybe* is muscarine, a quarternary ammonium compound. This was first isolated and named in 1869, from *Amanita muscaria*. It is, however, present only in insignificant amounts in this fungus, but occurs in higher concentrations in other fungi, notably species of *Clitocybe* and *Inocybe*. Confusion over the toxic constituents of these fungi continues to the present day, sometimes with serious results, when atropine, a specific antidote for muscarine, is given in cases of poisoning by *Amanita muscaria* the activity of whose chief toxic constituent, ibotenic acid, is potentiated by atropine.

Poisoning   Muscarine acts by inhibiting the conduction of impulses between nerve cells. The symptoms of muscarine poisoning develop within 15 minutes to two hours of ingestion. The combination of perspiration, salivation and lacrimation is diagnostic for poisoning by muscarine-containing fungi[60] and is sometimes referred to as the PSL syndrome. Other symptoms include abdominal pain (sometimes with vomiting), watery diarrhoea, reduced blood pressure and heart rate, profuse sweating, asthmatic wheezing and blurred vision.[60 61] A mortality rate of approximately 5% has been estimated.[62]

Of the fungal poisons, only muscarine has a specific antidote, atropine, which should be given as soon as the cause of poisoning has been established with certainty, and thereafter as required.

The copper trumpet *(Omphalotus olearius)*, a very rare fungus in Britain, (sometimes known as *Pleurotus olearius* and classified previously as *Clitocybe olearia)* also contains muscarine-like toxins. In this country it grows in clumps at the base of oak trees. The funnel-shaped cap is up to 15 cm across and the gills run down the stem. The whole fungus is coppery orange, but the spores are whitish. One report cites 25 cases of poisoning by this fungus that were treated in Yugoslavia in September 1969.[63] In addition to the symptoms described for muscarine poisoning, several patients noticed unpleasant, sometimes metallic tastes, and tingling of the fingertips.

The importance of correct identification cannot be over-emphasised as many cases of poisoning result from eating muscarine-containing fungi instead of the edible chanterelle *(Cantharellus cibarius)* which some of them resemble.[63]

Common Ink Cap *Coprinus atramentarius*

The fruit bodies of this fungus grow in clusters adjacent to rotting tree stumps from late spring to late autumn. The pale greyish, bell-shaped cap of the fungus is up to 5 cm high, ribbed radially and indistinctly scaly, especially near the centre, where it is often tinged light brown. As it matures, the edge of the cap becomes ragged and moist as the black gills (whitish when young) degenerate into an inky fluid containing the black spores. The stalk grows up to 20 cm high and is 1-2 cm thick, tapering upwards from the slightly bulbous base.

Poisonous principles   An amino acid derivative (N^5-(1-hydroxycyclopropyl) glutamine), named coprine, has been isolated from *Coprinus atramentarius*.[64] The toxic effect of coprine is exhibited only in the presence of alcohol (ethanol) and is similar to that induced by the drug disulfiram (Antabuse) used in the treatment of alcoholism. In the past it was suggested that the fungus actually contained disulfiram, but biochemical studies and experimental work with mice have shown that this is not the case.[64] Without alcohol, the common ink cap is good to eat. A similar reaction with alcohol has been reported after eating *Clitocybe clavipes*.

In coprine poisoning, the reported intervals between eating the fungus and taking alcohol are very variable, ranging from an hour or two before, to several days after. The consumption of alcohol at the same time as this fungus rarely has any undesirable effect. It appears that the time of occurrence and severity of the reaction are related to the blood alcohol level at the time the coprine reaches the liver. In common with many other potentially poisonous fungi, there is considerable variation in the reaction of different individuals, some being unaffected by the coprine/alcohol combination,[65] while others who have eaten the fungi are affected after taking alcoholic drinks[66] or simply by the alcohol in such preparations as salad dressings or skin lotions.[67]

Poisoning   The first effect is flushing of the face and neck (sometimes extending to the chest and arms). This is accompanied by a rapid, throbbing pulse, perspiration, dizziness and coldness, sometimes with tingling of the extremities, particularly the fingertips. There may also be nausea, vomiting, severe headache and mental confusion. It is usual for the reaction to develop within 30 minutes of taking alcohol and to last for 1-2 hours. Recurrences of the reaction may be experienced if alcohol is taken again within the next few days.

It is often stated that only cooked *Coprinus atramentarius* will elicit this reaction, but, contrary to some reports, coprine does not require heat for its activation and the consumption of raw fungi can also produce the characteristic effects.

Treatment As spontaneous recovery is usually fairly rapid, simple symptomatic treatment is usually all that is required.

Club Foot Mushroom *Clitocybe clavipes*

This fungus can be recognised by its grey-brown, top-shaped cap, yellowish gills and bulbous, club-shaped base of the stem.

Poisoning occurs only when alcohol is taken a few hours or days after eating the fungus. This reaction is usually associated with the ingestion of the common ink cap *(Coprinus atramentarius)* with alcohol. The effects are similar to those induced by the drug disulfiram (Antabuse) used in the treatment of alcoholism. It has been stated that the effects of eating *Clitocybe clavipes* with alcohol are only nausea and vomiting[68] and are therefore different from coprine poisoning, but typical Antabuse symptoms, including flushing of the face, a sense of puffiness in the hands and throbbing of the head and neck have also been experienced. There were three incidents of this type of poisoning in three different years in Britain.[69] In one case the reaction occurred when alcohol was taken seven hours after eating 4-6 fruiting bodies of the fungus. Specimens of the same fungus, collected from the same location in previous years, had not produced symptoms under the same conditions. The reasons for this variation are not known. In treatment, propranolol may be required to relieve the symptoms.

Cloud Cap *Clitocybe nebularis*

This fungus, also known as the clouded agaric, is generally considered good to eat, but should be taken with caution, as in some sensitive individuals it can cause severe diarrhoea.[70]

GASTROINTESTINAL POISONING

Fungi of several genera may cause gastrointestinal disturbances. The severity of the reaction depends on the state of the fungus (i.e. raw or cooked, fresh or old) and the sensitivity of the individual.

Yellow-staining Mushroom *Agaricus xanthodermus*

This fungus grows in clusters in autumn in pastures, woods and gardens, often on leaf mould. The fully expanded white cap (sometimes slightly grey at the centre) may be up to 15 cm across (usually 5-8 cm) and is broadly domed or convex. The gills change from whitish, to greyish-pink and finally greyish-brown as the purple-brown spores mature. The stem is 6-15 cm high and bears a prominent membranous ring.

This fungus is similar to the field mushroom *(Agaricus campestris)* and the horse mushroom *(Agaricus arvensis)* but differs from them in the bright, deep yellow coloration that develops on the cap and stem (particularly at the base) when bruised.

Agaricus xanthodermus is best avoided because, although eaten without ill effects by some individuals, in others there is abdominal pain and vomiting;[61] dizziness, faintness and a severe headache (with pain behind the eyes) that persisted for several hours, developed in two people who ate, as an experiment, one eighth of a cooked cap each.[71]

Agaricus placomyces, which also shows a bright yellow colour change on bruising, has a cap which is densely covered with minute greyish-brown or sooty-brown scales on a white ground. The wood mushroom *(Agaricus silvicola)* has a cream cap, bruising yellow, and smells of aniseed. While some individuals are unharmed, ingestion of these two fungi may cause indigestion and diarrhoea.[72] Another similar mushroom *(Agaricus nivescens)* is good to eat, stains lemon yellow when bruised and has flesh smelling of almonds.

Correct identification should be made and caution exercised when contemplating eating yellow-staining species of *Agaricus*.

Stomach lavage or emesis should be performed if *Agaricus xanthodermus* is eaten. Fluid replacement, together with other symptomatic measures, may be required.

Boletus spp

These fleshy fungi usually have a thick stalk, bearing the cap which has, on its underside, instead of radiating gills, closely crowded vertical tubes, opening by pores, so appearing sponge-like.

Many *Boletus* species are edible. Some, although not poisonous, are not edible because of their bitter taste, and at least one is poisonous.

This is the devil's boletus *(Boletus satanas)* which is not common in Britain but may be found in beech woods on calcareous soils, particularly in the South.

The fungus has a pale greyish cap, which may extend up to 20 cm across. The stalk is strikingly bulbous and covered with a red network. At maturity the pores are bright red. The spores are golden-brown. Because of the danger of confusing this species with other similar edible ones, it is advisable to avoid any *Boletus* which has red pores.

If eaten, the devil's boletus causes gastrointestinal disturbance and irritation.

Entoloma spp

There is considerable variation in size among these fungi, some of which are small and delicate and others robust. They often have a mealy smell. The gills are pink at maturity and, depending on the species, may terminate at the stem or extend down it. The elliptical spores are pink and angular. Fungi of this genus are also widely reported in the literature under the (unacceptable) generic name *Rhodophyllus*.

Entoloma sinuatum

This fungus, sometimes referred to as *Entoloma lividum,* has a thick stalk and a yellowish or greyish-ochre cap up to 15 cm across, with a central boss. It has a smooth, moist surface and may have an undulating edge. The gills are whitish-yellow at first but become flesh-coloured at maturity. The taste of the fungus is pleasant, initially, but it can cause severe vomiting, abdominal pain and diarrhoea. There may also be difficult breathing, slow pulse and coma.[73]

Hebeloma spp

The cap of the crustlike or fairy cake hebeloma *(H. crustuliniforme)* is usually 3-7 cm across, convex with inrolled edges when expanded, pallid or tinged light brown at the centre and slimy when moist. The stem is approximately 0.5 cm thick, white, often larger near the base, and bears powdery granules particularly near the top. The gills change with age from pale clay coloured to dull brown and often bear droplets of moisture on the edge in damp weather. The spores are pale brown and warted. *Hebeloma crustuliniforme* has an acrid taste and can cause poisoning. Members of this genus are not generally considered edible, although as with some other fungi, they are not necessarily poisonous to all individuals.

Sulphur Tuft *Hypholoma fasciculare*

This fungus is common in Britain and grows in dense clusters all through the year on or near stumps of broad-leaved trees. The caps are up to 7 cm across, sulphur-yellow and often have a dark tan centre. The gills are yellow at first, but become greenish. The spores are brownish-purple.

Sulphur tuft has a bitter taste and is often considered poisonous. Two dogs which ate the fungus suffered severe vomiting.[61]

Milk Caps *Lactarius* spp

Members of this genus are mostly reddish-brown or grey in colour and have white or yellowish spores. The fungi are characterised by having a depression in the centre of the cap and by exuding a milky white, or sometimes coloured juice, especially from the gills, where broken. This milk varies in taste from mild to acrid or peppery. While some species are edible those with a peppery taste, like *Lactarius piperatus, Lactarius pyrogalus,* and the woolly milk cap *(Lactarius torminosus)* are considered inedible and may cause vomiting and diarrhoea.

Morel *Morchella esculenta*

The oval, yellowish-brown cap of this fairly large fungus (up to 15 cm high) is deeply and irregularly pitted and the stem is thick and usually yellowish.

It is usually considered good to eat, although a report concerning poisoning of dogs given the cooked fungus or the liquid in which it was cooked may have involved this species.[74] The symptoms included vomiting and blood-stained diarrhoea and urine.

Roll Rim *Paxillus involutus*

This fungus is particularly common under birch trees. The cap is convex at first and has a strongly incurved margin, but expands up to 12 cm across, with a central depression. Initially the rust-coloured or olive-brown cap is downy, but it becomes smooth, except sometimes at the edges which are often grooved. The stalk is short, slightly paler than the cap and may be eccentric. The gills, which change from yellowish to brown, run from the cap down the top part of the stalk. The spores are brown. This fungus is poisonous to some individuals when eaten raw, but is apparently edible when cooked.

Pholiota squarrosa

This fungus grows in autumn in clusters from the base of the trunk of old broad-leaved trees. The cap, which is up to 10 cm across, is convex at first but flattens during growth except at the margin which remains incurved. Both the cap and stalk are dark yellow and are covered with darker brownish shaggy scales. The gills are yellow at first, but become rust coloured or tinged olive later. The spores are brown. Eating this fungus does not cause serious poisoning but it is indigestible and acts as a gastrointestinal irritant.

Fairy Clubs *Ramaria* spp

These erect, densely branching pinkish or orange-coloured coralloid fungi may grow up to 25 cm high from the basal stalk, which is stout and paler in colour. The flesh is usually pale orange but bruises brownish or black. The spores are brown and ornamented.

A few of these fairy club fungi are edible, but at least one, *Ramaria formosa*, sometimes known as the handsome clavaria has a particularly bitter taste when cooked and is poisonous.

Brittle Gills *Russula* spp

Many of the fungi in this large genus have brightly coloured caps, and the gills, usually all of the same length and running the entire distance between cap margin and stem, are remarkably brittle. Their spores are white to dark yellow. They resemble *Lactarius* species but no milk is exuded when the flesh or gills are broken. Several species are good to eat but others, like the sickener *(Russula emetica)*, *Russula fellea* and *Russula nauseosa* have a hot or acrid taste and are best avoided as they are gastrointestinal irritants and cause vomiting. All *Russula* species are said to be safe to eat after cooking and discarding the cooking liquid.

Earthballs *Scleroderma* spp

Fungi in this genus are more or less spherical or pear-shaped structures with coarse, root-like threads at the base.

Earthballs are fleshy when young, but develop a thick, tough, yellowish, leathery skin, with a scaly or grained surface. The interior of the fungus varies in colour with different species at maturity from purplish black to dark umber, and consists of a mass of spores traversed by white threads. When mature the leathery coat splits open irregularly to release the dry, powdery spores. Earthballs have an acrid smell and taste and are considered poisonous. In the USA, a young man who ate a small piece of raw *Scleroderma cepa* developed symptoms including abdominal pain and nausea. Tingling progressing to rigidity affected the whole body. Rapid recovery occurred after vomiting.[75] Several of the superficially similar puffballs *(Lycoperdon)* are edible, and earthballs may be confused with these.

Stropharia coronilla

This fungus grows in similar situations and is superficially similar to the field mushroom *(Agaricus campestris)* with which it is sometimes confused. *Stropharia* is probably poisonous. It can be distinguished from the field mushroom by its yellowish cap and stem, and by the gills which tend to run a short distance down the stem or are joined to it by a tooth, while those of the edible mushroom are free from the stem. The spores are dark brown.

Verdigris Agaric *Stropharia aeruginosa*

When young the cap of this fungus is covered with a bluish-green slime and often has small whitish scales, especially round the edge. The cap is rounded at first, then flattens and expands to about 6 cm across and has a central boss. As it ages the colour changes to a dull yellowish-green. The stalk is tinged bluish green and has a distinct ring. The gills are dark brown, sometimes edged with white. The spores are dark brown. Although apparently eaten in some Continental countries, this fungus is generally considered poisonous.

Tricholoma spp

In this large genus, most of the fungi are fleshy and have well-spaced gills which develop a distinct notch just before joining the stalk. Some are edible and good, notably the St. George's mushroom *(Tricholoma gambosum)*, which is more correctly classified as *Calocybe gambosa*, and the blewits *(Tricholoma nudum* and *Tricholoma saevum)* which are now usually referred to the genus *Lepista*. However, other species, including *Tricholoma album* and *Tricholoma sulphureum* are gastrointestinal irritants.

Symptoms, including dizziness, warmth, muscular stiffness, numbness and tingling of extremities, weakness, headache and incoordination when walking, developed, when dried *Tricholoma sulphureum* was cooked and eaten.[76] Stomach pains were experienced later. Deep sleep preceded recovery. Susceptibility of individuals to these fungi appears to vary and *Tricholoma personatum*, another name for *Lepista saeva*, eaten raw or cooked, has caused abdominal pain, vomiting and diarrhoea.[61] *Tricholoma* species should be avoided unless positively identified.

ERGOT

Ergot *Claviceps* spp (photo 1)

Claviceps is a parasitic fungus that infects, with varying severity, many grasses and cereal crops in whose flowers hard, elongated, blackish-purple spurs of fungal material develop, replacing the ovary and sometimes protruding from the seedhead. These hard masses, the 'ergots', are sclerotia, the resting stage of the fungus, from which, after overwintering in the soil, spores develop and infect new plants. The species found in Britain is *Claviceps purpurea,* but several other species that also produce ergots occur elsewhere.

Symptoms typical of ergot poisoning in man have been recorded for centuries[1] [2] even before a definite connection between the disease and consumption of grain parasitised by the fungus was recognised. In the past the disease was usually associated with rye, a decline in its incidence coinciding with an increase in the use of wheat flour,[2] but wheat and other cereal crops may also be parasitised by *Claviceps.*[3]

Because of its well known and long-standing reputation for poisoning, reports of ergot in crops usually receive considerable publicity and cause alarm, even when the incidence of the fungus is low. It is, therefore, difficult to make an accurate assessment of the prevalence of ergot in the country. *Claviceps* in wild grasses that could be a reservoir of infection for cereal crops, and the reluctance of farmers to send infected grain to millers (some of whom reject grain containing even a trace of ergot) are further complications. Grain with a small percentage of ergot is sometimes used in animal feed mixes, since the quantity of infected material eaten would be too low to produce clinical signs of poisoning. The danger to livestock is, however, intensified by some grain dressing operations in which, during grading and cleaning, ergots may be concentrated in the residual material, which may be fed to animals.[4]

In Britain, *Claviceps purpurea* has not been common or extensive in home-grown cereal crops for many years, although sporadic outbreaks have been reported. However, from the late 1970s onwards there have been increasing numbers of reports of ergot infection,[4] mainly in winter wheat. The disease in this crop was prevalent initially only in Scotland and northern England but it has now spread south. In 1982 *Claviceps* infection was more widespread in Britain than for many previous years. Crops in many parts of the country, including Wales and south-west England, were affected as well as some in the north.[5] [6] Recommended precautionary measures for farmers and grain merchants have been distributed.[7] The only effective treatment of land when *Claviceps* is present is deep ploughing (25 cm) after harvesting, as ergots buried deeply in soil will not germinate. There is considerable variation in the susceptibility to ergot of different varieties of cereals. Open-flowered varieties acquire the infection more readily. Work is in progress on producing resistant plant strains.

Poisonous principles

Claviceps contains alkaloids of which over 40 have been isolated, although not all are toxic. Many of these have been given names derived from the common name of the fungus (ergo-) and some are indicative of their structure or behaviour e.g. ergotamine, ergocristine, ergonovine (ergometrine). There are several synonyms in current use. The ergot alkaloids can be divided, according to their structure, into two groups: acid amide derivatives of lysergic acid, and clavines, in which the carboxyl group of the lysergic acid has been reduced to the hydroxymethyl or methyl group.[8] [9] It is of interest that a derivative of lysergic acid is the powerful hallucinogenic agent lysergic acid diethylamide (LSD), a drug whose use and misuse has been publicised widely. The total alkaloid content and the type of alkaloids present vary considerably in ergots of different strains and species of *Claviceps,* on different plant hosts and according to the environmental conditions. Thus it is not surprising that there are no precise figures available on the quantity of ergot considered safe for various classes of livestock or for human consumption. In some instances concentrations in grain of less than 1% ergot (by weight) have caused poisoning.

Some ergot alkaloids stimulate the action of smooth muscles, with consequent local restriction of arterial blood flow. This property is responsible for some of the adverse effects of ergot, but is also of pharmacological value, ergot derivatives being used to stimulate muscle contractions and control bleeding, particularly in obstetrics and in the treatment of conditions involving dilation of blood vessels (e.g. migraine). Ergotamine tartrate and ergometrine maleate are examples of preparations in general use. Most of the alkaloids available commercially are now obtained from *Claviceps* grown in laboratory culture rather than as a parasite on grass or cereal seed heads. Prolonged or excessive use of the drugs can induce symptoms of poisoning. So far, only the lysergic acid derivatives, and not the clavine alkaloids, have been used therapeutically.[9]

Poisoning in animals

The effects of ergot poisoning vary according to the concentration and type of alkaloids present and the duration of exposure to infected pasture or grain and grain products (including flour). Ergot appears to be unpalatable, as feed intake is usually reduced if it is present. Animals may lose weight and condition[10] [11] but more specific signs usually occur. Animals and man are affected similarly and two disease syndromes have been recognised, both called 'ergotism'. These are described variously as acute or chronic; nervous (convulsive) or gangrenous. Although there may be some general symptoms in common, it is unusual for the characteristic features of the two types of ergotism to occur in one outbreak. Animals are affected mainly by the gangrenous form of ergotism. When a relatively

47

large amount of ergot is eaten in a short time, irritation of the digestive tract, accompanied by abdominal pain and vomiting, occurs.[3] [12] The nervous symptoms include loss of balance, incoordination, muscle tremors and convulsions, which are often followed by drowsiness and temporary paralysis.[3] [8] The diminished blood supply that results from eating smaller amounts of ergot over a longer period, causes progressive degeneration of tissues, especially in the body extremities, where circulation is weakest. Initial pain and inflammation are followed by coldness, numbness and the development of dry, gangrenous lesions. It is not uncommon for portions of ears, tails and feet to be sloughed off. It is sometimes necessary to slaughter severely lame animals. It has often been stated that the consumption of ergot can cause abortion, but this is now considered unlikely as ergot alkaloids do not induce contractions in an inactive uterus, although they appear capable of increasing the strength of uterine contractions during birth.

In cattle the acute form of ergotism does occur,[13] but the gangrenous form is the more common, with lameness being a prominent feature.[14] [15] The milk yield of lactating cows may fall drastically.[15]

Selective grazing by sheep, which tend to avoid coarse-headed grasses, is an indirect protection against ergot poisoning, although it can occur to a limited extent in these animals.[16] A convulsive syndrome with 25% mortality occurred in a Lincolnshire flock[17] and symptoms included diarrhoea, reddening of the skin followed by hair loss and necrosis of ear pinnae, general weakness and incoordination. Some deaths occurred in Finland in sheep pastured on grasses with a high (0.2%) alkaloid content.[18] In experimental work, ergot sclerotia were well tolerated by housed sheep, but severe lameness developed in an animal pastured in cold, wet conditions while being given ergot containing 0.5 mg ergotamine per kg body weight daily. It was suggested that the low environmental temperature also reduced peripheral circulation so that the effect of the alkaloid was more pronounced.[19]

In general, pigs do not develop the gangrenous syndrome or lameness, but there may be reduced feed intake and consequent weight loss (or reduced rate of weight gain),[11] [20] [21] and interference with nitrogen metabolism.[20] [21] When rye ergot sclerotia were fed (up to 4% of the diet) to sows in early pregnancy, the embryos were unaffected, but when given later in pregnancy the sows lost condition and the number of piglets per litter was low. Some piglets were born dead or were premature and there was almost total failure of mammary gland development, teat enlargement and milk production.[22] [23] In separate incidents, piglets being suckled by sows that had eaten ergot developed necrosis of the tips of the tails and ears[24] or lacked vitality, were anaemic and had watery diarrhoea.[23]

Feeding chicks with a diet containing more than 0.3% of ergot depressed growth rate and increased mortality. Blackening of the nails, toes, shanks, beaks and combs was reported. In laying hens, feed consumption, body weight and egg production decreased, but there was no mortality, even with feed containing 9% of ergot.[25]

Reports of ergot toxicity in horses are mainly in the older literature. Acute poisoning after eating hay containing ergot sclerotia has been recorded.[26] The hooves, tail and mane were affected.

Human poisoning Ergot poisoning in man has been known for many centuries[1] and was known as St. Anthony's Fire, after the saint who is said to have suffered from it. This name refers to the burning sensations that may be experienced in the mouth, digestive tract and extremities after eating food containing ergot. Although ergotism in man still occurs in many parts of the world, no outbreak of epidemic proportion has been recorded in Britain since the late 1920s, when Jewish immigrants in Manchester were affected after eating bread made from ergot-infected rye grown in Yorkshire.[27] Millers in Britain are aware of the danger of ergot and it is unlikely that contaminated grain would be ground into flour for human consumption. However, a return to simpler living in rural areas by increasing numbers of people, who grow and grind their own grain on a small scale, could result in a recurrence of human ergotism in this country. Although it is clear that both the gangrenous and nervous forms of ergotism described in animals can occur in man, the reported symptoms vary greatly from a mild tingling in the extremities, and burning sensation in the mouth to severe convulsions, and extreme mental confusion.

Treatment This should include symptomatic and supportive measures, and, where necessary, vasodilators such as nitroprusside; amyl nitrite inhalations may be required.

MYCOTOXINS

Another type of poisoning results from the consumption of secondary metabolites of the microscopic fungi (referred to colloquially as moulds) that may be present in foodstuffs or animal feeds. These toxic metabolites of moulds are called mycotoxins, although, by derivation, all fungal toxins, including the antibiotics, are mycotoxins.

It was only comparatively recently that the potential for mycotoxins to cause diseases (mycotoxicoses) in animals was recognised. Aflatoxin, a mycotoxin, was shown to be the cause of death of thousands of poultry in Britain during 1960. It was found subsequently that this toxin also induced tumours of the liver, and research on aflatoxin and other mycotoxins gathered momentum. Today there is a vast literature on mycotoxins and mycotoxicoses too great for the subject to be dealt with in detail here. For more information recent reviews should be consulted.[1][2][3] This description has been included, however, since it is by the ingestion of plants or plant products that poisoning by mycotoxins arises. In the past, the plants themselves were assumed to be responsible for some diseases now known to be mycotoxicoses.

Aflatoxicosis   The fungi that produce aflatoxin are mainly strains of *Aspergillus flavus* or *Aspergillus parasiticus*. The clinical signs of aflatoxicosis vary among animal species, but reduced growth rate is common to most. The duration of exposure to aflatoxin in feed before the appearance of clinical signs is extremely variable and depends on the species of animal and the level of contamination of the feed. The disease is more likely to be chronic than acute, as in Britain the levels of aflatoxin in animal feedingstuffs are low. Aflatoxin has been shown to cause liver tumours in a variety of laboratory animals and there is some circumstantial evidence from other countries linking aflatoxin with such tumours in man. Aflatoxin B_1 is metabolised by animals and is excreted as aflatoxin M_1 in the faeces, urine and milk.

Awareness of the risk of aflatoxicosis in Britain led to the general acceptance, in the early 1960s of a voluntary code of practice which limited the use of ground nuts, thus preventing excessive aflatoxin contamination of animal feeds. These voluntary measures were replaced in 1976 by government regulations[4] stipulating maximum concentrations of aflatoxin B_1 (estimated by a standard analytical method) in feedstuffs for sale. Separate tolerances were given for several domestic animals and poultry based on their susceptibility to aflatoxin. In 1981, however, an amendment to these regulations prohibited the importation of groundnut and cotton seed and their derivatives. These stricter regulations resulted from a report which showed that liquid and dried milk was still frequently contaminated with aflatoxin M_1 even though at very low levels. In 1982, a further amendment allowed the importation of groundnut (and its derivatives) in which the level of aflatoxin B_1 does not exceed 0.05 mg/kg.[5]

Various detoxification processes of mouldy feedstuffs have been used in attempts to reduce their aflatoxin content, but only treatment with ammonia gas (usually of grain) has had sufficient effect to warrant its use commercially.

Many other mycotoxins have been identified from moulds, some of which, such as ochratoxin, citrinin, zearalenone and trichothecenes have been isolated from animal feeds. In Britain the climatic conditions, agricultural practices and import regulations for feed materials are limiting factors, so that mycotoxins are only potential causes of disease, infrequently realised. They do, however, present a potential hazard in that imported feeds may be contaminated on arrival in Britain, and home-grown feeds may become contaminated if improperly dried and stored; fungal contamination of crops before harvesting could also occur. Mycotoxins have now been found in a wide variety of foods, including cereal grains and nuts, and in the milk, meat and offal of animals that have eaten contaminated feed. In Britain, however, with the exception of aflatoxin, the evidence connecting the presence of mycotoxins in feed and the occurrence of specific disease in animals or man is only circumstantial.

It must be emphasised that feed may contain mycotoxins even though not visibly mouldy, and conversely, the presence of moulds in growing plants and stored or processed foods does not necessarily indicate the presence of mycotoxins. These are produced by only a limited number of fungi (mainly species of *Aspergillus, Penicillium* and *Fusarium)* but not all strains of these fungi are capable of producing toxins; many environmental factors can also influence their production. Relatively complicated laboratory analysis of feed samples is the only means of determining the type and extent of mycotoxin contamination. Some of the mycotoxins that occur in animal feeds in Britain have definitely been described as causing disease in other countries. They include ochratoxin and citrinin, produced by some species of *Aspergillus* on barley and probably acting together to produce kidney fibrosis in pigs; zearalenone (F-2 toxin), which is oestrogenic and may cause reproductive disorders (particularly in pigs); and trichothecenes which are irritant and may cause lesions in the mouth and stomach. Some of these have recently been implicated in disease in Britain.[6] In the winter of 1980-81, reduced growth rate, poor feathering and abnormal behaviour in broiler fowls in Scotland were associated with feed contaminated with *Fusarium* species which produced the mycotoxins zearalenone, deoxynivalenol, and diacetoxyscirpenol.

Apart from the possibility of mycotoxins being present, there are other potential dangers in using mouldy feed and bedding materials. If inhaled, the spores of *Micropolyspora faeni* can produce an allergic respiratory condition (farmer's lung) in cattle and man, and those of *Aspergillus fumigatus* can cause respiratory disorders in mammals and birds and lead to systemic infection and abortion in cattle.

PTERIDOPHYTES

Within this botanical group, the poisonous members in Britain are in the families Equisetaceae, Aspidiaceae and Dennstaedtiaceae.

EQUISETACEAE

Horsetail *Equisetum*

Other common name: Mare's Tail

Horsetails are found throughout the country and are troublesome weeds of pastures and arable land, especially in damp areas. At least ten species occur in Britain, the common horsetail *(Equisetum arvense)* and the marsh horsetail *(Equisetum palustre)* being widely distributed, while the others are more local.

Horsetails have a branching, underground rhizome from which ascend green, vegetative, jointed stems which are hollow, ridged longitudinally and up to 80 cm tall. Whorls of slender green branches radiate from the main stem at the joints (nodes). The leaves are represented only by a small, toothed sheath extending 4-12 mm up the main stem above each node, and by minute scales at the nodes of the branches. Erect, fertile branches also develop. These are usually brownish in colour, have toothed sheaths, but no whorled branches at the nodes, and terminate in a cone-like structure which consists of closely crowded rings of spore-bearing organs.

Poisonous principles   The plants contain varying quantities of silicates, rendering them harsh to touch and rather unpalatable in the fresh state. A variety of toxic principles have been extracted from horsetail, the most important one being an enzyme, thiaminase,[1] which also occurs in bracken *(Pteridium aquilinum),* and which destroys vitamin B_1 (thiamine). The clinical signs of poisoning caused by eating horsetail closely resemble those of vitamin B_1 deficiency.

Poisoning in animals   Despite the similar action of different horsetail species, it is most usual for horses to be poisoned by *Equisetum arvense,* and cattle (and to a less extent, sheep) by *Equisetum palustre.* Poisoning results less frequently from ingestion of the growing plants than from hay in which as little as 5% horsetail may produce symptoms. The poisonous principle is not destroyed by drying and storage, and a case is reported in which bullocks were poisoned by eating hay containing horsetail which had been stored for at least 16 months.[2] Horses may eat the plant from their bedding in preference to clean hay.[3] However, *Equisetum* poisoning is rarely reported in Britain. The symptoms in poisoned animals may be acute or take several weeks to develop. It is said that grain-fed animals are less severely affected than those not given grain.[4] Horses develop general unthriftiness, weight loss, weakness and incoordination (especially of the hindquarters). This may progress to posterior paralysis, muscular exhaustion and rigidity, and inability to stand despite extreme efforts made to do so. The appetite is not usually lost; there may be either constipation or diarrhoea. In severely affected horses there may be a rapid, weak pulse, opacity of the cornea of the eye, coldness of extremities and, in extreme cases, convulsions, coma and death.[4] [5] Pregnant animals may abort.[6]

Cattle are less severely affected than horses, but may lose condition, and develop diarrhoea and muscular weakness, particularly of the hindquarters.[4] [7] The milk yield of lactating animals falls, and the milk may be watery and have a bitter taste.[8] In addition, sweating and swaying were prominent features in calves poisoned by eating growing horsetail.[9] Poisoning in sheep is rarely described, but the symptoms are similar to those in cattle.[8]

Post-mortem findings These are not specific, but include varying degrees of jaundice of the subcutaneous connective tissue, degenerative changes in the brain, liver and kidneys, congestion of the lungs,[6] catarrhal inflammation in the digestive tract,[5] and exudation of serum from the membranes around the brain and spinal cord.[10]

Treatment Administration of large doses of vitamin B_1 or yeast, or preferably the intravenous injection of thiamine, is recommended. Injection of 25 ml (2.5 g) thiamine hydrochloride solution was effective in saving six of seven horses and a calf.[11] Recovery, particularly without treatment, is often slow.[5]

ASPIDIACEAE

Male and Buckler Ferns *Dryopteris* spp

Several of the *Dryopteris* spp. native in Britain are uncommon or limited in their distribution, but the male fern *(Dryopteris filix-mas)* occurs throughout the country and is common in woods, hedges and rocky places including steep hillsides, usually on acid soils. There are other similar, though taxonomically distinct ferns, often bearing an older generic name, such as *Aspidium*, and the specific name *filix-mas;* hybrids of plants within the group are found. Various buckler ferns also occur, but less commonly than the male fern.

Male Fern *Dryopteris filix-mas*

The bright, deep green leaves, grow from a short, stout, scaly underground stem (rhizome), forming a crown. Each leaf is composed of rows of numerous leaflets that are themselves deeply divided, almost to the stem. Spore-bearing structures develop in a row down each side of the small subdivisions of some leaves. The stalk is almost as long as the spreading blade of the leaf and together they may sometimes exceed 150 cm in length. The stalk bears brownish or orange scales. Some leaves may persist into the winter.

Poisonous principles

These ferns contain thiaminase, the agent responsible for thiamine deficiency in horses and pigs that have eaten bracken *(Pteridium aquilinum)* but thiamine deficiency has not been reported with *Dryopteris* spp. The active constituent of the ferns that has produced the adverse effects reported in cattle is not known. Extracts of male fern have anthelmintic properties and have been used medicinally; the toxicity of these extracts is well recognised.

Poisoning in animals

There are few reports of *Dryopteris* poisoning. All have involved cattle and occurred in winter, when the ferns were eaten as fresh food was scarce. It was reported in Ireland in three herds in 1964-5, when cattle on pastures with very little available herbage fed on rhizomes of buckler fern *(Dryopteris* sp.) growing in the hedgerows.[1] Poisoning due to male fern *(Dryopteris filix-mas)* occurred in Kirkudbright, Scotland, in 1967[2] and in 1976.[3] In both Scottish outbreaks the cattle were on an adequate diet of winter feed (silage and hay), but appear to have eaten growing rhizomes of the fern to satisfy a desire for fresh feed. The 1976 outbreak was more severe than that of 1967, possibly due to the combined toxic effects of male fern and rusty male fern *(Dryopteris borreri)*, which were growing together in the same field.

Clinical signs found in this type of poisoning are blindness often with widely dilated pupils, staggering gait, and hard, dark brown faeces; in some cases the animals stand or lie in water. Mortality is low. The blindness, which is sometimes permanent, is a characteristic feature of *Dryopteris* poisoning. Results of detailed examination of eyes of blind calves[4] revealed haemorrhages of the retina, oedema of the optic disc, and damage to the optic nerve.

Post-mortem examination of a cow from the 1967 outbreak[2] showed the animal to be in good condition. The rumen contents were very dry and contained partly chewed pieces of male fern. The walls of the abomasum and small intestine were thickened and acutely inflamed, the gall bladder was enlarged, and there was a small haemorrhage on the heart. In animals that died or were slaughtered in the 1976 outbreak,[3] there were numerous small haemorrhages along the major blood vessels of the thorax and abdomen and on the heart; ulcers were found in the digestive tract. Microscopic examination of the brain showed spaces around the nerve cells and blood vessels, particularly in the cerebrum.

Treatment Apart from a few animals that remain permanently blind, recovery is usually spontaneous after removal from access to the ferns. B complex vitamins and calcium have been injected, but with no apparent effect. This form of treatment may have been applied because of the known thiaminase content of the ferns, but, in ruminants, thiamine deficiency does not occur from this source as it is synthesised by ruminal bacteria. Purgatives can be given to treat the constipation.

DENNSTAEDTIACEAE

Bracken *Pteridium aquilinum* (photo 7)

Bracken is the commonest fern in Britain, and is found on light, acid soils in a variety of habitats including woodland, heath, moorland and hills up to about 600 m. No accurate, up-to-date figures are available for the area infested by bracken in Britain, but it is known to be increasing and approaching 400 000 ha.[1] [2]

Bracken is a coarse fern with a creeping underground stem (rhizome) from which the leaves develop annually in spring and die down when brown in autumn. The young leaves bear numerous coarse brown scales and are rolled tightly inwards from the tip. The scales are lost as the leaves uncurl. When fully grown their height may exceed 2 m, but varies according to the habitat, usually measuring 1 m or less. The leaves have a long, tough stem with (usually three) main pointed fronds near the top. Deeply indented leaflets arise in one plane on the stems. Brown, spore-bearing structures develop all round the margins of the segments of some leaves.

Poisonous principles The whole plant contains toxic constituents, at least some of which remain after cutting and drying. There are several harmful constituents in bracken, but the only ones that have been identified satisfactorily are a cyanogenic glycoside (prunasin) usually present in harmless quantities, an enzyme (thiaminase) that leads to thiamine deficiency in horses and pigs, and two carcinogens (quercetin and kaempferol). The toxic agent responsible for an acute haemorrhagic disease in cattle and sheep has not been identified, but evidence indicates that it is a naturally occurring radiomimetic substance (i.e. it mimics the effects of radiation);[3] the fraction containing it has also been shown to be mutagenic and carcinogenic.

Prunasin Cyanogenic glycosides are toxic because they yield hydrocyanic acid (HCN) when hydrolysed by enzymes released if the plant tissue is crushed. The presence of prunasin appears to act as a deterrent to grazing, but bracken shows a phenomenon known as biochemical polymorphism, and although most populations of the plant are cyanogenic, some are not because they lack the enzyme and/or prunasin. When non-cyanogenic plants dominate in a population, bracken is grazed heavily.[4] In some parts of the country sheep are said not to graze bracken at all under normal circumstances, but under some conditions, usually when there is no other fodder available, they will graze it[5] and seem to become addicted to the plant.[6][7] This preferential eating of bracken has been reported recently in a horse.[8] Despite the fact that the prunasin content of bracken is usually too low to harm grazing animals,[4] sudden death, thought to be due to hydrocyanic acid, has been recorded in animals fed on young fronds.[9]

Thiaminase Bracken contains thiaminase type I, an enzyme capable of destroying thiamine (vitamin B_1) and thus inducing thiamine deficiency in non-ruminant animals such as the horse and the pig.[10] Thiaminase activity is highest in the rhizomes and young buds, and decreases rapidly in the fronds as the aerial parts of the plant unfold.

Carcinogens Of various fractions isolated from bracken, quercetin and kaempferol have been shown to induce tumours.[11][12] Quercetin, a flavonol found in many food plants as well as in bracken, is thought to be a primary carcinogen (i.e. it does not require metabolic activation by enzymes for its activity). Kaempferol, a flavonol occurring in bracken in the glycoside complexes astragalin and tiliroside, does require enzyme activation. Although quercetin and kaempferol have been shown to cause intestinal and bladder cancers in the rat, it is not clear whether they are the carcinogen(s) causing the tumours associated with the ingestion of bracken in cattle and sheep.

Other toxins An active fraction, isolated from fronds and rhizomes, induces the acute haemorrhagic form of poisoning by bracken and is also carcinogenic and mutagenic.[13] It is soluble in alcohol and thus distinct from thiaminase. It is also very soluble in water, and its passage into milk and urine has been demonstrated in cows grazing or fed on bracken.[14] This fraction may also be responsible for a chronic form of poisoning in cattle, characterised by haematuria (blood in the urine) and tumours of the bladder. It is not clear whether this is also the agent inducing tumours of the digestive and urinary tracts of cattle and sheep.

56

Acute poisoning

Before the 1960s, only the acute (rapidly fatal) forms of poisoning by bracken were clearly recognised. There are two distinct forms of acute disease: thiamine deficiency (in horses and pigs) resulting from the presence of the enzyme thiaminase in the plant, and the haemorrhagic syndrome (in cattle and sheep) for which no specific poisonous principle has been identified. The latter, however, may be the same as that responsible for the chronic disease of cattle known as enzootic haematuria.

Thiamine deficiency This occurs sporadically in Welsh mountain ponies and other horses on bracken land.[10] The main clinical signs are incoordination, very pronounced heart beat after mild exercise, and, as the disease progresses, severe muscular tremors. These are followed by convulsions, opisthotonos (backward flexing of the neck) and death. These clinical features have given rise to the name 'bracken staggers' for the condition in horses. There is usually a rapid, dramatic response to the administration of thiamine if given at the onset of symptoms.[10]

Bracken-induced thiamine deficiency in pigs appears to be rare, mainly as a result of the conditions under which pigs are generally kept, but, even when it does occur, it is not easy to diagnose because of the non-specificity of the clinical features. In the few cases that have been reported in Britain, the pigs were either found dead or died quickly, after a short period of heavy breathing.[15] The condition has been reproduced experimentally by feeding a diet containing 25-33%, by weight, of dried, powdered bracken rhizomes.[16] Loss of appetite and vomiting appeared after about seven weeks on this ration, and listlessness after eight weeks. Terminal signs of recumbency and heavy breathing appeared suddenly at 8-10 weeks, after which death occurred within six hours. The most striking post-mortem lesions were in the heart, which was enlarged and mottled with yellow and red patches. Histologically, the heart lesions were similar to those described in experimental thiamine deficiency in pigs. If bracken poisoning is suspected in pigs, they should be removed from the bracken-infested land and given thiamine. The thiaminase in bracken does not induce thiamine deficiency in cattle and sheep; under normal conditions these animals are not dependent on a dietary source, as thiamine is synthesised by rumen bacteria.

Acute haemorrhagic syndrome This is often referred to simply as 'bracken poisoning', but the latter should be avoided as it is a non-specific term and bracken can have several different toxic effects. In Britain in 1893, during a severe drought in which bracken was eaten as it was the only food available,[17] a haemorrhagic syndrome was reported in cattle, and it was suspected that bracken was the cause.[17] In 1894, the disease was reproduced by feeding bracken,[18] but because of later failure with experimental feeding, and because of some confusion with anthrax, this explanation was not generally accepted until over 50 years later, when indisputable experimental evidence was obtained.[19] An increase in cases of poisoning by plants, including bracken, was reported in Britain during the drought of 1976.[20] The numbers of outbreaks recorded by the Veterinary Investigation Centres in this country from 1975 to 1981 indicate seasonal variations with most cases occurring in late summer and autumn.[21]

Clinical signs of this syndrome do not usually develop until animals have been eating bracken for several weeks, and sometimes not until they are no longer grazing the plants. Once clinical signs have developed, however, death may occur within a week; even more rapid death (within 48 hours) has been recorded.[22] Poisoning usually follows eating green bracken fronds, but rhizomes of the plant, exposed during ploughing, have caused death;[23] fronds cut when green and dried for use as bedding can cause poisoning when eaten (dry brown bracken, cut in winter, is safe to use for this purpose).

Internal haemorrhage, the principal effect, is revealed by the presence of blood in faeces (firm at first, then fluid) and sometimes in urine. Initially there is often a watery discharge from the eyes, nose and mouth, followed by bleeding from these sites and from the genital tract. Small haemorrhages are usually apparent on visible mucous membranes. Affected animals often lose their appetite, rumination ceases and they become weak and unable to stand; the pulse is often feeble, and body temperature may rise (indicating septicaemia). This 'enteric' form of the disease is more common in adult cattle. It is more usual for calves to develop a 'laryngitic' form of the disease, with oral and nasal discharge of mucus and oedematous swelling of the throat, leading to difficult, noisy breathing. The cause of the haemorrhages is a blood coagulation disorder originating in the bone marrow;[24] [25] fewer blood platelets are produced, resulting in an increase in blood coagulation time. A reduction in white blood cells leads to a greater susceptibility to infection, and a decrease in red blood cell formation, to anaemia; the term 'aplastic anaemia' is sometimes applied to this disease.[26] An increase in the level of heparin-like anticoagulant substances in the circulating blood[27] may be an additional cause of the haemorrhages.

The acute haemorrhagic syndrome also occurs in sheep that eat bracken, although it is a much rarer occurrence in this species than in cattle. On the North York Moors, losses have been recorded among sheep grazing pastures containing bracken, and in a survey in 1964,[5] the haemorrhagic syndrome was present in 16 of 43 dead sheep that were examined. The white blood cell and blood platelet counts of five severely ill sheep were consistent with the disease.

Post-mortem examination of cattle and sheep reveals extensive bleeding in many sites.

Chronic poisoning   In the 1960s, it was established that bracken is the cause of two chronic conditions: enzootic haematuria in cattle (possibly caused by the same agent as that responsible for the acute haemorrhagic syndrome) and 'bright blindness' (retinal degeneration) in sheep. These conditions had been recognised as specific diseases much earlier, although their cause was not known. More recently bracken has also been associated with intestinal tumours in cattle and sheep. Chronic poisoning by bracken may well prove to be of greater economic importance than the acute condition, but at present there is little information on the prevalence of this type of poisoning.[28]

Enzootic haematuria   This is a chronic form of bracken poisoning, found in cattle and sheep, after prolonged feeding of bracken in small amounts. In addition to loss of blood in the urine, it is associated with the development of benign and malignant tumours in the wall of the bladder. It has been suggested that the haemorrhagic and haematuria syndromes are two clinical forms of the same disease, and that the different symptoms are associated with differences in amounts of bracken eaten.[29] Carcinogens seem to be involved in chronic enzootic haematuria, but it is not known whether these are the same factors as those that cause the intestinal tumours reported in cattle and sheep that have eaten bracken.

Enzootic haematuria is found in cattle throughout the world, but is always limited to areas where cattle graze on bracken or where it is used as bedding.[29] The extent and importance of haematuria in cattle in Britain is not known.[30] Affected animals excrete red or brownish urine, but show no obvious disturbances of their general condition. In contrast to haemoglobinuria, in which the urine is clear and varnish-coloured, in haematuria the urine is always cloudy and opaque, because of the excretion of whole blood, and sometimes it is floccular as well. Cattle with haematuria do not show jaundice. Red blood cells can be detected microscopically in urine weeks or even months before the obvious appearance of blood in urine, and diagnosis can be confirmed by cystoscopy (endoscopic examination of the bladder wall in a living animal). During haematuria there is a fall in the number of red and white blood cells and in the haemoglobin concentration of the blood. In advanced cases there is also slight to moderate reduction in the numbers of blood platelets. The course of the disease is generally intermittent, with each episode being worse than the preceding one. Later, during a stage of severe bleeding, the flow of urine may be temporarily or permanently interrupted by blood clots.[29]

Post-mortem examination shows characteristic bladder lesions consisting of small red to black haemorrhagic foci. In some cases these may measure up to 1 cm across. Histological examination of the bladder shows dilation of blood capillaries, angiomatous (an angioma is a tumour formed of blood vessels) cavity formation, and growth of tumours infiltrating the whole bladder wall. Bleeding occurs from the angiomatous capillaries. The link between bracken and bovine enzootic haematuria was demonstrated in 1960 in feeding trials.[31] Prolonged (more than one year) feeding of cows and calves with bracken led to signs typical of enzootic haematuria, but some animals finally died with signs of acute haemorrhage indicating that haemorrhage and haematuria are two clinical manifestations of poisoning by bracken.[29] In a five-year investigation of tumours in sheep, five of eight animals fed on dried bracken (prepared in a pellet form) died of uraemia following haematuria, and one died half-way through the trial with the acute haemorrhagic syndrome.[32]

Bright blindness Another long-term effect of bracken feeding is 'bright blindness' of sheep, a progressive degeneration of the retina of the eye. It was first described in 1965 in hill flocks in the West Riding of Yorkshire, although it was said to have been known to Yorkshire hill sheep farmers for at least 50 years.[30] It is also well recognised in the Yorkshire Dales, Lower Weardale and Teesdale and in the Lake District. By 1971 it had been confirmed in 253 flocks in northern England and in one in Scotland. Although found widely in northern England, it has also been reported from South Wales.[7] The term 'bright blind' signifies absence of cloudiness of the eye which characterises some other forms of blindness.[2] The sheep are permanently blind. They adopt a characteristic, alert attitude. Both eyes are affected and the pupils become circular, responding poorly to light. Histological changes are confined to the retina. When advanced, the layer of the rods and cones and the outer nuclear layers are completely destroyed, together with parts of the inner nuclear layer.[33] The condition was reproduced experimentally in sheep by feeding them with a concentrate ration containing 50% dried bracken at about 1kg/day for up to 63 weeks.[6] The peak incidence of bright blindness is found in sheep 3-4 years old, indicating that most sheep require to graze on bracken for two or three summers before blindness develops. In 1978 bright blindness was reported in sheep in South Wales for the first time (on two farms, with little bracken, in Gwent).[7] These sheep had been bought from local hill farms where they had had access to heavy growth of bracken. The previous apparent absence from Wales of bright blindness is interesting in that hill sheep there often have ready access to bracken, but are rarely seen to eat it. This outbreak may have been caused by the drought of 1976 when grass was very scarce and sheep were forced to look for other food; they must also have continued to eat bracken in the following year. Sheep with bright blindness have very low blood platelet and white blood cell counts. A condition resembling bright blindness has been reported in cattle grazing on bracken land in south-west Wales.[25]

Tumours In addition to the association between bracken feeding and bladder tumours in cattle with enzootic haematuria, bracken feeding also seems to be related to the very high incidence of tumours of the digestive system of beef cows in upland areas of northern England and Scotland.[34] This has been found only on farms with bracken-infested land. The lowlands next to these areas show almost no incidence of these particular tumours. In a study of 80 cases,[34] four types of tumour were found, of which the most widespread was squamous carcinoma (a malignant tumour developed from squamous epithelium and having cuboid cells). Large numbers of cows had these tumours in the mouth, oesophagus and rumen. Co-existent tumours of the intestine and bladder were found in a large proportion of cases. Papillomas (benign tumours derived from epithelium) were found in the upper alimentary tract of 96% of cows. A virus has been isolated from the papillomas; these tend to increase in number and become malignant. It has been suggested that bracken has an immunosuppressive effect, so that the animal is not able to mount its normal immune response to such tumour-producing viruses. More than 70% of the cattle with tumours were found on farms on the west coast of Scotland, particularly in Argyll, and, where it was possible to trace the farm of origin, all had bracken-infested land. Argyll, with about 40 000 ha of bracken has 15% of all the bracken-infested land in Scotland.[7] Sheep in north-east Yorkshire have also been found with tumours of the intestine (adenocarcinoma) and the jaw (fibrosarcoma), and bladder tumours and fibrosarcoma have also been induced experimentally in sheep by feeding them on bracken for a long period.[32]

Treatment   Thiamine deficiency (the poisoning in horses by bracken) should be treated by daily injection of 100 mg thiamine (vitamin B_1). This is very successful if begun at the onset of clinical signs. Injection of thiamine is of no use in cattle and sheep. In cattle, batyl alcohol, a substance known to stimulate the activity of bone marrow, was found to be effective in some trials when injected subcutaneously at 1 g in 10 ml olive oil for five consecutive days, or in suspension given by slow intravenous injection daily.[35] However, doubts have been expressed about its efficacy and there are various problems involved in its use. Other treatments which have been suggested are combined therapy consisting of intramuscular injections of mepyramine, streptomycin, penicillin and prednisolone, and intravenous injections of toluidine blue (250 mg in 250 ml saline) and batyl alcohol (500 ml dispersed in saline). Blood transfusions (4.5 litres of citrated blood, followed by a second transfusion of half this quantity) can be given, together with a single intravenous injection of 10 ml of 1% protamine sulphate to counteract the anticoagulant effect of the heparin released. Supportive therapy consists of injections of B complex vitamins and oral administration of a drug to stimulate appetite. For the other types of poisoning by bracken, prevention seems to be the only course, either by preventing access to these plants or removal from bracken areas as soon as symptoms are seen. Milking cows should not be allowed to graze bracken at all, because of the danger of transfer of harmful agents to milk.

Control of bracken Mechanical and chemical control of bracken is sometimes used to prevent disease in grazing animals, but the areas involved are so large that control is very expensive and often impracticable.[2] The chemical commonly used is asulam (methyl 4-aminobenzenesulphonyl carbamate), an aqueous solution of which sprayed on to thick stands of bracken gives a reasonable kill without affecting other herbage too much.

Human poisoning The existence of carcinogens in bracken has important public health implications.[12] The fern is consumed as a food in several parts of the world, notably Japan and the north-eastern United States and Canada. In certain prefectures of Japan, human consumption of bracken has been associated with an increased incidence of oesophageal and stomach tumours.[36] The part of the plant commonly eaten is the uncurled frond (known as fiddleheads in the USA) and this contains high concentrations of carcinogenic agents. Indirect exposure might also occur since the active material is readily passed into the milk of cows fed or grazing on bracken[14] as well as through the placenta in mice.[36] Thus the human foetus could be exposed to the carcinogen when pregnant women eat the fern. Exposure of babies and children could also occur through mothers' milk, and people of all ages could be exposed to it by consumption of milk from cows grazing bracken-infested pastures. The presence of the carcinogen in the urine of cows grazing bracken has also been reported.[14] The possible risks to man through water supply, milk and animal products are being investigated.[37]

CONIFERAE

Few of the coniferous trees and shrubs which cause poisoning of animals in other parts of the world are native in Britain, but because of their use in forestry and as ornamentals, hedges and windbreaks, animals may come into contact with them. They are generally considered unpalatable and seldom eaten while growing, except in times of food shortage, but animals are often attracted to them and eat them in considerable quantities if they are lopped or felled.

Details of the more important poisonous members of the Coniferae are given under their family names: Cupressaceae, Pinaceae and Taxaceae. Other conifers, including spruces *(Picea)*, firs *(Abies)* and redwoods *(Sequoia)* are occasionally referred to as potentially toxic, but poisoning associated with them has not been reported in Britain.

Poisonous principles Conifers contain a variety of tannins, resins, oils and acrid irritant substances to which their toxic properties are attributed, but their precise nature and mode of action have not been determined.

ALLIACEAE

Garlic and Onion *Allium* spp

Plants of this genus usually have a bulbous stock enclosed by a thin, papery covering. The shape of the leaves varies considerably among the species, being long, narrow and flat in the leek *(Allium porrum)*, long, thin, more or less cylindrical and hollow in the cultivated onion *(Allium cepa)* and stalked, oval and pointed in ramsons *(Allium ursinum)*. All the leaves have parallel veins. The inflorescence is usually a terminal head, either globular or hemispherical, and has white or pale purple flowers in spring or summer.

Ramsons *Allium ursinum* (photo 8)

Other common name: Wild Garlic

This plant is common throughout Britain in woods and damp, shady places where it is sometimes dominant. The plants grow from a single, narrow bulb and have (usually two) bright green, oval leaves, pointed at the tip. They may grow up to 25 cm long (usually shorter) and are up to 7 cm broad. The leaf stalks are 5-20 cm long and twisted. The flat-topped inflorescence, borne on a semicylindrical or three-angled stalk, is composed of 6-20 small white flowers.

Crow Garlic *Allium vineale*

This is another fairly common species that grows in England and Wales beside roads or in arable land, where it may be a troublesome weed. It has a main bulb with smaller ones (offsets) growing from it. The leaves are grooved, hollow and up to 60 cm long. The rather loose inflorescence bears greenish flowers, bulbils, or both, depending on the variety.

Other wild *Allium* species (some introduced) also occur in Britain, but are rare or more localised in distribution. All parts of the plants have the characteristic smell of garlic or onion, especially when crushed.

Poisonous principles The major constituent of the volatile compounds in onion *(Allium cepa)* is n-propyl disulphide, but other related substances are also present, and have a similar action. These include methyl disulphide, allyl disulphide, allyl alcohol and allyl monosulphide. At least some of these compounds are present in other species of *Allium*.

Poisoning in animals

Farm animals, particularly sheep, appear to enjoy eating onions, and are often fed with them over long periods without ill effect. Poisoning usually occurs when animals are fed with them exclusively, or in large quantities; their use as part of a mixed diet is unlikely to cause problems. Domestic pets (especially dogs), however, seem more susceptible, and it is inadvisable to give them food containing onions.

The main effect of onions (or n-propyl disulphide) on all animal species is the precipitation of haemoglobin and the formation of minute inclusions, called Heinz bodies, within red blood cells. These cells are destroyed and removed from the circulation, and this can lead to severe anaemia. This so-called haemolytic anaemia is characteristic of onion poisoning, and the presence of Heinz bodies in red blood cells (demonstrated by appropriate staining of blood smears) is a diagnostic feature. The toxic constituents also cause disturbances in fat metabolism and enzyme activity in the liver.[1][2]

Allium species seldom cause illness of animals in Britain, but eating any plant in this genus may result in a taint in both milk and meat.

Wild onions *(Allium validum)* have caused poisoning of horses[3] and sheep,[4] in the USA and elsewhere, and *Allium vineale* was strongly suspected as the cause of outbreaks in cattle in East Anglia.[5] Annually recurring episodes of illness, with a drastic drop in milk yield, were associated with the animals being turned on to poor pasture containing crow garlic. Affected animals had a weak pulse, cold skin, jaundice and black diarrhoea, becoming watery and yellow.

Most outbreaks of *Allium* poisoning involve the cultivated onion *(Allium cepa)*, whose cooked or uncooked bulbs (occasionally whole plants) are sometimes fed to animals. In one recent outbreak,[6] cows and calves showed depression and paralysis and a bull died after being fed onions for two weeks. In a bullock fed with onion foliage and bulbs,[7] rumination, urination and defaecation ceased and there were muscular tremors, subnormal body temperature and pale conjunctiva. Blood-stained urine was observed in another bullock. Onion peelings[8] or rotting onions[9] have also caused illness in cattle.

Sheep appear to be less susceptible than cattle to onion poisoning. Ewes given cultivated onions with their feed for about four months[10] remained clinically normal, even when pregnant, and their lambs were unaffected. Anaemia developed in the ewes within three weeks, but recovery of red blood cells had begun before the end of the feeding period. Other ewes fed with dried or fresh wild onion lost weight and appetite and became anaemic.[11]

Horses are also susceptible to onion poisoning. One of two animals died after being fed cultivated onions when pasture was covered with snow,[12] and in another outbreak seven of nine horses died with symptoms including increased respiration rate when forced to move, jaundice of oral mucous membranes and conjunctiva, and coffee-coloured urine.[13]

Dogs have been used in experimental work on poisoning with onions[14] or n-propyl disulphide,[1] but there are several incidents recorded of accidental poisoning of domestic pets given portions of their owner's food. Ingestion of onion soufflé resulted in depression, increased frequency of urination, dark urine and anaemia in one dog,[15] and a puppy with a preference for raw onions collapsed on exercise and was anaemic.[16] Cats can be affected similarly but less severely than dogs. Onion soup given to two cats[17] resulted in anaemia although they remained clinically healthy. The condition was reproduced by experimental feeding of onion soup or raw onion to other cats.

Anaemia has also been seen in poultry fed on boiled onions.[13] No mention has been found of the effect of onions on pigs.

Post-mortem findings These are similar in all species and include jaundice of mucous membranes, subcutaneous tissues and muscles, inflammation of the digestive tract, dark or blood-stained urine, enlarged kidneys and fatty degeneration of the liver, which is usually pale brown in colour. In all cases the tissues have a strong odour of onions.

Treatment Symptomatic treatment may be given, but, in most animals, gradual recovery occurs spontaneously after removal of onions from the diet. In rabbits fed on boiled onions, an improvement of the anaemic state induced was achieved by treatment with methionine.[18]

Human poisoning Apart from the well-established culinary use of onions, leeks, chives and garlic, the leaves or bulbs of ramsons and other wild *Allium* species are sometimes eaten raw or cooked. No specific case of poisoning of man by any member of this family has been recorded, although possible antithyroid activity of the volatile constituents of onion has been reported.[19] The sulphur-containing volatile oils commonly found in *Allium* species have a local irritant effect on the nose and eyes, and can cause dermatitis.[20]

AMARYLLIDACEAE

This family includes the spring-flowering bulbs, daffodil *(Narcissus pseudonarcissus)* and snowdrop *(Galanthus nivalis),* both of which are native, although localised in distribution, in Britain. Many varieties are grown commercially.

Poisonous principles

The whole plant, particularly the bulb, contains toxic substances. These include the alkaloids narcissine (lycorine) and galantamine and a glycoside scillaine (scillitoxin).

Poisoning in animals

The growing plants are seldom eaten by animals, although the death of a tortoise, 11 days after eating leaves of wild daffodil *(Narcissus pseudonarcissus)* is reported.[1] The animal gradually lost its appetite, stopped defaecating and became lethargic. Post-mortem examination revealed severe gastritis and ulceration of mucous membranes. In the Netherlands, deaths were reported in cattle given *Narcissus* bulbs to eat when food was scarce during the Second World War.[2]

Human poisoning

Consumption of cooked or raw *Narcissus* bulbs, usually as a result of mistaking them for onions,[3] has caused symptoms including dizziness, abdominal pain, nausea, vomiting and diarrhoea.[4] It is reported that trembling, convulsions and death may occur,[5] but spontaneous recovery usually occurs within a few hours.

Stomach lavage or the use of suitable emetics, such as syrup of ipecacuanha, is recommended.

AQUIFOLIACEAE

Holly *Ilex aquifolium*

Holly grows wild, as an evergreen shrub or tree, throughout Britain and its varieties are widely cultivated as ornamentals.

The bark of the tree is dark grey and the leaves are thick, dark green and glossy above. They vary in shape from oval, with a smooth edge and terminal point, to those of more characteristic shape, having a deeply undulating margin with spine-pointed teeth. Small clusters of inconspicuous white flowers develop in spring and bright red, spherical berries often remain throughout the winter.

Poisonous principles The berries contain the toxin ilicin which, on ingestion, can cause vomiting, diarrhoea and drowsiness.

Poisoning No cases of poisoning involving animals have been found, but children are attracted by the berries and if more than about 20 are eaten they can have an emetic or purgative effect.[1] A two-year-old girl experienced nausea lasting for about two hours after ingesting two berries.[2] In a survey in 12 American states, 21 of 1051 cases of ingestion of poisonous plant parts by man in 1959-1960 involved holly.[3] The symptoms are usually mild, but if large quantities of berries have been eaten, vomiting should be induced with a suitable emetic (syrup of ipecacuanha). With stomach lavage, berries may block the tube.

ARACEAE

Cuckoo Pint *Arum maculatum* (photo 9)

Other common names: Wild Arum; Lords and Ladies; Wake Robin

Cuckoo pint is generally distributed throughout Britain, except for Scotland where it is relatively uncommon, particularly in the north. It is a shade-loving plant, growing in woods and hedge banks and may be a persistent garden weed. The leaves appear on long stalks in spring from the perennial white rootstock. The leaf blades are dark green and glossy, up to 20 cm long, triangular or arrow-shaped and often spotted dark purple. The flowers, which appear in late spring consist of an erect yellowish green partial sheath (spathe) usually 15-25 cm long, within which is a dull purple cylindrical structure (spadix). The fruits develop at the base of the spadix as a closely clustered group of green berries which become reddish orange when ripe, at which time the leaves and spathe die down. (The common name lords and ladies relates particularly to the fruiting stage of the plant.)

Poisonous principles

An acrid juice which acts as an acute irritant when applied to the skin or eaten is present in all parts of the plant; drying or boiling reduces but does not eliminate its activity. Starch extracted from the roots was used formerly for laundry work but was abandoned because of the irritation it caused to the hands. Food preparations from the baked and powdered root were known as Portland arrowroot and Portland sago. The nature of the toxic principle is uncertain, but most reports suggest that a saponin (saponic glycoside), aronin(e) or aroin, which occurs in all parts of the plant, is the active substance. Little is known about aronin except that it is volatile and unstable and that ultimately it affects the central nervous system. In other poisonous members of the Araceae family that are not native to Britain but produce similar symptoms to *Arum maculatum* poisoning, calcium oxalate has been identified as a toxic agent.[1]

Poisoning in animals

Poisoning by *Arum maculatum* is rare as, under normal circumstances, animals make no attempt to eat the plants, probably being discouraged by their pungent taste. Outbreaks of poisoning have been reported in spring among cattle on poor pastures and grazing hedgerows where *Arum maculatum* was abundant.[2] The symptoms were not constant, which may have been due to different amounts of the plant being eaten. They included salivation, swelling of the neck, incoordination and convulsions, followed by collapse and death. Post-mortem examination revealed inflamed mucous membranes of the mouth, abomasum and intestines and inflammation of the gall bladder.

Arum poisoning was suspected in seven separate cases in horses in Britain over a period of five years.[3] All were pregnant mares which aborted about five days after the onset of symptoms, which included inflammation of the conjunctiva of the eyes and the mucous membranes, particularly those of the mouth. Initial constipation was followed by scouring. Five of the horses died. In Romania, horses were poisoned after eating *Arum maculatum* growing at the edge of a wood;[4] an aqueous extract of the plants injected into dogs caused a fall in blood pressure, and respiratory changes led to asphyxia.

Human poisoning

This usually involves children who eat the attractive berries which are particularly poisonous.[5] However, a small boy was poisoned after chewing the leaves;[6] he developed a sore mouth and abdominal pain and became drowsy. The acrid juice is a deterrent to eating large amounts of cuckoo pint, but if sufficient of the plant is eaten there may be sore throat, gastrointestinal irritation and pain, with severe diarrhoea, irregular heartbeat[7] and, in extreme cases, coma and death.[8]

Poisoning is not usually severe, however, and treatment is rarely necessary. In serious cases the use of a suitable emetic (such as syrup of ipecacuanha) to induce vomiting, and the subsequent oral administration of demulcents are recommended.

ARALIACEAE

Ivy *Hedera helix*

Ivy is a native woody evergreen plant which creeps along the ground, often forming dense mats, or climbs up trees or walls by means of numerous short roots which grow from the stem. The plant is very tolerant of shade. The leaves which arise from the main stems, are 4-10 cm across, dark green above and paler beneath, and have 3-5 triangular lobes, the central one being the longest; those on the flowering stem tend to be more oval in shape. The flowers grow in autumn in a terminal group on the stem. They have yellowish-green petals 3-4 mm across, and smooth, black, globular fruits 6-8 mm in diameter develop after flowering.

Poisonous principles   The plant contains saponins (hederasaponins A and B) which undergo partial hydrolysis, with loss of sugars, to form the toxic substances α and β hederin.

Poisoning in animals   In small quantities, the plant is not considered harmful to livestock and is said by some to be beneficial. Ivy poisoning has been reported in cattle, deer, sheep and dogs[1] with symptoms that include vomiting, diarrhoea, excitement, muscular spasms, paralysis and initial dilation and later contraction of blood vessels. After consuming large quantities of leaves and berries, when pasture was scarce, two dairy cows started to stagger, became excitable and occasionally bellowed loudly as if in pain. A strong odour of crushed ivy leaves, both in the breath and in the milk, persisted for about three days, after which recovery was complete and uneventful.[2] Another report states that ivy seeds were responsible for the death of poultry in France.[3]

Human poisoning   Ivy is often listed among plants which can cause poisoning in children who eat the berries. Emetic and purgative effects have been reported, together with laboured breathing, excitation, convulsions and coma,[4] but no recent reports of such severe symptoms have been found. The sap of the plant can

69

cause dermatitis in man, sometimes with severe blistering and inflammation.[5]

Treatment   If a large number of berries has been eaten, vomiting should be induced with a suitable emetic (ipecacuanha syrup). Stomach lavage may also be performed, but the berries are liable to block the tube.

BERBERIDACEAE

Barberry *Berberis vulgaris*

Barberry is a spiny shrub 1-2.5 m high, with pointed oval leaves, 2-4 cm long, that have serrated edges, the serrations often terminating in a small spine. Clusters of yellow flowers, 6-8 mm in diameter appear in summer, and rectangular, red fruits, 8-12 mm long, develop in autumn. The plant occurs locally throughout Britain, where it is probably introduced rather than native. Many varieties are cultivated in gardens.

Poisonous principles   An isoquinoline alkaloid, berberine, has been isolated from the roots and bark of many *Berberis* species, but the berries are not toxic.[1]

Poisoning   Reports of children having eaten the berries of wild barberry or those of cultivated species and varieties of *Berberis* are among the most frequent enquiries received by poison information services,[2] but no authenticated cases of poisoning, of animals or man, by any parts of the plant have been found. Injury by the spines can cause papular dermatitis in man,[3] although it is possible that this may be due, at least partly, to the introduction of bacteria or fungi from the spines into the skin.

BORAGINACEAE

Comfrey *Symphytum officinale* (photo 10)

This erect, coarsely hairy plant, 30-120 cm high, grows in damp places, often beside streams, and is generally distributed throughout Britain, although found less commonly in the north. The leaves are 15-25 cm long, tapering towards the tip and narrowing towards the base which continues down the stem, giving it a winged appearance. The flower heads form in summer at the ends of the branches, where a cluster of blue, pink, purple or yellowish-white bell-shaped flowers are borne on separate stalks. The comfreys grown commercially, mainly for use in a variety of herbal preparations, are vigorous hybrids, usually crosses between *Symphytum officinale* and the rough comfrey, *Symphytum asperum (or asperrimum)*. The name Russian comfrey has been applied to this cross and also to another, designated *X. Symphytum uplandicum (or Symphytum X uplandicum)*.

Poisonous principles This plant and other species of *Symphytum* contain pyrrolizidine alkaloids, including heliosupine and cynoglossine. Quantitative studies of the hybrid Russian comfrey *(Symphytum X uplandicum)* showed that concentrations of alkaloids are highest in small, young leaves early in the season, decrease as the leaf grows heavier and are lowest in the large mature leaves.[1] Nitrates may accumulate in some species of the plant.

Poisoning Comfrey appears to cause poisoning in animals only rarely, as it is unattractive to eat due to its bristly hairs. Nitrate-nitrite poisoning has been reported in pigs given rough comfrey *(Symphytum asperum)* as green fodder.[2] (This species is seen occasionally in Britain where it has become naturalised in waste places.) General apathy, laboured breathing and cyanosis, typical of nitrite poisoning, were seen. The blood was dark reddish-brown indicating the presence of methaemoglobin, a stable compound (of nitrites and haemoglobin) that does not take up oxygen.

Therapeutic veterinary use of the plant has been reported. Preparations (sometimes called kytta) made from comfrey roots have been applied topically to promote healing of tongue ulcers in cats,[3] and skin lesions associated with lameness in cattle,[4] or given internally for the treatment of inflammatory conditions of the digestive and reproductive systems.[5] These healing properties are attributed to the allantoin(e) said to be present in the plant.[3 6]

In man, comfrey has long been regarded as a mild astringent, and extracts of boiled roots or leaves have been used as herbal teas and to treat internal inflammation. Applied to the skin, comfrey root preparations are said to have healing properties. The plant is listed as edible[7] and has been grown commercially in Britain and abroad for medicinal use; its potential as a food plant for man and animals has been investigated.[8] However, since publicity was given to experiments on laboratory rats[9] in which root extracts of *Symphytum officinale* increased the incidence of liver tumours, the plant has fallen into disrepute.[10] The carcinogenic response followed continuous high dosing over long periods, and it is unlikely that human consumption of comfrey in much smaller amounts would cause liver damage, and no examples of poisoning by the plant have been reported. The external use of comfrey preparations should be safe, as the toxic metabolites of the alkaloids are released only by the action of liver enzymes after ingestion. Contact with the bristly hairs of the plant is known to cause dermatitis in man.[11]

Hound's Tongue *Cynoglossum officinale*

This erect biennial grows up to 90 cm high and is covered with long, silky hairs, giving it a greyish appearance. Purple funnel-shaped flowers develop in summer.

Poisonous principles
The plants contain pyrrolizidine alkaloids, variously named as cynoglossine, consolidine, echinatine and heliosupine.

Poisoning in animals
Hound's tongue began to thrive in Britain in the mid 1950s as myxomatosis killed the rabbits, which had previously kept it in check. In 1959, a herd of pregnant Friesian cows were poisoned when they gained access to waste land where hound's tongue was growing in profusion.[12] When found several hours later, the animals had staring expressions, rapid breathing, varying degrees of tympany and diarrhoea. Increased thirst was a prominent symptom and a drop in milk yield was recorded. Post-mortem examination of animals that died revealed congestion of the lungs and large quantities of hound's tongue leaves in the rumen, where there was considerable inflammation. Other parts of the stomach were inflamed, and mesenteric lymph nodes were swollen, oedematous and haemorrhagic. Cattle which grazed hound's tongue growing with sainfoin in the USSR[13] developed nervous symptoms and diarrhoea 12-24 hours (6-12 hours in calves) after first eating the plants. Many cattle in the herd had failed to recover three months later and were slaughtered.

Purple Viper's Bugloss *Echium lycopis*

Other common names (in Australia): Paterson's Curse; Salvation Jane

This plant is still often known by its old name *Echium plantagineum*. Although a native plant growing near the coast in a few places, or occasionally as a garden escape, purple viper's bugloss has not been associated with poisoning of animals in Britain. It contains the pyrrolizidine alkaloids echimidine or echiumidine, and its ingestion has caused the death of horses in Australia.[14] In all cases the animals gradually lost condition and appetite and became listless over a period of 4-6 weeks.

Nervous symptoms including incoordination, circling and blindness were seen in some cases. Examination of dead animals revealed liver damage with bile duct proliferation. In Australia, ingestion of the plant has caused liver damage in sheep,[15] and nervous symptoms in a colt.[16] The rough hairs of the plant can cause dermatitis in man.

Common Viper's Bugloss *Echium vulgare*

This plant grows scattered throughout Britain and is common in some places. It contains pyrrolizidine alkaloids, including heliosupine, but no cases of poisoning associated with it have been found.

Other members of the Boraginaceae, notably species of *Heliotropium*, occasionally found naturalised as garden escapes in Britain, have caused poisoning in other countries. *Heliotropium europaeum* has been associated in Australia in sheep[17] and cattle[18] with outbreaks of a syndrome of toxic liver cirrhosis that closely resembles poisoning by ragwort *(Senecio jacobaea)*, a plant that contains a large number of pyrrolizidine alkaloids.

BUXACEAE

Box *Buxus sempervirens* (photo 11)

Box is an evergreen shrub or tree which is native in Britain but limited in its distribution to a few areas of southern England, where it is locally abundant on chalk or limestone in beech woods and scrub. Box is cultivated widely as an ornamental or hedging plant. The bark is grey and the twigs are angled and covered with short hairs. The leaves, borne close together on short stalks, are elliptical or oval in shape, 1-2.5 cm long, darker green and somewhat glossy above, paler and dull below. The inconspicuous flowers are borne in clusters in the axils of the leaves, each cluster terminating in a female flower with several male flowers below it. The fruit is an ovoid capsule containing shining black seeds.

Poisonous principles All parts of the plant are poisonous. The active agent was believed to be an alkaloid, buxine, but this is now recognised to be a complex group of steroidal alkaloids rather than a single substance. Many names, derived from the generic name *Buxus* have been applied to individual alkaloids within the group, but nomenclature based on their structure is also used.

73

There is still little known about the toxicity of the individual alkaloids.

Poisoning   Box is usually avoided by animals because of its disagreeable odour, when bruised, and bitter taste, but poisoning has been reported in horses,[1] cattle,[2][3] and pigs,[2][4] generally as a result of gaining access to garden hedges or hedge clippings. A fatal dose for a horse is reported to be 750 g of leaves.[5] Symptoms have included vomiting, abdominal pain, diarrhoea, incoordination, convulsions and coma. Death from respiratory failure may occur very rapidly. Aquarium fish have been killed by sprigs of box being placed in their tanks.[1] Post-mortem examination reveals acute irritation of the gastrointestinal tract, with box leaves in its contents, and congestion of the lungs. Treatment is symptomatic.

CANNABACEAE

Hemp *Cannabis sativa*

Hemp is an erect annual, generally unbranched and growing 1-2 metres in height, the varieties grown for fibre often being considerably taller. The leaves are alternate on the upper, and opposite on the lower part of the stem, and are compound, being divided into up to seven long narrow lobes with serrated margins; they are rough to touch. The male and female flowers are usually borne on separate plants in the axils of the leaves, the male flowers being in loose clusters, while the short spikes of the female flowers open only enough for the small feathery stigmas to protrude. After flowering, the leaves on the male plants turn yellow and these plants die, while the female plants remain dark green for about a month longer until the fruits ('hemp seeds') ripen.

In the warmer parts of the world, hemp is cultivated for fibre production and its oil-rich seeds, as well as for the narcotic, cannabis. The species is highly variable, and varieties have been developed for these different end-products. In addition to illegal cultivation in Britain, it is occasionally found growing wild around rubbish dumps and places where birds have been given seed mixtures containing hemp seed not rendered completely incapable of germination.

Cannabis is one of the earliest known narcotics. It was used in human and veterinary medicine as a hypnotic and sedative, but is now used almost solely for its psychedelic effects.

Poisonous principles   The active agents are tetrahydrocannabinols, which are found in the resin and occur in greatest concentration in the female flowers. The

74

tetrahydrocannabinol content varies with the variety of the plant, its stage of growth, and the climatic conditions. When grown for drug production, the male plants are removed as soon as they can be distinguished. In the Middle East and North Africa the resin is called hashish, though this name is often applied to any cannabis preparation. The term marijuana is used to refer to any part or extract of the plant that induces psychic changes. These are generally mild, with visual effects and a brief elevation of mood, followed by sedation; large doses can lead to coma.

Poisoning in animals The plant has a bitter taste and is generally avoided by animals, although there is a report from Greece of poisoning in horses and mules who ate illegally grown plants and showed excitement, respiratory distress, muscular tremors, hypothermia, foaming at the mouth, sweating, and recumbency; they died 15-30 minutes after the appearance of symptoms.[1] Recently, cases of poisoning have occurred in dogs which had access to cannabis preparations (hashish, 'hashish cookies', marijuana cigarettes) used by their owners.[2 7] Symptoms included muscular weakness, ataxia, salivation, vomiting, drowsiness, mild hypothermia, prostration and coma; some animals showed muscular tremors and convulsions, some had diarrhoea. Recovery usually occurs within 24 hours, and oral doses of 3 g of crude marijuana extract per kg body weight have not been lethal for the dog.[8]

Treatment There is no specific treatment, although the use of a central nervous system stimulant such as pentetrazol (leptazol; 0.25 mg intramuscularly) has been reported to aid recovery in the dog.

CAPRIFOLIACEAE

Common Elder *Sambucus nigra*

Elder is a common shrub or small tree which grows up to 3-4 m tall on waste land and in hedgerows, scrub or woodland, especially on alkaline and nitrogen-rich soils. The branches are often arched and have brownish-grey, deeply furrowed corky bark. The twigs are stout and greyish, and prominent brown or white pith is apparent when cut. The leaves are compound, each being divided into oval, pointed leaflets usually numbering 5-7. The inflorescence is flat-topped, with five primary rays, and is composed of numerous cream-white flowers which develop into purplish-black globular fruits which hang in conspicuous clusters in autumn.

Poisonous principles   The plant contains sambunigrin and other cyanogenic glycosides from which hydrocyanic acid is released by enzyme action.

Poisoning in animals   Elder appears to be unattractive to animals, which seldom eat it (possibly because of its unpleasant odour when bruised or crushed) but the bark, leaves and berries may cause poisoning. In Romania, pigs that ate young elder leaves developed signs of poisoning the following day.[1] Salivation, vomiting, abdominal pain, diarrhoea, accelerated respiratory and heart rates, paralysis of hindquarters, trembling and unsteadiness were recorded. Of the 50 animals affected, 14 died. Cases have also been reported in turkeys[2] and cattle,[3] but most are not well authenticated.

Human poisoning   The roots and stems of elder have caused poisoning in man, and have a reputation as purgatives. Berries eaten raw can cause nausea and vomiting.[4] Both berries and flowers, however, have long been used, apparently safely, after cooking or in wine-making, despite incomplete elimination of cyanogenic material.[5]

Snowberry *Symphoricarpos rivularis*

Snowberry is often still referred to by its synonym *Symphoricarpos albus*. This bushy shrub (1-3 m tall) is not native to Britain but is cultivated here and has become naturalised in many places. It has dull green oval leaves, small pink flowers and characteristic waxy, white, spherical berries, up to 1 cm in diameter.

Poisonous principles   A reputedly poisonous substance, viburnin, is found in the plant. Several alkaloids, including chelidonine, a narcotic constituent of greater celandine *(Chelidonium majus)*, are also found in *Symphoricarpos* but the toxicity of most of these has not been determined.[6] Saponins, tannins, terpenes, triglycerides and coumarins are also stated to be present.

Poisoning   Snowberry is said to cause gastrointestinal irritation, vomiting and blood-stained urine.[7] *Symphoricarpos* berries have a long-standing reputation for poisoning, an early report from Norfolk[8] describing gastrointestinal symptoms, delirium and a semi-comatose state in four children whose 'vomit left no doubt of their having eaten largely of snowberries'. (The plant in this report is mistakenly spelt *Lymphoricarpos* and has the old specific name *racemosus)*. More recent cases of snowberry poisoning have been recorded in children in the USA and Poland,[9] and in Britain, where vomiting, slight dizziness and mild sedation occurred after a child ate three berries.[4]

Other members of the family are popularly considered to be poisonous, e.g. honeysuckle *(Lonicera* spp*)*, danewort *(Sambucus ebulus)*, wayfaring tree *(Viburnum lantana)*, guelder rose *(Viburnum opulus)* and queries relating to these plants, especially their berries, are often received by the veterinary and medical professions. However, the plants must be considered harmless or of very low toxicity as no definite reports of their causing poisoning have been found. Honeysuckle can cause dermatitis in man.[10]

CARYOPHYLLACEAE

This family contains the soapworts *(Saponaria)*, sandworts *(Arenaria)*, stitchworts and chickweeds *(Stellaria)*, corn cockle *(Agrostemma githago)*, and well-known garden plants such as pinks and carnations. All members of the family contain saponins but, with the exception of corn cockle, they have only very rarely been associated with poisoning.

Corn Cockle *Agrostemma githago* (photo 12)

Although not native in Britain, this plant spread extensively and was formerly a common weed among cereal crops. As a result of changes in agricultural practice and the use of weedkillers, it has now disappeared from British arable land and is rarely seen in this country. It is included mainly for historical reasons because, in the past, it was an important cause of plant poisoning in animals and man[1] in Britain, and still is in some other parts of the world.

Corn cockle is an erect annual plant, growing from 30-100 cm in height. The stem is simple or sparingly branched, and both it and the narrow, pointed leaves, are covered with white hairs, giving the plant a greyish-green appearance. The leaves are narrow and pointed, up to 12 cm long, and, at the base, they clasp the stem from which they usually arise in pairs. The flowers, 3-5 cm in diameter, are borne singly at the end of the main stem or branches and have purplish-pink petals. The plant is readily recognisable by the single pink flowers, the buds which have a slightly bulbous base and long, pointed, leafy teeth at the tip, and by the seed capsule, which becomes light brown on drying and opens by five more or less erect teeth to reveal the black seeds, 3-3.5 mm across. The seeds used to be threshed out with cereal grains and either sown with them for future crops or ground with them into flour.

Poisonous principles
These are colloidal glycosides with the properties of saponins. They are so called because, although they do not dissolve in water, they remain suspended in it and impart to it a lathering or frothing action, similar to soap. The saponins are not inactivated by heat, and the consumption of bread made with contaminated flour can cause poisoning. Such flour has a greyish colour, a bitter taste and an unpleasant odour.[2] Should these saponins enter the blood, they cause a breakdown of red blood cells (haemolysis).

Poisoning in animals
Between 1951 and 1963, thirty outbreaks of corn cockle poisoning were recorded in Poland, resulting in high mortality among pigs, cattle, horses, silver foxes, fowls, geese and ducks.[3][4][5] Poultry are said to be more sensitive to corn cockle poisoning than carnivores, while carnivores are more sensitive than herbivores,[6] the young of all species being more sensitive than adults. Saponin-containing plants are not eaten readily, probably because of their bitter taste. When poisoning does occur, however, the symptoms are similar in all animals and include salivation and gastrointestinal disturbances (often with ulceration and frothy diarrhoea); general paralysis may develop.

Post-mortem findings
Necrotic lesions may be found in the liver, spleen and lungs as well as in the intestines, which are often severely inflamed. The blood may be haemolysed.

Treatment
This is mainly symptomatic, and similar to that used for any poison causing gastrointestinal irritation. Demulcents, sedatives and pain-killing drugs may be given; stimulants may be required after the acute stage has passed. If laxatives are needed, only very mild ones should be given until it can be reasonably supposed that ulceration of the intestinal walls has healed. Obviously the use of contaminated feed, or access to the plants, should be discontinued.

Human poisoning
A chronic form of poisoning, known as githagism, can occur in man.[2] It is caused by the presence of ground corn cockle seeds in flour. Lassitude, yawning, weight loss and gastrointestinal disturbances are the chief symptoms, the patient weakening progressively and possibly dying if the contaminated diet is continued.

CELASTRACEAE

Spindle *Euonymus europaeus* (photo 13)

Other common name: Skewer Wood

Spindle is found in woods, scrub and hedges throughout Britain, mostly on calcareous soils. It is a deciduous shrub or small tree growing from 2-6 m high, with many erect branches, giving a stiff appearance. The bark is grey and smooth and the young twigs green and four-angled. The leaves are 3-13 cm long and arranged in pairs on the stem. They are oval, with pointed tips and short stalks and usually turn reddish in the autumn. The small, inconspicuous yellowish-green flowers, up to 1 cm across, form in summer in clusters near the tips of the twigs. The fruit capsules are dark pink, four-lobed and 10-15 mm across. When ripe, they split open from the top, revealing a bright orange fleshy substance (the aril) with one seed in each lobe. The wood is hard and was sought after for the manufacture of spindles, knitting needles, skewers and pegs, and for burning, to make charcoal sticks for drawing.

Poisonous principles

All parts of the plant are said to be poisonous, although the precise nature of these principles is uncertain. In early literature[1] a toxic substance, evonymine (the plant name being given as Evonymus) is mentioned, while later publications refer to evobioside, evomonoside, evonoside, euonymin and triazotin or triacetin. From the effects of poisoning by *Euonymus*, it is clear that some of these toxic substances are glycosides. An unnamed glycoside isolated from *Euonymus europaeus,* given by intravenous injection to pigeons and cats, stimulated the action of the heart muscles.[2]

Poisoning in animals

Sheep and goats have been poisoned by eating the twigs and leaves of the plant,[3] and fatal poisoning in two horses which ate shoots of the plant is recorded.[4] The horses were adequately fed in stalls, but allowed out to graze in the evenings in a meadow, on the edge of which spindle bushes were growing. A considerable amount of the shoots was eaten, and the animals became restless and suffered paralysis of the digestive tract, with consequent constipation. Their pulse became rapid and both animals died four days later. Inflammation of the intestines was evident at post-mortem examination.

Human poisoning

This usually involves digestion of the berries, which is followed 10-12 hours later by diarrhoea, vomiting and stimulation of the heart. In severe cases, persistent vomiting, hallucinations, sleepiness and loss of consciousness may occur, and convulsions and symptoms similar to meningitis have been reported.[5] In one fatal case, blood-stained diarrhoea and convulsions preceded death. Stomach lavage and the administration of purgatives and demulcents are recommended for treatment.

CHENOPODIACEAE

Mangels and Beet *Beta vulgaris*

Other common names: Mangold; Mangel-wurzel; Mangold-wurzel; Fodder Beet; Sugar Beet

These are plant breeding selections and varieties of the subspecies *vulgaris* or *maritima* of *Beta vulgaris*. They are distinguishable visually by the size, colour and shape of the roots, and by the proportion of the swollen root (or lower stem and root) visible above the soil surface. The other main difference is in the dry-matter content of the roots, which is lowest in mangels, intermediate in fodder beet and highest in sugar beet. Varieties known as mangels have been cultivated for animal feed in Britain since early last century; sugar beet was introduced in the 1920s and fodder beet around the middle of this century. The roots of mangels and fodder beet and the tops (leaves and crown of the root) of sugar beet are used for animal feeding, the main part of sugar beet roots for sugar production. Sugar beet pulp, a by-product of processing for sugar, is an excellent, but expensive feed. It should be emphasised that these plants are a valuable and generally safe livestock feed, and it is only under certain circumstances that their consumption can give rise to adverse effects that include lactic acidosis and ketosis as well as true poisoning.

The high carbohydrate content of the roots of these plants can lead to increased acidity in the stomach of ruminants, due to accumulation of lactic acid (lactic acidosis), if this feed is introduced too rapidly into the diet. Decreases in appetite, milk yield and fat content of milk may be associated with this condition.[1] A high lactic acid content in the rumen occurred in sheep given fodder beet juice, equivalent to 11.7 g sucrose per kg live weight.[2] Because of their high dry-matter content, excessive amounts of *Beta* roots in feed may cause rumen impaction. Ketosis (a metabolic disorder in which the ketone content increases and that of glucose decreases in blood) may occur among cattle fed on freshly harvested fodder beet,[3] sugar beet tops[4] and sugar beet pulp.[5]

Poisonous principles Nitrates (readily converted to toxic nitrites) accumulate in these plants and are present in freshly harvested roots and sugar beet tops; oxalates occur in the roots and foliage, and saponins in leaves. Nervous disorders

80

sometimes occur and may be due to one of these or to another unidentified substance; goitrogens are also present.

Poisoning in animals

Nitrate-nitrite poisoning Freshly harvested *Beta* roots may contain high levels of nitrates. These, and possibly other constituents of the roots, have an irritant action and can cause severe diarrhoea (sometimes fatal) in cattle.[6] To avoid this, the roots need to be 'ripened' by storage in clamps for 3-4 months before feeding. It is also recommended by some that fodder beet should be allowed to mature before feeding.[7] Sugar beet tops should be left to wilt for at least a week before feeding in order to avoid severe diarrhoea in cattle.[7] Spraying beet crops with the herbicide 2,4-dinitrophenylhydrazine (2,4-D) can lead to accumulation of toxic levels of nitrates (up to 8.8%) in the foliage.[8]

Nitrates are reduced to highly toxic nitrites in the rumen of cattle and sheep. Nitrite poisoning is characterised by weakness, laboured breathing, staggering and recumbency and can be fatal. The nitrites combine with haemoglobin in the blood to form methaemoglobin, preventing the uptake of oxygen and giving the blood a characteristic brownish colour. In an outbreak of nitrite poisoning in Canada,[9] 41 of 70 cattle were poisoned by eating frosted, green sugar beet tops that contained 1-6% nitrate. Despite treatment by intravenous injection of 10-30 ml of a 2% aqueous solution of methylene blue, 19 of the affected animals died. The conversion of nitrates to nitrites does not occur to any great extent in pigs. During cooking of roots containing nitrates, at too low a temperature or for too short a time, nitrites are formed. Feeding with such cooked roots has led to poisoning in pigs, which are more susceptible to nitrites than are other farm animals.[10]

Oxalate poisoning Some species of Chenopodiaceae, including the beets, contain soluble sodium oxalate and insoluble calcium and magnesium oxalates[11] in the roots and leaves (beet foliage may contain up to 12% oxalates).[12] Soluble oxalates are very largely detoxified in the rumen, being converted into carbonate and bicarbonate. If a large enough quantity of oxalate is ingested, some of it will be absorbed unchanged and thus lead to oxalate poisoning. The ability of the rumen to prevent this depends on the state of nutrition of the animals and the efficiency of ruminal function. Oxalate poisoning can occur in several forms:[11] [12] calcium deficiency (hypocalcaemia), leading to rapid death; breakdown of red blood cells (haemolysis); kidney damage due to blockage of tubules by calcium oxalate crystals; and crystallisation of oxalates in brain tissue, causing paralysis and other disorders of the central nervous system. In castrated male sheep and cattle fed on mangels, particularly those grown on chalky soils, the urethra may become obstructed by calcium oxalate crystals. In Yugoslavia, metabolic disorders and poisoning occurred among cattle which had been fed intensively for a long period on sugar beet leaves.[13] An acute form of oxalate poisoning occurred, with lesions in the central nervous system, the digestive system and organs involved in blood formation;[13] there were disturbances in blood chemistry and blood coagulation.[14]

Other toxic effects   A chronic form of poisoning, also seen in the cattle in Yugoslavia,[13] and attributed to saponins, was characterised by bone diseases resulting in lameness, reduced fertility, increased incidence of milk fever (paralysis at parturition, due to hypocalcaemia), dark coloured urine and a tendency to haemorrhages.

Feeding cows on sugar beet leaves (40-70 kg for 46 days) has produced slight goitrogenic effects, but without clinical signs of goitre; by the end of the trial the yield of milk and its fat content had fallen.[15]

Sugar beet can be a very dangerous feed for horses. In 1934-36 in Hungary, hundreds of horses fed ensiled sugar beet tops died, with nervous symptoms: throat paralysis and, more frequently, spinal paralysis.[16] Horses may also choke on sugar beet pulp.[10]

If fed to dairy cows, sugar beet tops should always be given immediately after milking, to avoid taint.[7]

Fat Hen *Chenopodium album*

Fat hen is a common plant of waste places and poor cultivated land and is by far the most frequently occurring *Chenopodium* species in Britain. The whole plant, including the tightly clustered flower heads, is green with a powdery appearance. It often exceeds 50 cm in height. The form of the plant is variable, but it is usually branched, the terminal spike being the largest. The leaves are oval or diamond shaped with variably toothed edges. The stem, leaf stalks and upper leaves are sometimes tinged reddish-purple.

Poisonous principles   Although known to accumulate nitrates,[1] [2] the high oxalate content of *Chenopodium* is thought to be responsible for most of its poisonous properties. When absorbed during digestion, soluble oxalates combine with calcium, resulting in a reduction in the blood calcium concentration (hypocalcaemia).

Poisoning in animals   Ingestion of the plant has caused muscular incoordination among lambs in Australia,[3] shallow respiration, weak heart beat, recumbency and death in ewes in the Netherlands,[4] and similar symptoms, with loss of consciousness and death in some cases, in cattle in the west of England.[5] In New Zealand, listlessness and staggering when driven were observed the day after 40 milking cows had eaten considerable amounts of fat hen.[6] Milk production decreased and two animals became deeply comatose. A soluble oxalate content of 7.22% was found in the plants.

In most cases of poisoning reported in livestock, the affected animals had been allowed to graze in pastures heavily overgrown with fat hen. For treatment, calcium borogluconate should be given intravenously.

Human poisoning

Consumption of the plant, either raw or cooked, followed by exposure to sunlight has caused a photosensitisation reaction characterised by severe necrotic ulceration of the skin.[7] [8] Gangrenous areas developed and the lesions were slow to heal. In general there were no effects on internal systems, but blood-stained diarrhoea occurred in two cases.[7] In both the reports cited, fat hen had been eaten in fairly large quantities during a time of acute food shortage in Poland. Under similar conditions in Dresden in 1947, *Chenopodium album* and the related plant common orache *(Atriplex patula)* were eaten 2-3 times a day.[9] Weakness and fatigue developed gradually, followed by oedema, particularly of the head, hands and legs. A yellow pigmentation appeared on parts of the skin exposed to light.

COMPOSITAE

This family includes one of the most important poisonous plants in Britain, that is ragwort *(Senecio jacobaea)*. Other members of the family that are native in Britain, or are commonly grown here, are also described, although they are only potential causes of poisoning in this country.

Ragwort *Senecio jacobaea* (photo 14)

Other common names: Benweed; Staggerweed, Tansy Ragwort; St. James's Wort

Ragwort is abundant throughout Britain on waste land, beside roads and in pastures, where it is a troublesome weed. No accurate estimates have been found of the amount of ragwort in the country as a whole, but surveys conducted annually from 1979 in north-east Scotland indicate a strong natural tendency to increase, although herbicide spraying is keeping the level fairly constant at around 18% of the grassland area.[1]

Ragwort usually grows as a biennial, but if flowering does not occur in the second year (e.g. because of grazing) it can be perennial. It is an erect plant usually 30-90 cm high, but may exceed 100 cm. The stems are tough and often tinged red near the base, but brighter green and branched above the middle. A basal rosette of leaves usually dies before flowering but the stem leaves persist. They are deeply dissected, with irregular, jagged-edged lobes (hence the most common name, ragwort). All the leaves are dark green and rather tough and may be sparsely hairy on the lower side. The inflorescence is a conspicuous, large, flat-topped head of densely packed flowers with ray florets and disc florets, all of which are bright yellow. The seeds are borne singly and have a downy appendage (pappus) making them readily dispersable.

Poisonous principles

These are pyrrolizidine alkaloids many of which have been characterised and named, often from the name of the plant (e.g. senecionine, seneciphylline, jaconine, jacobine), but many more have been detected[2] (mainly by chromatographic methods) and require more detailed study. The most toxic pyrrolizidine alkaloids are cyclic diesters. Although their toxic effects are most apparent in the liver, it has been suggested that the alkaloids themselves are not hepatotoxic, but that they may be metabolised in the liver to bound pyrrole derivatives that are toxic. These metabolites are either soluble (detectable in urine) or insoluble (detectable in body tissues).[3] The poisonous principles are not destroyed by drying or storage.

Poisoning in animals

The signs of ragwort poisoning are usually slow to develop, and may not become apparent until animals have been eating it for several weeks or months; signs may even appear after consumption of the plant has ceased. Occasionally, however, poisoning develops only a few days after eating ragwort. Once clinical signs have appeared, it is not unusual for affected animals to die within a few days. The disorders of the digestive and nervous systems that result from eating the plant bear superficial resemblances to some other diseases. It is not surprising, therefore, that the association between the disease syndrome and ragwort was not recognised until this century. The discovery was made in Canada in 1906, where the condition (known as Pictou disease, after the town of that name in Nova Scotia) became established following the introduction of ragwort from Scotland in 1852.[4] The occurrence of poisoning by ragwort in Britain was first demonstrated in 1917,[5] although the poisonous properties of this plant had been suspected before this.

At pasture, poisoning is most likely to occur when there is heavy infestation of ragwort and alternative plants are scarce. Under such conditions ragwort may be grazed heavily, despite its apparent unpalatability. Some animals develop an addiction or preference for the plant once they start eating it. The toxicity of ragwort remains after ensilage or drying;[6] in one outbreak hay containing 5% ragwort caused poisoning, with some mortality in heifers.[7] Dried grass, hay or silage are the most common sources of ragwort poisoning in Britain.

Cattle[4][8] and horses[9][10] are most often involved in ragwort poisoning, although sheep[11] and pigs[12] are also susceptible. The practice of allowing sheep access to ragwort-infested pasture to assist in clearing it of the plants is not recommended. Deer appear to be resistant to ragwort poisoning,[13] and experiments on rabbits showed that intestinal absorption of alkaloids was low[14] and urinary excretion efficient;[15] guinea-pigs were also resistant.[15]

Clinical signs of ragwort poisoning are similar in cattle and horses. Initially there are digestive system disturbances, usually including abdominal pain and diarrhoea (sometimes with blood) or constipation,[4] both associated with persistent straining, and often resulting in rectal prolapse.[6][8] There may be emaciation and jaundice. Nervous signs may develop, particularly in horses. They include restlessness and aimless, uncoordinated movement;[9] the names 'walking disease' and 'sleepy staggers' have been applied to this condition in horses. Affected animals of both species may appear blind, press their heads against solid objects[9][16] and become at least partially paralysed. Weakness progressing to recumbency[4] and 'hepatic' coma (due to an increase in blood ammonia) may precede death.[16] There appears to be little correlation between the severity of the reaction and the amount or duration of ragwort ingestion.[10] In experimental feeding, cattle tolerated up to 1.5% of their body weight of the dried plant, eaten in a 15-day period, but died if given 2% of their weight within 20 days.[17]

Post-mortem examination of cattle and horses reveals inflammation of the digestive tract, often with ulceration and small haemorrhages,[6] and cirrhosis of the liver, with characteristic histological changes.[6][9] Accumulation of ammonia, as a result of liver damage, is responsible for a spongy degeneration of the brain and spinal cord.[16][18]

Sheep, fed experimentally with 3 g dried *Senecio jacobaea* per kg body weight daily for 16 days did not develop clinical signs, but liver function was impaired and there was 70% mortality during the next six months.[11] A severe disease with emaciation and, terminally, aggressive behaviour, occurred in Iraq in sheep grazing vegetation, one third of which was *Senecio cineraria*.[19] Post-mortem examination revealed congestion and inflammation of the liver and superficial haemorrhages of abdominal organs.

Ragwort poisoning has not been reported in pigs under natural conditions, but their susceptibility to it was demonstrated experimentally[12] by the inclusion of 5-10% dried ragwort in the diet of seven pigs for 1-3 months. The animals developed laboured breathing and fluctuating, elevated body temperatures. In contrast to the post-mortem findings in sheep and cattle, the only lesion in the liver was enlargement of cell nuclei. The most severe effects were in the lungs, which were firm, heavy, reddish purple and haemorrhagic.

In chicks fed, from one week old, for six weeks on a diet containing 7% dried, ground ragwort, there were progressive degenerative changes in the liver.[20]

Treatment

There is no specific treatment for ragwort poisoning, but supportive treatment for the digestive disturbances, and removal of affected animals from pasture containing ragwort may assist in recovery. It is recommended that dietary protein be limited[16] at this time as exacerbation of the nervous disorders often follows intake of a high protein feed. In rats it has been shown that the inclusion of 1% cysteine in the diet provides some protection against ragwort poisoning by enhancing the pyrrole-conjugating ability of the liver.[21]

Human poisoning

A disease, called seneciosis, is recognised in some parts of the world but it is doubtful if there are any adverse effects of ragwort on man in Britain. The question of the transfer of alkaloids to milk from cattle grazing ragwort remains open. The presence of at least one alkaloid (jacoline) was demonstrated in the milk of cows given 10 g of dried ragwort per kg of body weight by stomach tube daily for two weeks, but careful monitoring did not reveal any change in their calves.[22] In rats given the milk of goats fed for four weeks on a diet containing 25% dried, ground *Senecio jacobaea*, there was a reduction in the activity of some liver enzymes.[23] The potential danger to man of the consumption of milk from poisoned animals is generally considered to be slight.

In the USA, toxic alkaloids from *Senecio jacobaea* have been detected in honey produced from the nectar of the plant and are considered a potential health hazard.[24] In some States, bees visit ragwort particularly from mid to late summer when there is a dearth of other suitable flowers. These conditions may occur during drought in Britain, when ragwort survives better than clover. The resulting honey is deep yellow in colour and has a strong, unpleasant taste and smell.[25] There is, however, no evidence that, in this country, such honey contains sufficient quantities of ragwort alkaloids to be toxic.

Control of ragwort

Hand-pulling and removal of the plant from pasture is practised to some extent, but is obviously impracticable for heavy infestation or large areas. Ploughing of infested pasture is recommended and herbicide spraying is effective, but expensive. There is evidence that, at least in north-east Scotland, spraying areas where 22% (or more) of the fields are infested with ragwort decreases the level of infestation, but the infestation increases where less than 22% of infested fields are sprayed.[1] The herbicides MCPA and 2,4-D are recommended, but a single spray treatment is not necessarily sufficient as there may be regeneration of plants from residual roots.[26] Animals should not be allowed on to recently sprayed pasture as they will eat wilted plants or those treated with weed killer even more readily than fresh plants. An increase in water-soluble carbohydrates (and hence greater palatability) has been demonstrated in ragwort after treatment with 2,4-D; there is also evidence that the weed killer increases the alkaloid content of the plants.[27]

Ragwort was designated as an injurious weed in the Weeds Act, 1959, as, particularly in cattle, ragwort poisoning is said to cause higher economic losses in Britain than all other plants combined.[19] Under the Act, a landowner can be required to prevent the plant from spreading, and failure to do so within a specified time renders him liable to prosecution and a fine.[26]

Great Burdock *Arctium lappa*

This native plant occurs in waste places and beside paths or roads throughout the lowlands of Britain. The lesser burdock *(Arctium minus)*, with many variable forms including the burdock formerly known as *Arctium pubens,* also occurs in this country.

Attachment of burs (flower heads with hooked bracts) to the coats of animals can cause skin irritation, and symptoms of varying severity develop on the tongue and oral mucous membranes if burs enter the mouth. Granular stomatitis, with clinical signs including salivation, oral discomfort on eating and ulceration of affected areas, is said to be a common condition[1] resulting from contact with burdock, but is rarely reported. Mechanical obstruction of the oesophagus with burs has caused mortality in pheasants.[2]

Yellow Star Thistle *Centaurea solstitialis*

Other common name: St. Barnaby's Thistle

This plant occurs only occasionally in Britain as a weed on cultivated land, but several other *Centaurea* species are native in this country.

Yellow star thistle, and to a lesser extent, some other species of *Centaurea* are responsible for a nervous syndrome (nigropallidal encephalomalacia), of sudden onset, in horses.[3] Affected animals may be sleepy or move aimlessly, and involuntary movements of the mouth, with puckering of the lips and protrusion of the tongue are characteristic signs. The outcome may be fatal, and areas of necrosis can be seen in the brain.

The nature of the poisonous principle is not known. Poisoning has been reported mainly from California and Oregon in the USA, but horses in Argentina and Australia have also been affected.[3] As the disease occurs only after prolonged ingestion of the plants under climatic conditions that do not permit good growth of other forage plants, it is unlikely that horses would be affected in Britain.

Chicory *Cichorium intybus*

This plant is probably native to Britain and is sometimes cultivated, the leaves being used in salads and the dried, ground roots in beverages.

Cattle readily eat the leaves,[4] but feeding the roots to heifers in Poland (18 kg per animal daily) resulted in loss of appetite, thirst, diarrhoea, paralysis of extremities and, in some cases, death.[5] At post-mortem examination, gastrointestinal inflammation, oedema and congestion of the liver, kidneys and lungs were seen. After chicory was withdrawn from the feed, the remaining animals recovered within a few days.

Common Sunflower *Helianthus annuus*

Sunflowers are not native in Britain, but are cultivated for their oil-bearing seeds or as ornamentals; escapes sometimes grow in a semi-wild state. The plants are known to accumulate nitrates.

Cattle have been poisoned by eating sunflower plants in several countries including Germany[6] and the USSR.[7] In these outbreaks the plants were young and the seeds not formed or still green. Symptoms included circulatory failure, swaying of hind quarters and excitation, with subsequent collapse, 1-3 hours after eating the plants. Post-mortem examination revealed oedema of the lungs, dark-coloured blood, congestion of intestinal blood vessels and small haemorrhages, typical of poisoning by nitrites, to which nitrates are converted in the rumen.

Ploughman's Spikenard *Inula conyza*

This plant grows, and is locally common, on some types of chalky soil in Britain. The toxic principle is not known with certainty, although a substance isolated from elecampne *(Inula helenium)* and designated helenin(e) (probably a lactone of a volatile, aromatic oil) was toxic for laboratory animals.[8] Large-scale poisoning of cattle which ate *Inula conyza* growing with lucerne was reported from Poland.[9] In Germany, 16 cattle died or were slaughtered 7-12 hours after eating green fodder containing about 30% of *Inula conyza*.[10] Salivation, gastrointestinal disorders with blood-stained faeces, circulatory disturbance and muscular tremors were the principle symptoms. At post-mortem examination, swelling and degeneration of the liver, kidneys and heart and haemorrhages of the intestinal mucous membranes were found. Also in Germany, in a separate incident, ten sheep died or were slaughtered, with similar symptoms, after grazing pasture on which *Inula conyza* was abundant.[10] The related plant stinkwort *(Inula graveolens)* is reported as poisonous in Western Australia.[11]

Milk Thistle *Silybum marianum*

This is not a native plant but has become naturalised in some parts of Britain. It has caused poisoning in cattle in New South Wales[12] and South America,[13] where affected animals developed gastrointestinal disturbances, slow heart beat and difficult breathing. Post-mortem examination revealed congestion of the stomach and intestines with chocolate-brown coloured blood. Cases of poisoning have occurred only in winter. Nitrites produced in the rumen from nitrates in the plants are thought to be the poisonous principle. Treatment by frequent injection of 2-4% methylene blue is recommended; dramatic recovery has resulted from the use of a 20% solution of this dye.[14]

Cocklebur *Xanthium strumarium*

The seeds of *Xanthium* have been so widely distributed, unintentionally, by attachment of the burred flower heads to animals or clothing, that the true place of origin of the plants is difficult to determine. In Britain cocklebur is described as an introduced plant with local distribution.

A glycoside, named xanthostrumarin, was first thought to be the poisonous principle, and later hydroquinone was suspected, but carboxyatractyloside has now been demonstrated to be the toxic agent.[15]

No reports have been found of poisoning by this plant in Britain, but in the USA all classes of domestic livestock have been affected.[16] Pigs[17][18] exhibit loss of appetite, gastrointestinal disturbances, hyperexcitability, weakness, muscular incoordination, prostration and, in severe cases, convulsions and death. Gastrointestinal inflammation and haemorrhages of the liver and kidneys are seen at post-mortem examination.

Although the toxin is also contained in the seeds, these are rarely eaten as they are surrounded by the burs of the flower head, but depression, after eating cocklebur seeds, has been reported in poultry.[18] The toxicity of the plant remains after drying.

Some other members of the Compositae, including various thistles *(Carduus* and *Cirsium)* and golden rod *(Solidago)* are known to accumulate nitrates[19] in potentially toxic amounts, but no reports of their having caused poisoning have been found. Mugwort *(Artemisia vulgaris)* and the Jerusalem artichoke *(Helianthus tuberosus)* both of which occur in Britain, have poisoned animals in other countries. Several plants in the family can cause an unpleasant taint in the milk of dairy cows.[20] Human poisoning has occurred by medicinal use of the aromatic oil or infusions of tansy *(Chrysanthemum vulgare).*[20]

CONVOLVULACEAE

Dodder *Cuscuta* spp

Large dodder *(Cuscuta europaea)* is a slender twining annual parasite which is reddish in colour and twists in an anti-clockwise direction. In Britain it is found chiefly on nettles and hops, to which it attaches by suckers; but it is stated to be rare and is probably decreasing. Common dodder *(Cuscuta epithymum)* is similar but smaller (its stem diameter is 0.1 mm compared to that of 1.0 mm for large dodder) and is common locally on gorse *(Ulex)* and heather *(Calluna).* The poisonous principle is not known. Dodder poisoning has not been reported in Britain, but species in Russia, including *Cuscuta europaea,*[1] that parasitise lucerne, have caused chronic poisoning in horses when more than half of the plants fed have been affected. Symptoms are those of gastroenteritis, with loss of appetite, diarrhoea, constipation, and colic; death has resulted from intestinal perforation or intraperitoneal haemorrhage.[2] Horses are said to be more susceptible than other animals.

Morning Glory *Ipomoea purpurea*

This twining plant with heart-shaped leaves up to 12 cm long and clusters of 1-5 purplish-blue funnel-shaped flowers up to 8 cm long is not native in Britain, but is commonly cultivated out-of-doors or under glass.

Poisonous principle

The seeds of the plant contain d-lysergic acid, which is a well known hallucinogen.

Human poisoning

There are no reports of consumption of any parts of the plant by animals, but in man cases of the deliberate ingestion of up to 300 seeds are often reported. The symptoms produced include stomach ache and nausea, but are mainly a result of disturbances of the central nervous system, such as agitation, disorientation, blurred vision, dilated pupils and hallucinations.[3] Altered perception of surroundings and permanent psychological disturbance, sometimes leading to death, have been recorded.[4] Stomach lavage is indicated where the patient is not hallucinating. Sedation may be required.

CRASSULACEAE

Sedum spp

Common stonecrop *(Sedum acre)* is a small, evergreen perennial with numerous creeping stems, often forming mats 15-30 cm across, and bearing short succulent leaves which often develop a yellow or reddish tinge. The flowers are about 12 mm in diameter and have bright yellow, pointed petals.

Poisonous principles

This plant, and some other species of *Sedum,* have a hot bitter taste and are reputed to be poisonous. There is some justification for this as the alkaloids sedamine and sedridine are found in the plants.[1]

Poisoning

Because of the habitat of many of the species, which grow in crevices in walls and rocks, the plants are often inaccessible to animals and are unlikely to be eaten in sufficient quantity to cause poisoning. No actual case reports of poisoning by members of this family have been found in recent literature, and it is probable that the reputation of stonecrop as a poisonous plant is attributable to old reports[2] of clinical signs including salivation, muscle tremors, rapid respiration and coma in dogs fed with 7 g of *Sedum acre* per kg of body weight. In man, the sap of the plant is irritant to the skin.[3]

CRUCIFERAE

The name of this family is derived from the cross-shaped arrangement of the four petals of the flowers. It contains about 1900 species, including many garden flowers (stock, wallflower, candytuft), and weeds of arable land (charlock, wild radish) as well as plants which provide food for man and animals: vegetables (cabbage, turnip, radish), condiments (mustard, horseradish), forage plants (kale, rape) and oilseed plants (rape). In the period 1975-77, crucifers accounted for 57 of the total of 145 cases of plant poisoning referred to the Veterinary Investigation Centres of England and Wales. These included 17 cases of *Brassica* poisoning in sheep and 38 in cattle, and a single case of horse radish poisoning in birds.[1]

Most of the crucifers are herbaceous, with spirally arranged, lobed leaves, the terminal lobe being the largest. The earliest flowers appear as a compact group which gradually lengthens into a loose inflorescence with the youngest flowers at the apex. The flowers have four yellow or white petals. The fruit is usually a capsule which is divided into two cells by a thin longitudinal partition. Seeds usually occur in one or two rows in each cell. The shape of the fruit is important in distinguishing between species.

Poisoning may be due to mustard oil, as in the weeds charlock and wild radish, and the condiment plants white mustard and horse radish. Another type of poisoning is associated with the forage and oilseed crops. The chief toxic constituents are glucosinolates, although kale also contains a haemolytic toxin.

All species of Cruciferae so far investigated contain glucosinolates, which usually occur as potassium salts. By hydrolysis with the plant enzyme, thioglucosidase[2] (sometimes still referred to by the older names myrosinase or glucosinolase), potentially toxic substances are released. These include isothiocyanates, nitriles or thiocyanates. Glucosinolates occur in all parts of the plant, but are usually more concentrated in the seed.[3] Thioglucosidase does not normally come into contact with glucosinolates, unless the plant cells are crushed in the presence of water. The first glucosinolate to be isolated was named sinigrin (allyl glucosinolate) from black mustard *(Brassica nigra)*. On hydrolysis this yields mustard oil (allyl isothiocyanate), the pungent substance that contributes to the characteristic flavour of black mustard and other cruciferous plants. Most plants which produce allyl isothiocyanate are listed as poisonous to livestock. The immediate effect of mustard oil on contact with the skin is acute inflammation.[4] Most of the known glucosinolates are converted to stable isothiocyanates or nitriles, but some isothiocyanates are unstable and react further to form either ring compounds or the thiocyanate ion (SCN^-). Prior treatment of the plant material, and the conditions under which the hydrolysis occurs, influence the course of the reaction.[1]

The main compounds formed from the glucosinolates, and their effects in animals are: goitrins and the thiocyanate ion that cause thyroid enlargement; isothiocyanates that are irritant to skin and mucous membranes, and are also goitrogenic; nitriles that interfere with growth and cause pathological changes in the liver, kidneys and other organs, without any effect on the thyroid gland.

Rape *Brassica napus*, Turnip Rape *Brassica campestris*

Other common names: Cole; Colza

Almost all of the rape grown in Britain is the swede rape, *Brassica napus*, but the turnip rape, *Brassica campestris*, also occurs. Both of these plants are polymorphic, and there are several cultivars and hybrids to which a variety of other common names is applied. These differ in their growth habit and their suitability for use, either as forage or as an oilseed crop. Forage rape is usually eaten as a standing crop by sheep and cattle. Oilseed rape is grown for its seed, from which the extracted oil (often called colza oil after an alternative name for the plant) is widely used for human consumption or industrial purposes (including lubrication). The residue of the seeds after extraction (rapeseed meal) is incorporated into animal feeds, mainly for pigs and poultry. Rapeseed meal is a good source of protein, but the amount used at present is limited by its toxic effects. Work is in progress to produce varieties of rape with lower concentrations of potentially toxic substances, so that it can be fed in larger quantities.

Poisonous principles
Although rape is a valuable and widely used feed, all parts of the plant can contain toxic levels of several potentially harmful substances. The foliage contains glucosinolates, S-methyl cysteine sulphoxide (SMCO) and, under certain growing conditions, nitrates; the seeds contain glucosinolates, sinapine (the choline ester of 4-hydroxy-3,5-dimethoxycinnamic acid and usually associated with the glucosinolate complex) and tannins and saponins (whose effects have not been investigated);[5] rapeseed oil contains erucic acid, a long-chain fatty acid.

Of the glucosinolates, the most important in rape are progoitrin, gluconapin and glucobrassicanapin; these yield the goitrogens 3-butenyl isothiocyanate and 5-vinyl-2-oxazolidenethione, respectively. Isothiocyanates are not only goitrogenic, but are also irritant to the skin and mucous membranes. Goitre does not occur in animals grazing on rape, but can develop among pigs and poultry given feed containing a high proportion of rapeseed meal. This is probably because the leaves contain less progoitrin than the seeds. Under some conditions, progoitrin is hydrolysed to organic nitriles instead of goitrins, and these nitriles have been shown to damage the liver and kidneys of rats. SMCO is a haemolytic factor which was first identified in kale; there is much less SMCO in rape than in kale. There is variation in the toxicity of rape between season, year and crops, this being attributed to differences in the content of glucosinolates and SMCO. The glucosinolate content is also influenced by the age of the plant, the environment and genetic factors.[6] The SMCO content of rape plants increases with age.[7]

Poisoning in animals   Several disease syndromes have been associated with rape, although in many cases it is not possible to correlate these with the individual toxic constituents. Rape poisoning is most likely to occur in cattle and sheep from forage rape, and in pigs and poultry from rapeseed meal.

Forage rape poisoning   Most accounts of this are based on observations made in Canada in the 1940s.[8] At that time four types of disease were recognised: respiratory, urinary, nervous and digestive. These designations remain applicable to current outbreaks except that, in older reports, the respiratory form may have been confused with fog fever (atypical interstitial pneumonia) or a similar condition in some cases, and that the urinary type refers to the haemolytic anaemia which is now associated with SMCO. It is now clear that these are not specific forms of rape poisoning and may occur concurrently or sequentially.

Anaemia   Particularly in the older literature, this is reported to be the commonest form of rape poisoning; it is often accompanied by haemoglobinuria. The anaemia results from the breakdown of red blood cells (haemolysis), due to the presence of SMCO; haemoglobin released from the red blood cells is excreted in the urine which becomes reddish or dark in colour. Affected animals may be jaundiced, and liver damage sometimes occurs; the photosensitisation reactions recorded are not necessarily related to this liver damage. The presence of a haemolytic substance in rape was suspected in the 1940s in Canada, where, particularly in Ontario, an association between overfeeding on rape and anaemia and haemoglobinuria in cattle had been recognised for many years. Experimental work has confirmed that feeding rape to ruminants induces anaemia but that haemoglobinuria occurs in only a few animals.[9] There is evidence that increased production of red blood cells can compensate for their loss by haemolysis.[10] In Britain, anaemia and haemoglobinuria have occurred in cattle,[11] and anaemia in sheep[12] after grazing rape.

Cattle are not often fed on rape and little work has been done on its toxic effects on this species. In addition to the haemoglobinuria type reported in cattle in Britain,[11] an outbreak has been described in which the main clinical feature was blindness, associated with dullness, lack of ruminal

94

1   Ergot (*Claviceps purpurea*) on barley
    TFP

2   Fly Agaric (*Amanita muscaria*)
    HCB

3   *Cortinarius speciosissimus*
    AIKS

4   *Inocybe geophylla* var *lilacina*. A common
    lilac variant of the whitish or pale
    greyish-fawn fungus
    ROYAL BOTANIC GARDEN EDINBURGH

3

4

5

6

5   Death Cap (*Amanita phalloides*)
    HCB

6   Grey Mottle Gill (*Panaeolus sphinctrinus*)
    on dung
    ROYAL BOTANIC GARDEN EDINBURGH

7   Bracken (*Pteridium aquilinum*)
    HCB

8   Ramsons (*Allium ursinum*)
    HCB

8

7

movements and constipation.[13] Diarrhoea is occasionally reported in cattle but constipation is a more common occurrence.[11]

In Scotland, jaundice developed in some sheep which had grazed on rape for a part of each day during a month; three died.[12] The symptoms were depression, rapid breathing, a rapid heart beat, and considerable diarrhoea. Visible mucous membranes were dark yellow or brown, and the skin was yellow. Haemoglobinuria was observed in one sheep. The haemoglobin content of the blood was 3.6 g/100 ml. The anaemia appeared to be associated with a low content of inorganic phosphate in the blood. A similar incident has been reported among lambs in New South Wales.[14]

Nervous type   This is characterised by the sudden onset of blindness, and can occur in both cattle and sheep. More severe nervous signs include head-pressing and violent excitement. The eyes appear normal on ophthalmoscopic examination. The pupils show some response to light and may or may not be dilated. Affected animals usually recover, but this may take several weeks.[13] [15] [16] This type has been found in sheep in Britain, blindness being the main clinical sign. On removal from rape, most of the animals recovered their sight.

Digestive type   This is seen 3-4 days after the consumption of excessive amounts of rape. The affected animal stops feeding, is constipated, and there are no ruminal sounds. The rectum and colon are empty, except for small amounts of sticky black faeces. Bloat may also occur. In Britain, bloat and constipation have been seen, along with other clinical signs of rape poisoning in cattle[17] [18] and sheep.[19]

Respiratory type   Despite confusion with fog fever in some cases, respiratory distress can be a feature of rape poisoning in both cattle[17] and sheep.[14]

Post-mortem findings   These vary slightly between the four types of poisoning. In all forms, however, there is inflammation of the intestinal tract, with patchy necrosis and congestion of the liver; often the bladder contains dark-coloured urine. There is also an accumulation of dark-coloured intestinal contents. In the digestive type, the rumen contains a black, solid, doughy mass, and there is no gas; the folds of the omasum have a burned appearance, and the mucous membrane peels easily from them.

Other conditions associated with the consumption of forage rape are nitrite poisoning[20] [21] and photosensitisation.[11] [22] Rape, in common with turnips and swedes, is capable of taking up large amounts of nitrate when grown on soil containing a lot of nitrogen, whether occuring naturally or as the result of application of nitrogenous fertiliser.[20] In this state it is not safe to feed it to cattle and sheep. The death of 20 lambs in a flock of 337 from nitrite poisoning, the result of feeding on second growth rape, has been reported from New Zealand.[21] In contrast to kale, there are no reports of goitre in animals grazing rape, except for one experiment with lambs,[23] although glucosinolates are also present in rape. A photosensitisation known as 'rape scald' occurs in lambs in New Zealand;[22] clinical signs include oedema and necrosis of the skin, but liver damage has not been linked with this condition. Photosensitisation has also been recorded in a cow in Britain.[11]

Rapeseed meal poisoning

Rapeseed meal is generally not so well accepted as other meals, such as the more expensive soya bean meal. The depression of weight gain associated with rapeseed meal feeding can occur without other clinical signs, and may be only the result of lower feed intake, because of unpalatability. Other explanations have, however, been suggested for this reduced weight gain. These include depression of thyroid activity, and the formation of toxic nitrites[2] from glucosinolates in rape seed.

Goitre The most common adverse effect of feeding rapeseed meal is enlargement of the thyroid gland (goitre), that occurs in pigs and poultry and, to a very small extent, in ruminants.[5] This condition is almost invariably associated with increased weight of the thyroid gland; it does not respond to treatment with iodine as do some other forms of goitre. The seed of *Brassica napus* is more goitrogenic than that of *Brassica campestris*, because it contains more oxazolidenethione, produced by hydrolysis of glucosinolates. It appears that the increase in size of the thyroid gland enables sufficient thyroxine to be produced, thus compensating for the depressing effect of rapeseed meal on thyroid hormone production, but further work is required to clarify this.[5]

Liver haemorrhage This is another effect seen in poultry fed with rapeseed meal; it is often responsible for high mortality. This condition caused widespread losses in British flocks in 1971-72[24] although it had been seen earlier, in experimental work.[25] The severity of the haemorrhages varies with different types of rapeseed and different breeds of bird. Higher mortality rates have been recorded in laying hens than in broilers or cockerels; it has been suggested that the transitory increase in blood pressure at egg-laying is responsible for this. The constituent of rapeseed responsible for this has not been identified with certainty, but the glucosinolate complex may be involved.

Leg abnormalities Perosis (shortening and thickening of bones) can occur in poultry fed rapeseed meal.[26] This condition is often associated with thyroid enlargement and growth depression. The legs are weak; bent hock joints are a typical feature. A higher incidence of leg weakness occurs in birds fed seed residues of *Brassica napus* than with *Brassica campestris*. The causative agent is not known, although the incidence of the condition is higher with high glucosinolate meals.

Effects on reproduction Diets containing a high (20%) content of rapeseed meals (particularly those from *Brassica napus*) depress egg production in pullets.[5] No adverse effects on reproductive efficiency have been reported in sows, but in gilts given 8-10% rapeseed meal there have been reductions in litter size and weight and in some cases, delayed conception.[27]

Egg taint An effect of feeding rapeseed to poultry that is of particular concern to poultry farmers is a taint in eggs, described as a *fishy, crabby* or *off* taste; only brown eggs are affected.[28] It was found in the early 1970s that this taint is due to the presence of trimethylamine in the eggs. Trimethylamine is a product of the breakdown of sinapine and other dietary sources of choline, by intestinal bacteria. Egg taint is linked with a genetic defect impeding the synthesis of the enzyme trimethylamine oxidase[28] that breaks down trimethylamine. Impaired thyroid function was thought to account for the reduced production of trimethylamine oxidase, but recent experiments have shown that the enzyme is inhibited by goitrin (from glucosinolates in the plants).[29] A biochemical test has been developed to identify, while still chicks, birds with defective trimethylamine metabolism.[30] [31]

Taint in meat The meat of sheep which have grazed on rape may have a disagreeable aroma and flavour, which could be due to metabolites of glucosinolates.[32] Similar taint has been suspected in the carcasses of broiler fowls fed on rapeseed meal.[26]

Effects on man Rapeseed oil is used for human consumption in foods such as margarine and cooking fats. The oil contains erucic acid that is not readily absorbed from the intestines and is therefore an undesirable constituent of food. Under experimental conditions, it has caused damage to the heart of pigs and rats,[33] but no adverse effects have been observed in man as a result of eating products containing it. New varieties of rape with low erucic acid content are being developed.[32]

Kale *Brassica oleracea* (photo 15)

The two main types of kale traditionally grown in Britain, marrowstem and thousand-head (tall and dwarf, respectively) were developed by selection and cultivation from the wild cabbage *(Brassica oleracea)*. Kale is an excellent, succulent feed for cattle, of high digestibility, rich in protein

(17% crude protein in the dry matter) and carotene.[34][35] It is particularly valuable as a green winter feed. Traditionally, marrowstem kale is grown for autumn use, and the more frost-resistant thousand-head late in the winter. The new kale cultivars, Maris Kestrel and Proteor, do not fit into these types. Maris Kestrel is a hybrid kale, the prototype of a short, winter-hardy thick-stemmed type.[36] Kale grows well under a wide range of conditions, but is found mostly in the south and south-west of England.[37] The area sown to kale increased greatly between 1948 and 1960, but declined rapidly in the subsequent decade.[37][38] Difficulties associated with harvesting, and wastage and soil damage during direct grazing were partly to blame, but the increased occurrence of so-called kale poisoning probably also contributed to this decline.[38] Problems have long been associated with the feeding of large amounts of kale over a prolonged period.

Poisonous principles   Toxic constituents of kale include an amino acid, S-methyl cysteine sulphoxide (SMCO), that is converted in the rumen during normal fermentation to dimethyl disulphide, which is a compound that destroys red blood cells,[39] and causes an acute haemolytic anaemia. Also present are goitrogens, mainly the thiocyanate ion, but also some isothiocyanates, derived from glucosinolates.[40][41] Glucosinolates which have been identified from kale include sinigrin, glucobrassicin, progoitrin, gluconapin, neoglucobrassicin, glucoiberin and glucobrassicanapin.[42] The SMCO content can vary with fertiliser application; it increases with nitrogen application but only when soil sulphate values are high.[43] Kale can accumulate nitrates; nitrate/nitrite poisoning has been reported in cattle in New Zealand.[22]

Poisoning in animals   The two main disorders produced by kale feeding are haemolytic anaemia and goitre. Adverse effects on fertility have also been described.

Haemolytic anaemia   When ruminants are fed largely or exclusively on kale, or on other brassica crops, such as rape, cabbage, Brussels sprouts and swede tops, they may develop severe haemolytic anaemia as a result of SMCO present in the plants. Symptoms depend on the extent of haemolysis (breakdown of red blood cells), and the ability of the animal to replace the cells destroyed. Recently calved cows or those in late pregnancy are at greater risk, as are animals with a high milk yield. An obvious clinical sign of this acute anaemia in cattle is the presence of haemoglobin in the urine (haemoglobinuria); the urine is reddish-brown or black. Other signs are loss of appetite, weakness, fall in milk yield, jaundice, increased heart rate, and diarrhoea. An affected cow soon becomes weak, and ceases to feed; this is followed by a rapid loss of condition. Collapse and sudden death may also occur.

The first evidence of anaemia, usually after 1-3 weeks of kale feeding, is detectable in the blood; microscopic examination reveals stainable granules (Heinz-Ehrlich bodies) in the red blood cells. Subsequently, blood haemoglobin falls, usually over 1-2 weeks, from the normal 11 g/100 ml to 6 g/100 ml or lower. If kale feeding is stopped, haemoglobin returns to normal in 3-4 weeks. If kale feeding continues even until haemolysis becomes severe, the animals may still recover by producing new red blood cells.

Post-mortem examination of animals that die reveals emaciation and jaundice. The bladder may contain black, tar-like urine, the spleen is pale brown, the liver swollen and pale (with distinct lobules), and the kidneys are a uniform dark brown. Histological examination of the liver shows wedge-shaped areas of necrosis. Extensive vacuolation of kidney cells and degeneration of nuclei in the renal epithelium are also seen, together with the presence of large, irregular masses of an iron-containing protein, haemosiderin, within macrophages of the spleen.[44] The findings are similar in another form of haemoglobinuria that occurs after calving, and is not always due to kale feeding.[45]

In a survey of 83 dairy farms in 1969 (49 in southern England and 34 in south-west Scotland), 6.4% of cows fed kale developed anaemia (as shown by a low haemoglobin content of blood), although in 36% the red blood cells contained more Heinz-Ehrlich bodies than normal. In most of the herds, the disorder was not serious because the animals were seldom fed kale alone.[46] The livestock most at risk are sheep and cattle fed almost entirely on brassica fodder crops.[47]

The SMCO content of kale increases as the plant matures, and as secondary growth and flowering begin. Flowers contain twice as much SMCO as the whole plant (up to 20 g/kg dry matter), and they are very toxic to cattle. At one farm in Scotland, yearling cattle strip-grazing on Maris Kestrel kale crossed an electric fence in order to eat the flowers, and several of them developed severe anaemia.[48]

Care should be taken when feeding kale and other brassica crops to ruminants, to limit the intake of SMCO by restricting the amount fed and/or by using cultivars low in SMCO (e.g. Maris Kestrel and Cauletta). It has been estimated that a daily intake of 15 g SMCO/100 kg live weight is required to produce acute haemolytic anaemia, and that 10 g or less produces only mild anaemia.[39] In one survey of kale cultivars and types, plants sampled at various stages of growth contained between 3.8 and 14.4 g SMCO per kg dry matter.[48]

Kale is one of the crops used for the production of leaf protein extracts and as a feedstuff for poultry. Heinz body anaemia similar to that found in ruminants has also been produced in adult fowls (male and female) fed with dimethyl disulphide at up to 600 μg/head per day for 12 days. Haemoglobin and haematocrit values were also reduced.[49]

Goitre This condition has been produced by kale in adult sheep,[50] in lambs born to ewes that had been fed on kale during pregnancy,[51][52] and in cattle.[53] The goitre is due to secondary iodine deficiency, because thiocyanate prevents accumulation of iodine in the thyroid gland. This effect can be corrected by feeding extra iodine.[41] There is some evidence to suggest that the goitrogen in kale is of the thiouracil type, that is it inhibits the organic binding of iodine rather than the absorption of inorganic iodide.[50] The thiocyanate content of kale varies according to part of the plant sampled and the time of year. Small, young leaves contain about five times more thiocyanate than large leaves, and twice the content of intermediate-sized leaves. Thiocyanate content doubles during late September and October, then declines subsequently. Variations between crops and years have also been noted.[54]

A common sign of iodine deficiency is the birth of offspring that are weak or die soon after birth. Such animals have an enlarged thyroid gland. The offspring may be born dead, or the thyroid gland may be so large that it interferes with breathing and sucking.[55] Loss of hair is another feature. Iodine deficiency is not now of major economic importance in Britain because it is easy to recognise and to correct.[56] Goitre takes a long time to develop in adult animals. Ewes fed unrestricted amounts of kale (daily intake averaging 4.5 kg) for 17 weeks developed thyroid enlargement, and histological signs of goitre; the thyroid gland and the blood contained subnormal amounts of iodine.[57]

Reduced fertility This has been associated with kale feeding in cows and ewes. A definite correlation between kale feeding and low winter fertility in cows, particularly Friesians, was established by a survey of 100 farms in Somerset in 1957-58,[58] and a similar effect was reproduced experimentally in Friesians each fed about 50 kg kale daily. Amounts of copper and haemoglobin in the blood were much lower than in cows not fed kale.[59] Herd infertility, manifested by prolonged absence of oestrus, may occur among cows with anaemia due to kale feeding.[60] Simultaneous deficiencies of phosphorus, copper, manganese and iodine can contribute to the infertility of kale-fed dairy cows.[34] Ewes fed kale have shown brief oestrus and an increased occurrence of abnormal embryos.[51] Feeding kale throughout the winter to a herd of goats in France was suspected to be the cause of the birth of mummified or weak, non-viable kids 5-15 days after the expected date of parturition.[61] Oestrogenic substances have not been demonstrated in kale,[62] and it appears that the goitrogenic properties of kale may be responsible for infertility, suppression of oestrus, reduced conception rate, embryonic mortality and stillbirth.[63]

Effects on man Goitrogens circulating in the blood stream are excreted in the milk of lactating animals fed goitrogenic plants. The milk of a goat fed on thousand-headed kale was found to contain 4.6 mg thiocyanate/100 ml.[64] Evidence from Tasmania in 1949-54 suggested that enlarged thyroids in children might have been caused by drinking milk from cows fed large amounts of marrowstem kale.[65] The pastures in Tasmania harboured various cruciferous weeds, particularly turnip weed *(Rapistrum rugosum)*, but extensive investigations failed to produce definite evidence of goitrogens in milk from cows grazing on kale or on cruciferous weeds.[66] In Finland, the thiocyanate content in milk was shown to increase from 2 to 5-8 mg/litre when cows were fed large quantities of brassica forage, but even at levels of 18 mg/litre, there was no evidence that the milk was goitrogenic, although the iodine content of the milk fell with the increase in its thiocyanate content. These findings indicate that iodine deficiency would develop in young children only if such milk were the sole source of nourishment.[40]

Charlock *Sinapis arvensis*

Charlock is an annual weed of arable land, and thrives on calcareous and heavy soils. It is less common than in the past. The leaves are rough and slightly hairy. The flowers are bright yellow, and flowering continues for most of the summer; the pods have a beak which takes up about one third of their length. The seeds are capable of remaining dormant in soil for many years, and germinate only when conditions are favourable. Selective weed killers have been aimed at this weed, particularly in cereal crops. Charlock is now easily controlled in cereals and in oilseed rape, a relatively new crop in Britain.

Poisonous principles Charlock is not poisonous until the pods have formed. The poisonous constituent of the seeds is the volatile mustard oil, allyl isothiocyanate.[3] This is released from sinigrin (allyl glucosinolate) present in charlock seed.

Poisoning in animals Toxicity has been demonstrated in chickens, especially when fed crushed charlock seed.[67] Sheep fed crushed seed developed slight bloat, while in those fed large amounts of the green plant (30-35 kg) rumination ceased.[68] Poisoning occurred in lambs folded on a field of rape in which charlock with well formed pods was abundant.[69] The symptoms were those of acute gastroenteritis: abdominal pain, slight frothing around the mouth and nose, grunting and diarrhoea. Post-mortem examination revealed acute inflammation of the rumen, intestines, and kidneys. Poisoning of horses by charlock has been reported in the USSR[70] and Yugoslavia.[71] Cattle have been poisoned by hay containing 20-30% of charlock; allyl isothiocyanate, however, has not been found in silage.[79] In Georgia, USSR,[72] cattle had access to charlock growing in profusion to a height of 70-80 cm in fields after the potato harvest. Temperatures were low (-5°C), so these plants had probably been frost-damaged. Small amounts eaten by cattle produced frequent urination, reddening of visible mucous membranes, and slight bloat. They recovered within 24 hours. When large amounts were eaten, animals died of asphyxia in 1-1½ hours. Clinical signs were bloat, open-mouth breathing, groaning, shuffling or standing with legs wide apart, bulging of eyes with dilated pupils, bluish coloration (cyanosis) of visible mucous membranes and inability to urinate. Treatment was symptomatic and included puncture of the rumen for bloat.

White mustard *Sinapis alba*

White mustard is the cultivated mustard, which is grown as a forage crop for sheep, as a green manure, and for the manufacture of the condiment, mustard. The stem grows to a height of 30-60 cm, and is usually covered with stiff hairs. The leaves are also rough, hairy, lobed and up to 15 cm long; the flowers have yellow petals, up to 15 mm across. The pod grows up to 40 mm long and 3-4 mm wide. It has a flat hairy beak which takes up over half of its total length, and contains one seed at its base.

Poisonous principle The seed of white mustard contains sinalbin (*p*-hydroxy-benzyl-glucosinolate). On hydrolysis, this forms an unstable isothiocyanate which breaks down into thiocyanate and *p*-hydroxybenzyl alcohol.[3] Under some conditions, toxic quantities of nitrates may be present.

Poisoning in animals In Britain, when lambs grazed for two days and nights on a white mustard crop in which seed pods had formed, five died and 40 were ill and unable to stand.[73] Others, which could walk, had frothy salivation and diarrhoea. Symptoms and post-mortem findings were almost identical with those of charlock poisoning.[69] Sheep fed 600 g of extracted mustard seed cake a day for several days, or 1-2 kg in one feed, had a blood haemoglobin value twice that of normal; respiration and pulse rates increased and the sheep died; oedema was found at post-mortem examination. However, 290 g of mustard cake fed every day for 100 days in 1 kg of concentrate, with maize silage and hay, produced no adverse effects. The seed cake contained 1.1% mustard oil.[74]

Poisoning has also occurred in cattle. Some bullocks died after grazing white mustard stubble. Post-mortem examination showed that the rumen was packed with coarse fibrous mustard stems and the lining membrane was more easily detached than usual. The abomasum was inflamed, there was patchy inflammation in the small intestines and some lung inflammation.[75] Eight of 54 dairy cows died within two and a half days of having had access to a heap of about 16 kg of white mustard seed, which had been deposited in the field where they were grazing.[76] Poisoning commenced with staggering and walking around in circles, then the cows became recumbent with arched neck and profuse salivation. There was no diarrhoea. Post-mortem examination revealed inflammation of the abomasum and intestine. There was patchy congestion and inflammation in the kidneys. The rumen was well filled with fibrous material, and abundant mustard seeds. Mustard seed poisoning has also been reported from India[77] in a bullock given 'conditioning powder' containing 50-60 g of mixed, ground mustard seed, once daily for some days. Clinical signs were those of severe gastroenteritis. In Switzerland, 19 of 48 heifers died two hours after being fed on white mustard.[78] This crop had been cut and fed to the cattle because development of the plants had been inhibited at the preflowering stage by a sudden drop in temperature. The plants contained 6.2% nitrate in dry matter, 10-20 times the toxic level; the glucosinolate content was below that considered dangerous.

Horse Radish *Armoracia rusticana*

Horse radish is a perennial with a long tapering root. The basal leaves are rough to touch but are not hairy; they grow up to 50 cm in length on stalks up to 30 cm long and are undivided. They are toothed at the edges, and 10-15 cm broad. The stems are 60-125 cm tall, and bear tiny white flowers in a terminal group. The pods, even if they form, seldom ripen in the British climate. Horse radish is cultivated for culinary use, but is also found wild in many parts of the country.

Poisonous principles The root and leaves of horse radish contain sinigrin (allyl glucosinolate) and 2-phenylethyl glucosinolate.[79] Allyl glucosinolate is hydrolysed to allyl isothiocyanate which is a potent irritant of the eyes and skin.

Poisoning Horse radish poisoning is rare because of the pungent, disagreeable flavour of the leaves and roots, but there have been reports in Britain of poisoning of cattle, ponies and pigs.[1] In cattle the symptoms were lowing and excitement followed by collapse and death. Six ponies, found dead after having broken into an orchard in which horse radish was growing in profusion, had large amounts of the leaves and flowering stems in their stomachs, which were acutely inflamed and smelled typically of horse radish. There were no other lesions. The animals had struggled violently before dying. Two fattening pigs were found dead about three hours after being fed uncooked hotel garbage. Post-mortem examination showed acute inflammation of the stomach walls, which even after washing in water smelled strongly of horse radish. There were no other lesions. It was estimated that the pigs had eaten 55-85 g of the grated root between them.

103

All the above members of the Cruciferae owe their poisonous properties to volatile oils, similar to oil of mustard, which are released by enzymatic hydrolysis of non-toxic glucosinolates. All of them are very strong irritants when allowed to come into contact with living tissues.

Treatment Demulcents are recommended, and purgatives may be required as constipation can occur in the early stages of recovery.

Wild Radish *Raphanus raphanistrum*

Wild radish is an annual or a biennial plant, 20-60 cm tall, very branched, with divided or lobed, rough leaves, which are larger at the base than near the top of the stem. The flowers are white or very pale lilac (occasionally pale yellow) with veined petals.

Poisonous principle The active constituent is allyl isothiocyanate, derived from the glucosinolate, sinigrin.

Poisoning There are no records of poisoning by wild radish in recent British literature, but it has always been regarded as harmful to livestock if eaten in quantity. However, lambs and adult sheep failed to develop signs of poisoning when fed large amounts of the freshly cut plants or ripe seeds. Similarly, no poisoning or abortion occurred among pregnant ewes given up to 600 g of wild radish pods a day, neither were yearling sheep poisoned by eating up to 1 kg of pods mixed with grain. The seeds contained 0.17-0.29% allyl isothiocyanate.[80] Poisoning in lambs was suspected after fifty lambs had been allowed to graze a field covered with wild radish in an advanced stage of flowering. One died on the same night and five others were found dead the next morning; others in the flock were unable to rise. Post-mortem examination within two hours of death showed the rumen to be filled with the plant, the abdominal muscles were congested and the tissues yellow in colour. The heart and lungs were normal, but the liver was friable, the kidneys were congested with blood and the bladder was filled with blood-stained urine.[81]

Other cruciferous crops

Cabbage *(Brassica oleracea* var. *capitata)*, Brussels sprouts *(Brassica oleracea* var. *gemmifera)*, swede *(Brassica napus* var. *napobrassica)* and turnip *(Brassica campestris)* all contain the haemolytic factor S-methyl cysteine sulphoxide

(SMCO),[82] but they are seldom eaten in amounts large enough to cause trouble. Haemolytic anaemia, with haemoglobinuria, has been reported in cattle,[83] [84] and in sheep[85] fed large amounts of cabbage and in cows given free access to Brussels sprouts.[83] Although swede roots have always been regarded as safe, anaemia can be produced experimentally in cattle and sheep[85] and in goats[84] by feeding them on swede roots and tops. The SMCO content of turnips is generally quite low, but one cultivar, Tokyo top, contains moderate amounts; mild anaemia occurred in lambs fed on young stubble turnip,[86] a *Brassica campestris* hybrid.

Turnip plants are capable of taking up and accumulating large amounts of nitrate, which can cause nitrite poisoning in cattle.[84] [87] When 22 cows were fed, in error, seeds of turnip and swede, they developed acute haemorrhagic gastroenteritis and colic, and seven died. This feed had been imported as 'linseed cake' from Ethiopia into Belgium, and it contained 0.5-0.7% isothiocyanate.[88]

Glycosides in shepherd's purse *(Capsella bursa-pastoris)* were thought to be responsible for milk taint in cattle in Australia.[89]

CUCURBITACEAE

White Bryony *Bryonia dioica* (photo 16)

Other common name: British Mandrake

White bryony is a climbing plant, common in England and Wales, except in some northern counties. It has been introduced locally in Scotland. The name and habitat of the plant cause confusion with black bryony *(Tamus communis)*, another climbing plant, but of a different family (Dioscoraceae).

White bryony has trailing stems, branching especially near the base and sometimes exceeding 5 m in length. The plant climbs by means of spirally coiled tendrils which arise from the stem beside the leaf stalks. The leaves are up to 10 cm across, have 3-5 pointed lobes and they, and the stems, are covered with minute, stiff hairs making the plant rough to touch. Greenish-white flowers appear in clusters in the leaf axils in summer, the males (12-18 mm across) and the females (10-12 mm across) being similar in appearance, but borne on separate plants. The flowers have pointed sepals, larger triangular net-veined petals and yellow anthers in the males and a prominent bifid stigma in the females. White bryony has a massive, tuberous root, consumption of which has caused poisoning when mistaken for parsnip or turnip, hence the French name 'navet du diable' (devil's turnip). The ripe fruit is a red berry with a dull surface and contains flat, black and yellow mottled seeds. The whole plant, but particularly the root, contains an acrid milky juice, the unpleasant odour of which persists after drying.

Poisonous principles
Little is known of these, except that they include a glycoside (variously named as bryonin, bryonine or bryonidin) which is a drastic purgative, and an alkaloid (bryonicine).

Poisoning in animals
Under normal conditions, poisoning of domestic animals by white bryony is rare, although early literature[1] reports that ingestion of the root by pigs, and the berries by poultry may prove fatal. Poisoning of a herd of 40 milking cows occurred when the animals had access to white bryony roots exposed during excavation for a pipe line.[2] Within a few hours the animals had collapsed, their bodies were cold and their eyes deeply sunk in their sockets. Despite treatment with stimulants all the animals became comatose and died. Post-mortem examination revealed large quantities of chewed, fleshy root in the rumen, the walls of which were inflamed. Two other cows which ate white bryony, but recovered, developed a craving for the plant and, during the following summer ate any part of it which was available. This caused acute digestive disturbance, with diarrhoea, and almost complete, but temporary, cessation of milk secretion. In another more recent case in Britain where white bryony foliage with berries had been eaten liberally from a hedge, a 5-year-old cow collapsed and was unable to stand until the following day.[3] There were signs of respiratory distress and milk production ceased for four days, after which it rose gradually, but never reached its former level.

In addition to diarrhoea, horses poisoned by eating white bryony[4] exhibit copious urination, sweating and, occasionally, complete cessation of defaecation. Other symptoms reported in horses are respiratory difficulty, incoordination and convulsions; intestinal ulceration has been seen.

In Romania, 18 ducklings gorged themselves on bryony when food was scarce.[5] All died within 10-24 hours, after showing apathy, staggering gait, recumbency, trembling, convulsions, diarrhoea and laboured breathing.

Treatment with stimulants and liquids, to replace fluids lost in diarrhoea, is recommended.

Human poisoning
The juice of white bryony irritates the skin[6] and poisoning has resulted from eating the root[1] and the berries, which are particularly attractive to children. Usually, fluid replacement is the only treatment necessary.

9 Cuckoo Pint (*Arum maculatum*). The orange-red berries which ripen in autumn are poisonous
JH

10 Comfrey (*Symphytum officinale*)
HCB

11 Box (*Buxus sempervirens*)
JH

12 Corn Cockle (*Agrostemma githago*). The small black seeds are poisonous
JH

10

11

12

13　14

13　Spindle (*Euonymus europaeus*)
HCB

14　Ragwort (*Senecio jacobaea*)
HCB

15　Kale (*Brassica oleracea*)
HCB

15

CUPRESSACEAE

Cypress *Cupressus* spp

There are many species and varieties of *Cupressus* of which the best known is probably the Monterey cypress *(Cupressus macrocarpa)*, sometimes referred to simply as macrocarpa. This evergreen tree may grow up to 25 m tall, has ascending branches, reddish-brown fissured or scaly bark, small scale-like triangular leaves closely pressed on one plane against each other and the stem, and unisexual cones which rarely exceed 3 cm across.

Poisoning in animals Poisoning by *Cupressus* has been reported mainly in cattle[1][2] in which loss of condition, weakness, staggering gait and sunken eyes are consistently found. The foliage and woody parts of felled cypress trees *(Cupressus sempervirens)* were responsible for the death of two heifers in Britain.[3] Cows which eat cypress in the last three months of pregnancy are liable to abort, and both the foetus and the adult animal may die. Persistent, severe straining occurs, the cervix does not dilate fully, the foetal membranes are retained, and the maternal cotyledons are greatly swollen. Animals that recover give very little milk initially. Post-mortem examination of foetuses aborted by cows which ate *Cupressus macrocarpa* revealed areas in the white matter of the brain in which the cells had softened and degenerated (cerebral leucomalacia).[4]

Juniper *Juniperus* spp

Juniper is a shrub or small evergreen tree with thin bark which often peels in longitudinal strips. Depending on the species, the leaves may be scale-like, resembling cypress, or needle-like, as in pines. The scales of the female flowers become fleshy and coalesce to form a berry-like fruit.

Poisonous principles The leaves and shoots contain juniper oil, terpene derivatives and a bitter substance, probably an alkaloid, called juniperine.[5]

Poisoning in animals Species of juniper, particularly *Juniperus sabina,* which is not native but sometimes planted in Britain, have poisoned animals. The clinical signs include gastrointestinal disturbances, muscular cramps and abortion,[6] especially in the last three months of pregnancy. Poisoning occurs most frequently in cattle, but has also been recorded in a goat which ate juniper and developed gastrointestinal disorders and blood-stained urine.[7] Post-mortem examination reveals inflammation of the digestive and urinary tracts.

Juniperus communis grows on calcareous soils throughout Britain, although it is rather local in distribution. It contains similar toxic principles to other *Juniperus* species, but no specific cases of poisoning have been attributed to it in this country.

CYPERACEAE

Sedge *Carex* spp

Sedges are rarely eaten by animals as they contain silicates which make them coarse and hard, and consequently unpalatable.

Poisonous principles
The plants contain cyanogenic glycosides. Saponins, tannin, resin and traces of an oil are also said to be present in the whole plant.[1]

Poisoning
Consumption of *Carex vulpina*, a sedge native in Britain, has poisoned some cattle in Romania[2] where 10 of 62 animals died or had to be killed after eating the actively growing green plant in early summer. The clinical signs described, which apply equally to cattle which have eaten other *Carex* species, are typical of cyanide poisoning. They occurred within a few minutes of eating the plant, and included excess salivation, clenching and grinding of teeth, dilation of pupils, congestion of mucous membranes, diarrhoea, muscular spasms, unsteady gait, posterior paralysis, recumbency, deep respiration becoming shallower, weak pulse and groaning. Coma usually preceded death which often occurred 30-60 minutes after eating the plants. Post-mortem examination revealed haemorrhages in the conjunctiva, muscles, bone marrow and intestines, the contents of which, in some cases, smelled of bitter almonds. The blood was bright red and the lungs were congested with blood and oedematous.

Treatment
If given immediately, and before too much sedge has been eaten, intravenous injection of sodium thiosulphate and sodium nitrite solutions may be effective in treating poisoned animals.

DIOSCOREACEAE

Black Bryony *Tamus communis* (photo 17)

Black bryony grows in scrub, hedgerows and at the edges of woods and is common throughout southern England, the Midlands and Wales, decreases in frequency further north and is absent from Scotland. It is a hedge climber and its common name is likely to cause confusion with white bryony *(Bryonia dioica)* which is also a climber with a similar habit and habitat, but is botanically a very different plant, belonging to another family (Cucurbitaceae).

The plant grows from an irregular, blackish tuber and climbs by means of its slender, unbranched stems which twine anticlockwise and grow up to 4 m long. Dark, shining, heart-shaped leaves are borne on long stalks along the stem, and yellowish-green, unisexual flowers appear in the leaf axils in early summer. The males are stalked and loosely clustered and the females have very short stalks, are fewer and more compact. The berries are up to 12 mm in diameter and are shining and green when first formed, but red when ripe. They contain 1-5 rough-coated yellow seeds.

Poisonous principle Very little is known about this, but it is sometimes stated to be a glycoside.

Poisoning in animals Reference is often made to the toxic nature of black bryony, but there are few reports of animals having been poisoned by it. Early literature[1] states that the leaves are eaten by sheep and goats without adverse effects, but that the berries are narcotic and irritant. Fatal poisoning was suspected in three horses which had grazed in fields where the stems, leaves and berries of the plant had been pulled from the hedge and showed signs of having been chewed.[2] In one case the plant was identified in ingested material taken at a post-mortem examination. The horses refused food and became dull; severe abdominal pain, accompanied by elevated temperature and profuse sweating, developed before death.

Human poisoning The sap can cause blistering of the skin and, if eaten, burning and blistering of the mouth, followed by vomiting and diarrhoea; death may result.[3]

Treatment Demulcents are recommended.

DIPSACACEAE

Devil's-bit scabious *(Succisa pratensis)* was reported over eighty years ago[1] to have caused damage to the tongues of cattle which ate it. There has been no record of its toxicity since then.

DROSERACEAE

Sundew *Drosera* spp

It is thought by farmers in Ireland (Co. Donegal) that a purulent dermatitis seen in lambs may be caused by photosensitisation after eating sundew.[1]

Contact with crushed leaves of sundew has caused human dermatitis.[2]

ERICACEAE

Rhododendron spp (photo 18)

Of the many hundreds of species and varieties in this genus, only one *(Rhododendron ponticum)* of those introduced to Britain has become naturalised, mainly in peaty and sandy soils. Many, including the azalea group, are grown as ornamentals.

Common Rhododendron *Rhododendron ponticum*

Other common name: Pontic Rhododendron

This plant is a branched, evergreen shrub, commonly cultivated and often planted in woods where it may become dominant beneath trees. It grows up to 3 m high, and has hard, elongated, elliptical leaves which are pointed at the tip and taper towards the stalk. The mature leaves are 6-12 cm long, dark green but not glossy above and paler green beneath. The young leaves are brighter green and less hard. The inflorescence develops in spring and is a hemispherical or more or less spherical group of wide-mouthed, bell-shaped flowers up to 5 cm across. They are dull purple in colour, spotted with brown, and have a cluster of stamens (usually 10) projecting from them. A wide range of flower colours are seen in cultivated varieties.

Poisonous principles   The leaves, flowers, pollen and nectar of many *Rhododendron* species contain several toxic diterpenoids (grayanotoxins). One of these, grayanotoxin I, is also known as rhodotoxin, acetylandromedol, or, more often, as andromedotoxin, although there is some confusion over the latter name, which has been used to describe two different toxic substances. Grayanotoxin I and, less frequently, grayanotoxins II and III are the toxins in poisonous honey,[1] produced by bees which have collected nectar from the flowers of some *Rhododendron* or *Azalea* species. The planting of ornamental rhododendron gardens in parts of Scotland has made bee keeping uneconomic there because of serious loss of bees in spring.[2] In 400 B.C., Xenophon reported poisoning of Greek soldiers who had eaten honey made by bees from wild rhododendrons. In the British Isles, however, human poisoning by honey is almost unknown; hive bees generally procure little nectar from rhododendron flowers, and the honey produced in spring is usually not taken from the hives but used by the bees themselves.[3]

Poisoning in animals   Animals rarely graze in woodland areas in Britain and are therefore unlikely to eat rhododendrons under normal conditions, but all classes of livestock are at risk if they gain access to gardens or garden refuse containing the plant. Under adverse conditions, when food is scarce, animals are more likely to eat evergreen plants including rhododendron. Poisoning is most common in sheep[4][5] and goats.[6][7][8][9] Losses have been reported annually in the north and west of Britain when hill sheep, brought down for the winter, eat rhododendron leaves.[4] Rams appear to be particularly susceptible to poisoning by this plant. Poisoning has been reported in south-west England among cattle that ate rhododendron leaves when they strayed into a plantation during severe weather,[10] and in calves and goats in Wales.[11] It appears that many animal species are susceptible to rhododendron poisoning which has been reported among buffaloes during drought conditions in India,[12] among wolves which ate leaves from a rhododendron hedge in a zoo in Germany[6] and in coypu given a few picked rhododendron leaves before feeding[13] at a time when green feed was scarce. It was estimated that the coypu had consumed 2-3 grams of the leaves per kilogram of their body weight. Symptoms developed very rapidly but began to decline after one hour, recovery being complete in three hours. When fed *Rhododenron* leaves experimentally, guinea-pigs ate reluctantly; rabbits ate readily initially, but soon stopped. The rapid development of adverse effects may act as a safeguard to animals and prevent them from consuming a lethal dose. Clinical signs seen in cases of poisoning are similar for all animal species and include salivation, vomiting (frequently projectile), abdominal pain (which is often intense), diarrhoea, constipation, trembling, weak pulse, slow and difficult breathing, staggering, falling and exhaustion. Vomiting, a very unusual occurrence in cattle, was seen in Wales in calves that broke into a thicket in which rhododendrons were abundant.[11] Milk production is reported to decline and almost cease for up to three days in poisoned cows.[10] In fatal cases, death is due to respiratory failure and may occur within a few hours of first eating the plant.

Post-mortem examination This reveals plant fragments in the stomach, but little inflammation, the vomiting being caused by the action of the toxins on the nerve endings of the stomach walls. Haemorrhages around the heart and inflammation of the respiratory system have also been reported in sheep.[14]

Treatment The administration of stimulants is recommended and surgical removal of stomach contents may prevent death.

In goats, subcutaneous injection of morphine (60-200 mg depending on the size of the animal) has been reported to bring about recovery within four hours.[9] The use of purgatives is recommended.

Human poisoning All parts of the plant can cause poisoning, the symptoms being similar to those in animals, including salivation, watering eyes, nasal blockage, vomiting, convulsions, slow pulse, low blood pressure and paralysis.[15] Stomach lavage or the use of emetics is recommended.

Other members of the Ericaceae, notably species of *Pieris* and *Kalmia* can cause severe poisoning, but they are not native in Britain, and are found only in gardens, where it is unlikely that animals would have access to them.

EUPHORBIACEAE

Several members of this family are poisonous, but the castor oil plant, whose seeds are responsible for many outbreaks of poisoning in animals, is the most important.

112

Castor Oil Plant *Ricinus communis*

This plant is not native in Britain, although it is sometimes grown indoors and in gardens as an ornamental. However, there is considerable interest in *Ricinus* as a poisonous plant in this country because oil expressed from the seeds (castor beans), and residues of the seeds (pomace) are fed to animals.

The castor oil plant is an annual herbaceous shrub which may, under favourable conditions, grow up to 3 m in height, although in Britain the plants seldom exceed 1 m. There are numerous cultivated forms which vary in their foliage, fruit and seed characteristics. On larger plants the leaves may be up to 1 m across. They are dark green, often tinged with red or purple, and are divided into up to 12 pointed lobes which radiate from the point of attachment of the stalk. The flowers are of separate sexes but borne on the same inflorescence. The males, which open to reveal a mass of stamens, are at the base and the females, with prominent red stigmas, are near the apex. The fruit is a green or reddish capsule with fleshy spines and contains glossy, elliptical seeds, up to 1 cm long, and attractively mottled in black, white, grey or brown.

Poisonous principles The chief poisonous constituent of the plant is a lectin, ricin, a simple protein (a toxalbumin) which is reputed to be one of the most toxic naturally occurring substances. The leaves of the plant are only mildly toxic, the ricin content being highest in the seeds. Ricin is soluble in water, and therefore not present in extracted oil, but remains in the husks, which may be incorporated into oil seed cake or meal for animal feed, or used in fertilisers. It has been known since the 1880s that substances extracted from castor beans (and some other seeds) coagulate red blood cells; these have therefore been called phytohaemagglutinins. It was thought until recently that ricin was both the toxic agent and the haemagglutinating agent, although it was known that the haemagglutinating activity of pomace disappeared before its toxicity,[1] [2] upon heat treatment. It is now clear that another lectin (other than ricin) in castor oil seeds is the haemagglutinin.[3] This protein is called ricinus agglutinin or sometimes, rather confusingly, ricine. Failure to distinguish between these two proteins may explain the apparent failure of some detoxification processes. Heat (usually steam) treatment of the pomace is carried out to denature the toxic protein before the product is used in feed preparations. However, the usual test made to check for completion of the detoxification process is a haemagglutination test, which indicates that only the agglutinin, and not necessarily all of the ricin, has been destroyed. The problem is decreasing as a result of more careful quality control of animal feeds. Accidental contamination by castor beans at harvesting of commercial crops (e.g. soya bean)[4] for human and animal consumption remains a problem in countries where the plant is widespread, but is unlikely to occur in Britain.

113

Poisoning There is wide variation in sensitivity to the toxin in different species[5] and different individuals of the same species, but in all cases the lethal doses are very small. It has been estimated that a dose as small as two millionths of the body weight would be fatal by injection,[6] the oral dose being somewhat greater due to losses of the toxin in the digestive tract. Experimentally, the lethal oral dose of ricin varies from 0.1 g/kg body weight in the horse, to 5.5 g/kg in the goat; the lethal dose for cattle, pigs, sheep, rabbits and fowls is between 1 and 2 g/kg.[7] Depending on the concentration of the toxin present, animals poisoned by eating feed containing ricin may show symptoms within an hour, or up to three days later. Those which do not die often take many weeks or even months to recover[8] due to severe tissue damage.[9] Ricin inhibits the synthesis of some essential enzymes,[7] increases the production of others and the level of bilirubin and blood urea nitrogen, and decreases blood sugar. As ricin is a protein, antibodies to it are produced by the body and animals can be immunised, by repeated small doses, to withstand up to 800 times the lethal dose.[6]

The oil fraction of castor beans contains hydroxy fatty acids, up to 90% being ricinoleic acid,[10] considerable amounts of which may be absorbed and utilised if fed to animals. Castor oil is a well known laxative, which has been used extensively in veterinary and medical practice. It acts by stimulating motor nerve activity of the small intestine, causing local irritation which may lead to diarrhoea. Because of this action, ricinoleic acid is sometimes classified as a toxic lipid.

The plant also contains a potent respiratory allergen, but, unlike ricin, repeated exposure to this increases sensitivity. The allergen remains stable in boiling water.[2]

Poisoning in animals Most outbreaks of poisoning in animals result from their being fed with improperly detoxified castor bean products. In one episode, traces of ricin were found in a batch of cattle cake.[11] The animals suffered severe diarrhoea with blood clots in the faeces. The milk yield was drastically reduced and there were two abortions. In another incident in which cows received 1 kg castor bean cake daily, 9 of 25 newborn calves died 1-2 days after birth.[12] Their clinical signs were weakness, feeble pulse, shortness of breath, watery faeces and swollen joints. Calves born to cows 10-15 days after withdrawal of the cake from their diet were healthy. After eating groundnut meal, later found to contain 25% castor bean husks, 10 cows died and another had to be killed.[13] The animals could not stand, were groaning and passing fluid faeces with blood and mucus. Their temperature was subnormal and their pulse fast and weak. The lethal dose was estimated as approximately 250 g of husks.

In contrast to cattle, sheep tolerate one-third castor seed meal in their diet, although such feed is not readily eaten.[14]

The symptoms in horses fed castor beans mixed with maize[15] were similar to those described for cattle. In the horse, the early symptoms of

114

castor bean poisoning could be confused with respiratory infection. Accidental incorporation of some castor beans with grain from burst bags in a shipping consignment resulted in the poisoning of 48 horses in a stud.[16] On the same premises, two chickens and a rabbit given the same food died. Clinical signs in the horses varied in intensity but included sweating, rocking gait, elevated temperature, rapid pulse, muscle spasms and abdominal pain. In Britain, castor beans were found in the stomach of a goat that died after showing acute abdominal pain and profuse diarrhoea.[17]

Poisoning occurred when three dogs ate 'biological' fertiliser,[18] containing 25% extracted castor seed, direct from the packs, also in two others that ate the product after it had been spread on the land. One dog died within 20 hours and two others were killed. It was estimated that the lethal dose was 1-2 g/kg body weight (100 g of the fertiliser for a 10-25 kg dog). There was gastrointestinal disturbance, with haemorrhage; death resulted from circulatory failure.

Pigs poisoned by eating meal, subsequently found to contain 0.3-1.4 g castor seed husk per 100 g, developed severe vomiting and diarrhoea and became weak and uncoordinated. One weaned pig died in a convulsion, and two of ten piglets of a poisoned sow also died.[8] On the same farm, poultry were also fed a mash made from the contaminated meal. Their condition deteriorated rapidly, with drooping wings, ruffled feathers and greyish combs and wattles. Their crops remained impacted for several days, they had diarrhoea, egg production ceased, moulting commenced and several birds died.[8] The surviving pigs and poultry had not completely recovered three months after the episode. Poisoning by feeding with castor beans or ricin had been induced experimentally in horses,[19] cattle,[20] rats[5] and mice.[21]

Post-mortem findings   These are similar for all animal species and include haemorrhages in the heart, degeneration of kidneys and liver, and intense inflammation and erosion of intestinal membranes.

Human poisoning   Chewing castor beans is the most frequent cause of poisoning by *Ricinus* in man.[22] (If swallowed without chewing, the hard seed coat prevents release of the toxin.) In the USA in recent years, 104 cases (of which 98 were children) were recorded of eating castor beans.[23] In two adults and two children, poisoning was fatal. A latent period of several hours or days is characteristic of ricin poisoning in man. The symptoms are similar to those in animals, with severe irritation and haemorrhage of the digestive tract, resulting in profuse vomiting and diarrhoea. Dehydration and scanty urination are often recorded. Severe poisoning occurs with only a few beans and ingestion of eight is usually fatal,[24] but an adult who partly chewed and swallowed 12 beans recovered after vomiting and subsequent hospital treatment.[25] Even two well chewed beans can be fatal.

A much publicised case of homicidal use of ricin involved a Bulgarian broadcaster who died as a result of a small, perforated metallic sphere being inserted forcibly into his leg.[6] The coroner was satisfied that the sphere contained ricin.

Respiratory allergy in man (mucosal irritation and asthma) has been reported among workers handling pomace in ports[26] or in oil mills.[27] Typical symptoms of ricin poisoning also occur in individuals exposed to castor bean products.[28]

All suspected cases should be admitted to hospital. Emesis should be induced or stomach lavage carried out immediately. Methods for eliminating the toxins from the blood should be considered.

Spurges *Euphorbia* spp

The *Euphorbia* genus contains over 1600 species, 17 of which occur in Britain, some having become naturalised after introduction. Unlike many temperate and tropical species, no British species are shrubs or trees. The earliest reports of the spurges refer to their medicinal uses, the plant having been named after Euphorbus, physician to King Juba II of Mauritania in A.D. 18.

Petty Spurge *Euphorbia peplus*

This small green annual is very common on waste and cultivated land throughout Britain. It grows from 10-30 cm tall, with a single or branched stem. The leaves are oval or rounded, 0.5-3 cm long and arranged alternately on the stem. The inflorescence (umbel) is three-rayed, with bracts similar to the leaves and more prominent than the insignificant yellowish-green flowers. The seed capsule is about 2 mm long and three-sided, with two narrow wings on each side. The seeds are pale grey and pitted.

Sun Spurge *Euphorbia helioscopia* (photo 19)

Sun spurge is similar in its distribution and general appearance to petty spurge *(Euphorbia peplus)* described above, but the plant is usually taller, growing up to 50 cm high. The leaves are larger and have finely toothed edges, and the inflorescence is 2-5 rayed and yellowish-green. The seed capsule is 3-5 mm long, smooth and somewhat three-sided but generally rounded. The seeds are brown.

Caper Spurge *Euphorbia lathyrus*

It is doubtful if caper spurge is native in Britain, although it appears to grow naturally in a few woodland areas. It is more common locally as a garden escape. The plant is a bluish-green biennial. The first year it has a short, erect, leafy stem and in the second year the stem elongates and the inflorescence develops. The leaves grow without stalks in opposite pairs on the stem and are narrow and up to 20 cm long, the upper ones being broader at the base than the lower ones. The prominent bracts are triangular, giving the 2-6 rayed inflorescence (umbel) a spiky appearance. The seed capsule is 8-20 mm across, three-sided and smooth; the seeds are brown.

Poisonous principles These three species, and others of the genus contain a milky latex, which exudes from the plant when it is cut or crushed.

The nature of the toxic principles requires further elucidation, but a resin, an alkaloid (euphorbin, euphorbine or euphorbane), a glycoside, a dihydroxycoumarin and a complex substance named euphorbiosteroid have been reported to occur in various *Euphorbia* species. More recent work has demonstrated that the latex of *Euphorbia* species contains polyhydric diterpene esters. The activity of the toxins is not affected by drying and storage, so that feeding dried fodder crops containing spurges could poison animals.

Poisoning in animals Despite their known toxic properties, very few cases of poisoning by *Euphorbia* species have been reported in Britain. Petty spurge *(Euphorbia peplus)* caused poisoning when fed experimentally to dogs and rats[1][2] and has caused illness and losses among horses and cattle in Australia and sheep in New Zealand.[3] In Britain, sun spurge *(Euphorbia helioscopia)* caused severe swelling and inflammation of the mouth, salivation and some diarrhoea in sheep allowed to graze a field of kale that had not grown well and in which sun spurge was the dominant weed. The animals recovered fully when transferred to good pasture.[3]

Human poisoning This has resulted from the use of the seed capsules of caper spurge, mistaken for true capers (the flower buds of *Capparis spinosa)* to which they bear a superficial resemblance. One of two children died after sucking the juice of sun spurge *(Euphorbia helioscopia).*[4] Both children experienced burning of the mouth, oesophagus and stomach, salivation, vomiting, stomach pain, convulsions, narrowing of the pupils and symptoms of lung oedema. Coma preceded death. The strong irritant nature of the latex has caused intense irritation and burning of the lips and tongue in children who have handled the plant then licked their fingers, and *Euphorbia* species are frequent causes of skin reactions.[5] Experimentally, pieces of leaf applied to the skin have caused rashes and blistering in man.[6] Application of the latex has been recommended in the past to remove warts. Preparations of the plants were taken formerly as purgatives and emetics, but the action was drastic and now they are rarely used.

Annual Mercury *Mercurialis annua*

Although possibly not a native plant, annual mercury is widespread locally in southern England in waste places and as a garden weed. In Wales and northern England it is rare. It is a smooth plant with erect, branched stems 10-50 cm high, elongated oval leaves, pointed at the tip and narrowing towards the stalk and arising in opposite pairs on the stem. The leaf margin may be slightly serrated and the surface bright green and slightly shiny. The inconspicuous, greenish male and female flowers are borne on separate plants in axillary clusters, the females having only very short stalks. The fruits are hairy, globular and 3-4 mm across.

Dog's Mercury *Mercurialis perennis* (photo 20)

This native plant grows throughout most of Britain, except northern Scotland. It is often the dominant ground cover plant in woods. The plant is similar to annual mercury but grows from a long, creeping rhizome; it has an erect, usually unbranched stem up to 40 cm tall, leaves that are lightly hairy, giving them a dull appearance, and female flowers borne in clusters on long stalks.

Poisonous principles Several constituents of *Mercurialis* have been incriminated, but their separate or combined effects have not been studied in detail. They are methylamine (isolated from the plants in the last century and named mercurialine), trimethylamine and several poorly defined substances including hermidin(e), saponins and a volatile oil.

Poisoning in animals Both annual and dog's mercury can poison animals, although the plants are not eaten readily (possibly because of their unpleasant odour when bruised) except when other feed is scarce; some animals seem to acquire a taste for them.[7] There is experimental evidence that, in cattle, acute poisoning only follows the feeding of seeding plants[8] but rabbits have been poisoned fatally not only by seeds but also by stems and roots.[9] *Mercurialis* poisoning has been recorded in several countries, including Britain where hill sheep in Wales ate dog's mercury when snow covered their pasture.[10] Other outbreaks in sheep have involved cut forage[11] and pasture heavily

118

contaminated with annual mercury.[12] Cattle are susceptible to poisoning by these plants;[13] [14] horses can be affected[15] and the plant has been suspected of poisoning goats.[16]

The effects are similar in all animal species. Initially there are acute gastrointestinal symptoms, accompanied by salivation, loss of appetite and watery diarrhoea (sometimes preceded by constipation). Affected animals become weak and lethargic; jaundice of oral and genital mucous membranes and eyes develops, followed by the most characteristic sign of pinkish or obviously blood-stained urine. Urination is often painful. In fatal cases, coma may precede death.

Post-mortem findings

Typically these are subcutaneous oedema, haemorrhages of liver, kidneys and heart, enlargement of the liver, degeneration and dark coloration of kidneys and gastrointestinal inflammation.

Human poisoning

There are some old records of irritant, narcotic poisoning, with some fatalities, after eating annual mercury.[9] Recently, two adults ingested a quantity of boiled leaves of dog's mercury which they had mistaken for brooklime *(Veronica beccabunga)*.[17] Symptoms developed within three hours and included profuse vomiting and diarrhoea, facial flushing, abdominal and bilateral loin pains and haematuria. The patients were given rehydration therapy; antihistamines and sodium bicarbonate were also administered. Particular support was given to renal function. Symptoms persisted for 24 hours, but full recovery was achieved within 48 hours. The possibility of human poisoning from eating meat from poisoned animals has been considered and condemnation of the offal recommended,[18] but no definite information is available.

FAGACEAE

Oak *Quercus* spp (photo 21)

There are two native oak trees in Britain, *Quercus robur* and *Quercus petraea*, both of which are deciduous. The former is a gnarled, spreading tree found on clay soils and is the common oak of the greater part of England and southern Scotland. The leaves have little or no stalk (peduncle), but the acorns are stalked, hence the alternative name pedunculate oak. *Quercus petraea* is a less spreading tree, with a straight trunk and stalked leaves with hairs on the underside; the acorns, however, have very short stalks, or none at all, hence the name sessile oak. It is the oak of light and shallow soils and is found particularly in the north and west of the British Isles. Where the two species occur together there áre many intermediates. Other species of exotic origin are naturalised in plantations and gardens; some, like the holm or holly oak *(Quercus ilex),* are more or less evergreen; others are little more than shrubs.

The leaves of most oaks have deeply indented margins, with rounded or pointed lobes with serrations, according to the species. All oaks have separate male and female flowers, both growing on the same tree. The males are in slender pendulous catkins and the females solitary or clustered, each one surrounded by small scales. The fruit, or acorn, is ovoid and protrudes from a woody cup formed from the scales.

Poisonous principles

These are said to be tannins of the gallotannin class, or their metabolites.[1] Tannic acid acts as an astringent when applied to tissues and coagulates blood and proteins. This property has been used for thousands of years, ever since leather was first made by tanning skins and hides with oak bark.

Poisoning in animals

This is usually seasonal, occurring in spring (when the tannin content of the sap is highest) from eating buds and young leaves, and in the autumn, from the ingestion of acorns. The tannic acid content of acorns is variable, but higher when they are green than when they are ripe.[2] Although in most years it is normal for animals, particularly horses[3] [4] to eat acorns as a highly nutritious pre-winter feed, severe poisoning may occur in some animals. The ingestion of small quantities of acorns and oak leaves may cause no symptoms at all or mild transient indigestion. Animals may acquire a craving for oak and even eat both leaves and green acorns directly from the trees.[4] [5] They may injure themselves in attempts to gain access to them, and poisoning may recur several times in the same season.[6]

Oak poisoning in cattle[7] occurs in many parts of the world and is of major economic importance in some places, e.g. south-western USA,[8] where young leaves and buds may be grazed in spring when pastures are short. In Britain, poisoning is more common in autumn when acorns are eaten. Acorn poisoning in cattle was more prevalent than usual in this country after the drought and bumper crop of acorns of 1976. The Veterinary Investigation Diagnosis Analysis records showed 18 cases in 1976-77 compared with only two cases in 1975-76.[9] Although their ingestion does not necessarily result in poisoning, it is more likely to do so when other feed is scarce or absent.[10] Calves are reputed to be more susceptible than older cattle, although there are reports of poisoning in lactating and dry cows. In one recent outbreak in Britain, ten of sixty cows in a herd became ill, and two died, after grazing parkland where many acorns had fallen.[11] In acorn and oak leaf poisoning of cattle, several days may elapse between eating them and the occurrence of symptoms which are progressive, beginning with cessation of rumination, lack of appetite and refusal to drink. After initial constipation, dark coloured faeces are passed in small quantities and in the latter stages may be accompanied by

120

a little blood. Other symptoms from case reports include dullness, distended rumen, weakness and staggering, stilted gait, pale mucous membranes, watery discharge from the eyes, nose and mouth, low body temperature and irregular, slow heart beat. In chronic cases there is considerable wasting. Cases which are likely to prove fatal show aggravated symptoms, with flatulence and abdominal pain, and death may occur suddenly during a convulsion. The milk from lactating animals is often bitter and unusable for any purpose.

As the grazing habits of sheep differ from those of cattle, they do not usually eat a significant quantity of leaves or fallen acorns. In Britain, however, cases of acorn poisoning were recorded in 1976-77[9] and in an earlier incident eight sheep died after grazing young oak shoots.[12] The sheep were in a semi-starved state when released on to land where the stumps of felled oak trees were sprouting. Local sheep farmers claimed that they had grazed sheep successfully on young oak shoots and that it was a recognised method for killing off old tree stumps. Poisoning of sheep has also been reported after eating green acorns in Germany[13] and Romania.[14]

Horses may also be affected, and numerous fatalities were reported in Britain in the autumn of 1976 when, after the exceptionally dry summer, there was a large crop of acorns and other food was scarce.[3] The symptoms included depression, flatulence, abdominal pain, loss of appetite and initial constipation often followed by diarrhoea. In severe cases the stomach may be ruptured.[15]

Occasionally, pigs have been poisoned by excessive quantities of acorns, but such an occurrence is very rare. These animals usually thrive on them, and many farmers turn pigs into the pastures and woods where acorns abound, to eat them as they fall. In many parts of Europe, particularly Germany, acorns have been gathered and dried, then ground into a meal for use in combination with other foods for pig feeding.[6]

Post-mortem findings
These are similar in all animal species and include intestinal inflammation and haemorrhage, thickening of intestinal walls and distension of the stomach with gas. Degenerative changes in the kidneys are characteristic and nephritis is often the final cause of death in chronic cases. The liver may be enlarged, pale and friable and body cavities often contain excess fluid (sometimes blood-stained).

Treatment
Feeding with bran and hay may reduce the risk of poisoning. In general, treatment is symptomatic, and demulcents and purgatives are often given. Calcium hydroxide, however, was effective in minimising the toxic effects of feeding oak leaf preparations to rabbits,[16] and experimental calves fed with foliage of post oak *(Quercus stellata)* with 15% (by weight) calcium hydroxide were unaffected, whereas similar animals fed with the oak alone became ill and some died.[17]

121

Beech *Fagus sylvatica*

This tree is found mainly in south-east Britain on calcareous soils, where it is often the dominant species in woods. Beech and its varieties (including the ornamental copper beech) can, however, grow on a variety of soils, and are often planted and used for hedges. It is a large 30-40 m high tree with a smooth, grey bark, spreading branches, slender elongated brown buds and stalked leaves that are broadly oval, 4-9 cm long, and have paired veins.

The seeds are triangular nuts, up to 1 cm long, covered by a brittle brown shell and contained, usually in a closely packed group of three, in a four-lobed woody husk covered with coarse bristles. Only the fruit and seeds (mast) of the tree have been reported as poisonous.

Poisonous principles

This is usually called fagin and has been known for many years. It is sometimes referred to as an alkaloid, though its precise composition has yet to be investigated. Saponins are also said to be present.

Poisoning in animals

Beech mast is less likely to cause poisoning now than formerly, when the residues left after extraction of oil from the nuts were used to make cake for animal feed. Most reported cases of poisoning refer to the ingestion of such cake, which was apparently particularly poisonous when made from residues which included the husk.[18] It is often stated that the nuts themselves are not poisonous, although there are conflicting reports on this point. Residues which have been boiled and the water discarded have been considered safe, but other sources state that the toxic principle is insoluble in water.

It is inadvisable to feed beech nuts or cake to horses, which seem particularly susceptible (300-500 g can be fatal);[19] most cases of poisoning reported have involved cattle, which may become critically ill. Local irritation and burning occur initially and affected animals have periods of severe abdominal pain, violent cramps and staggering, alternating with periods of complete paralysis, collapse and unconsciousness.[19][20] Death from asphyxia may occur within 12 hours; animals surviving longer than this usually recover. Post-mortem findings are not characteristic. They include signs of suffocation and sometimes severe oedema of the brain and spinal cord and inflammation of the intestines.

Human poisoning

If eaten in sufficient quantity, the kernels of beech nuts cause soreness of the mouth and throat, and the ingestion of 50 or more nuts can produce headache, abdominal pain, vomiting, diarrhoea, vertigo and elevated body temperature.[21] Extreme fatigue, pallor and fainting may also occur. The symptoms usually develop within an hour of eating the nuts and last for up to five hours.

Treatment   In both animals and man this is symptomatic; the use of purgatives and tranquillisers may be indicated.

FUMARIACEAE

Bleeding Heart *Dicentra spectabilis*

Other common name: Dutchman's Breeches

This plant is not native to, and rarely naturalised in Britain, but it, and other *Dicentra* species, are frequently grown in gardens, and have been recorded as escapes.

Poisonous principles   Various species of the plant have been shown to contain protopine and related groups of isoquinoline alkaloids,[1] protopine itself being the only alkaloid found in *Dicentra spectabilis*.

Poisoning in animals   Symptoms seen in cattle fed experimentally with *Dicentra cucullaria* and *Dicentra canadensis* (described under the old name for the genus, *Bikukulla)*[2] were similar to those reported in field cases in the USA where poisoning by *Dicentra* species is reported annually in early spring in areas where the animals graze woodland pastures. The plants are apparently unpalatable, but are eaten when other forage is scarce. The experimental animals refused the plants unless mixed with grass. Feeding the whole plant to a steer resulted in violent trembling, agitation and frothing at the mouth. Partly digested stomach contents were ejected forcibly. Convulsions with rigid extension of neck and limbs, difficult breathing, glassy eyes, abdominal pain and diarrhoea occurred. Other animals fed with the plants experienced only slight restlessness. In all cases recovery was rapid and complete.

Human poisoning   Incoordination, trembling, respiratory distress and convulsions occur in man,[3] but there are few reports of human poisoning as a result of eating *Dicentra*. Treatment should include removal of stomach contents; tranquillisers may be required. Contact with the plants can cause an allergic skin reaction in sensitive individuals.

GERANIACEAE

Storksbill *Erodium* spp

The common storksbill *(Erodium cicutarium),* whose taxonomy is not clearly definable, as there are subspecies and intermediate forms, is native in Britain, mainly on dry grassland and near the sea.

There have been no reports of disease in animals associated with this plant in Britain, but sporadic outbreaks of photosensitisation in sheep[1] and cattle[2] have been reported, mainly from Australia and New Zealand. Staggers, with leg weakness in lambs and cattle that had eaten the plant, has also been reported.[3]

GRAMINEAE

Although native grasses are the major source of food for many animal species and are often dominant plants in pasture, some of them are capable of poisoning animals.

Poisonous principles The plants themselves may contain substances that can lead to poisoning, if present in sufficient concentration. These include tryptophan, oestrogens, a metabolic inhibitor, cholecalciferol and compounds from which hydrocyanic acid can be released. Toxins from fungi that infect grasses can also have adverse effects on animals.

The action of ruminal microorganisms on the amino acid, tryptophan, produces a toxic metabolite, 3-methylindole, which is thought to be the cause of fog fever, a disease that can develop in cattle after consuming large amounts of tryptophan-containing herbage.

Significant concentrations of oestrogens occur in young plants of short-rotation ryegrass *(Lolium* spp) and perennial ryegrass *(Lolium perenne).* In Britain there are no reports of problems associated with oestrogens from grasses.

A metabolic inhibitor, which interferes with cellulose digestion and adversely affects the growth of lambs, has been isolated from cocksfoot *(Dactylis glomerata).*[1] Cholecalciferol, or a similar vitamin D-like substance, is the calcinogenic constituent of yellow oatgrass *(Trisetum flavescens)* which has caused calcinosis in cattle in the Alpine regions of Germany and Austria.

Poisoning Fog fever is an acute respiratory disorder of grazing cattle, particularly beef cows two or more years old; it usually occurs within two weeks of a

124

change from poor to better pasture in autumn.[2] At this time, cattle often become hungry and may consume large amounts of tryptophan-containing herbage. In a survey of 800 cases in Wales in 1971,[3] it was found that 10% of cows were affected in each herd, and 5-20% died. In another survey of 30 outbreaks over four years,[4] between 6 and 21% of the cows were affected, and 28 (2.9%) of 965 adult cows at risk died. Clinical signs include apathy, increased breathing rate (50-80/minute), and increased depth of breathing. Difficult or laboured breathing occurs only in severe cases. Post-mortem findings in the lungs are congestion of blood vessels, oedema and alveolar changes (formation of hyaline membranes, interstitial emphysema and epithelial hyperplasia). Fog fever can be avoided by preventing sudden transition from poor to lush pastures, and by reducing stress factors (such as removal of calf from cow) at this time. The addition of monensin to feed seems to prevent this disorder.[5]

Calcinosis (the abnormal deposition of calcium salts in tissues), first noticed in Austria in 1962, has been the subject of much research since 1970.[6] The cause of this calcinosis is yellow oatgrass, a loosely tufted perennial; it is common in England and Wales, but infrequent in Scotland and Ireland.[7] Although readily consumed by cattle and sheep it is not known to have any adverse effect on grazing animals in Britain. Young growing plants are much more calcinogenic than mature plants, while flowering plants and hay are not at all calcinogenic. In alpine pastures, flowering is delayed and leaf growth encouraged by increase in altitude, and this probably accounts for its calcinogenicity in cattle in these areas.

Among the grasses, compounds with cyanogenic potential are found in Britain in Yorkshire fog *(Holcus lanatus)* and reed grass *(Glyceria maxima)*. In this country these compounds are present at such low concentrations that they are usually harmless, but an incident in goslings has been reported from Romania in which *Holcus lanatus* caused nervous and respiratory signs and death from hydrocyanic acid poisoning.[8]

Under certain conditions, some grasses become infected with fungi whose toxic metabolites (mycotoxins) can have adverse effects on animals; in the past these effects were attributed to the plants themselves. Diseases now known to be linked with mycotoxins from fungal infection of grasses include ryegrass staggers, fescue foot, darnel poisoning and sweet vernal grass poisoning. These are mentioned because the grasses involved occur in Britain, although, with the exception of ryegrass and sweet vernal grass, diseases of animals have not been associated with them here.

Ryegrass staggers is a nervous disorder of cattle, sheep, horses and deer eating perennial ryegrass *(Lolium perenne)*. Affected animals show head and shoulder tremors when disturbed. Severely affected animals become uncoordinated, walk with a characteristic high-stepping gait and usually collapse in tetanic spasm.[9] The disorder usually occurs during hot dry weather when the condition of the pasture is poor and contains a lot of dead plant material, accumulated at the base of the sward. The disease occurs in New Zealand and according to recent research in that country and in Britain, this condition is probably caused by potentially tremorgenic fungi;[10] species of *Penicillium* have been implicated.[11] A similar condition has occurred in Britain, during hot, dry summers, among cattle and sheep grazing perennial ryegrass,[10 13 14] and in the Netherlands among sheep grazing Italian ryegrass *(Lolium multiflorum)*.[15] More recently, neurotoxins provisionally named lolitrems have been isolated from ryegrass infected with a fungus (a so-called *Lolium* endophyte).[12]

Tall fescue *(Festuca arundinacea)* is associated with 'fescue foot' in cattle. This is manifested by lameness, and it may progress to peripheral necrosis of affected limbs, with sloughing of the hooves, tail and sometimes ears. It occurs in New Zealand, Australia and the USA, but not in Britain. Mycotoxins also seem to be involved in this disorder.[16] Alkaloids in tall fescue, notably perloline, inhibit rumen fermentation and reduce feed digestibility.[17] Perloline and other alkaloids have also been found in perennial ryegrass.

The only British grass harmful to both human beings and animals is darnel *(Lolium temulentum)*, but this has become rare in Britain, and the following account is included for its historical interest. Darnel is an erect annual grass which grows to a height of 1 metre. It is an introduced species in Britain, and used to be a common weed of cereal crops. It can be distinguished from perennial and Italian ryegrasses by its longer, outer, empty glume and by the long awns on many of the other glumes.

The nature of the toxicity of darnel has not been elucidated satisfactorily. No recent work on the poisonous principles has been traced, its toxicity still being attributed to substances usually referred to as alkaloids,[18] including temuline, temulentine and loliin(e). Fungi in or on the seeds have, for many years, been implicated in the toxic reaction but the situation is still 'shrouded in uncertainty'.[19 20] It has been known from ancient times that human beings can be poisoned by eating flour or baked products contaminated with ground darnel seed.[18 19 21] Occasional cases of poisoning of livestock have been reported in this country and in Europe, but they are not well authenticated. No cases of darnel poisoning have been reported from the USA or New Zealand, where the plant is locally common. In South Africa, darnel is common and bread made with flour containing appreciable quantities of darnel seed is eaten regularly without producing any side effects. In feeding experiments in South Africa[22] and New Zealand[23] with laboratory and farm animals, darnel had no toxic effects, whether fungus-infected or not. There was an incident of poisoning among reindeer *(Rangifer tarandus)*, addax *(Addax nasomaculatus)* and gazelle *(Gazella soemmeringa)* kept in captivity, when fed oats contaminated with seeds of various plants, including 5% darnel.[24]

Some fungi that grow on poorly prepared hay or silage made from sweet vernal grass *(Anthoxanthum odoratum)* can break down natural coumarins in the plant to 4-hydroxycoumarin. This can be broken down further, in the presence of formaldehyde in the atmosphere, to dicoumarol (3,3'-methylene-bis-4-hydroxycoumarin), which interferes with blood clotting and leads to haemorrhage in animals that eat it.[25][26] This effect is usually associated with *Melilotus* spp., when it is known as sweet clover disease.

Sweet vernal grass grows in Britain, but has not, until very recently, been associated with animal disease in this country; most reports are from North America. The circumstances of the recent outbreak,[27] that occurred in cattle on a hill farm in south-west England, were unusual in that the hay contained 80-90% of sweet vernal grass, whereas the level in permanent pastures in this country is usually only 5-10%. Coumarin, *o*-coumaric acid and melilotic acid were identified in the hay, and *Aspergillus fumigatus* and *Aspergillus flavus,* fungi known to be capable of converting these to 4-hydroxycoumarin were also present. As cattle and sheep that grazed the pasture did not develop haemorrhages, it was assumed that the dicoumarol had been produced in the hay.

Clinical signs typical of dicoumarol poisoning developed in the cattle. Some animals died suddenly and post-mortem examination revealed extensive haemorrhages. The condition was reproduced experimentally when the hay was fed to calves; an increased blood clotting (prothrombin) time was recorded in three calves. Oral administration of vitamin K_1 reduced the prothrombin time, but the prophylactic use of the vitamin while giving feed containing dicoumarol would not be cost-effective.

Wheat *Triticum vulgare,* Oats *Avena sativa,* Barley *Hordeum vulgare,* Rye *Secale cereale,* Maize *Zea mays*

With the current increase in intensive husbandry, large amounts of home-grown and imported cereal grains are fed to farm animals in Britain. They sometimes cause digestive disorders and other problems that, although not strictly regarded as poisoning, will be described briefly.

No toxic substances are produced by any grain crop grown in this country, except for rye. Rye grains contain a substance capable of producing rickets in chicks,[28] and also pentosans[29] and alkylresorcinol,[30] which may depress growth, particularly in chicks. Chicks fed rye grain produce sticky black faeces, but this does not appear to affect growth. Any toxicity or serious digestive disturbances occurring in grain-fed animals are usually the result of feeding poor quality grain, which may have been badly harvested or stored or contaminated in some way, or is the result of overfeeding. Grain is usually processed (ground, rolled or pelleted) before feeding to animals, but processing is justified economically only if it aids digestion. For sheep, processing is not required, and may have adverse effects on carcass quality and on the rumen. In addition, processing interferes with cellulose digestion when cereals supplement forage. For cattle, processing of grain is usually required, but only to the extent necessary to improve digestibility; fine grinding (rather than just light rolling to crush the grains) may lead to rumenitis, parakeratosis and inefficient utilisation of roughage.[31]

Large amounts of grain, rich in readily available carbohydrates, can lead to acidosis in cattle and sheep through the accumulation of lactic acid in the rumen. Lactic acidosis occurs among feedlot cattle in the USA, and among sheep in Australia, where 'wheat poisoning' or 'wheat sickness' is seen after giving too much grain feed. Wheat seems to produce acidosis more often than other cereals. Acidosis is characterised by loss of appetite, diarrhoea, mucus in faeces, dehydration, incoordination and sometimes death. Rumen motility is inhibited, and salivation and intestinal motility are reduced. Acidosis affects the redistribution of water in the body and the elimination of toxic compounds. Tissues of the rumen, liver and other organs may be damaged.[32][33] In sheep rumenitis (inflammation of the rumen) may develop after feeding wheat grain,[34] and overfeeding can upset the lower digestive system and lead to diarrhoea as a result of reduced net absorption of water in the colon.[35] The rumen fluid of animals with acidosis also contains endotoxin released from Gram-negative bacteria normally present in the rumen. This endotoxin depresses blood pressure and motility of the rumen and intestines, and causes a pronounced drop in the number of white blood cells.[36] Livestock which break into fields of wheat before the grain has ripened are liable to develop severe digestive disorders, which may be fatal.

The barley beef system of rearing calves quickly to slaughter weight (85% rolled barley in the ration), which was widely adopted by British farmers in the 1960s, led to digestive disorders and other problems including vitamin deficiencies, allergic reactions (with clinical signs of acute respiratory distress and increased heart rate), liver abscesses, kidney necrosis, laminitis, rumenitis, overeating and bloat. These troubles largely disappeared when the ration was modified slightly to include 87% rolled barley of 17.5% moisture content (compared with 16% moisture in the former ration), 10% (instead of 15%) additional protein (soya and fish meal) and additional roughage (hay with feed, and straw instead of sawdust for bedding).[37]

Oats are the most suitable grain for feeding to horses. Other grains need more processing. Quite small amounts of uncooked wheat, barley or rye, if fed whole or ground into a meal, may lead to digestive disorders with the release of bacterial toxins that are absorbed rapidly into the blood stream and can lead to laminitis (inflammation of the sensitive laminae or layers by which the horny hoof is attached to the foot).

The best grain feed for pigs is barley, since its low oil content leads to a high quality carcass, and its fibre content is optimum. Feeding finely ground wheat or barley may cause stomach ulcers.[38] [39]

Maize (corn in the USA) is becoming increasingly popular as a valuable silage, forage and grain crop in Britain, but despite its high nutritive value, problems can arise from its use. Under certain conditions, particularly in drought or frost and in young plants, nitrates accumulate from which toxic levels of nitrites can be formed. High concentrations of cyanogenic compounds can be found during early growth (12-35 days).[40] Digestive disorders that may result from feeding maize are ruminal acidosis (production of large amounts of lactic acid from the easily digestible carbohydrate) and, from poor quality silage, ruminal alkalosis (production of large amounts of ammonia and simultaneous depression in the ruminal synthesis of amino acids). Both of these conditions can be accompanied by diarrhoea. Lactic acidosis has also been reported in cattle grazing unripe green maize standing in the field.[41]

Other problems that have occurred as the result of feeding cereals are: nervous disorders and diarrhoea among geese and cattle fed brewers' grains (a by-product of malting barley used for beer-making); rickets in lambs grazing on green oats; nitrate poisoning in cattle fed on oat straw;[42] biotin deficiency in chicks fed a wheat-based diet.[43]

HIPPOCASTANACEAE

Horse Chestnut *Aesculus hippocastanum*

This large, broad-crowned deciduous tree which grows up to 30 m tall is not a native of Britain, but has become well established in the country since its introduction. It is often planted in parks, gardens, streets and greens. The bark is dark greyish-brown and somewhat scaly on the trunk and older branches. The large oval buds, pointed at the tip, are often more than 2 cm long and are covered with characteristic, deep red-brown sticky bud scales. The leaves are compound with 5-7 coarsely veined leaflets (8-20 cm long) radiating from the stalk and broadening before terminating in a usually blunt point. When first emerging from the bud they are densely covered with woolly hairs. The white or cream flowers appear in spring in elongated upright clusters. At the base of each flower is a yellow patch which later turns red. Another similar *Aesculus,* a hybrid arising from common horse chestnut and the American red buckeye tree, has red flowers. The fruits are up to 6 cm across, green, tough and sparsely covered with coarse spines. They contain one or two shiny brown seeds (conkers) which have a prominent pale buff scar.

Poisonous principle

It is generally agreed that the poisonous principle of *Aesculus* is a saponin glycoside (7-hydroxycoumarin 6-glucoside) named aesculin, although it has been suggested that the tree also contains alkaloids. Aesculin yields aesculetin (6,7-dihydroxycoumarin) on hydrolysis.[1] Aesculin is closely related to the hydroxycoumarin found in spoiled sweet clover hay from which the anticoagulant rodenticides were originally developed.[2] The young leaves and flowers of the tree are usually considered the most toxic parts; the bark is said to contain more aesculin, but is probably rarely eaten.

Poisoning in animals

Despite its availability in certain habitats (e.g. to cattle and deer in parkland), horse chestnut rarely causes problems in Britain. In outbreaks in Maryland, USA, the leaves and fruit of the tree caused illness in cattle, some of which died.[3] Poisoning has been reported in cattle, horses and pigs, with clinical signs including inflammation of mucous membranes, vomiting (where possible), weakness, incoordination, muscular twitching, stupor and paralysis.[4]

Human poisoning

This can occur when conkers are eaten in mistake for sweet chestnuts, and is most common in children. The likelihood of such poisoning is often mentioned, but there are few authenticated cases.

A fatal case has been reported in a 4-year-old boy who became restless then slept deeply after eating horse chestnuts. When, two days later, he ate a further quantity, he became unconscious and died in hospital from respiratory paralysis.[5]

In suspected cases, an emetic, such as syrup of ipecacuanha, should be given.

HYDRANGEACEAE

Hydrangea spp

In Britain hydrangeas are commonly cultivated as garden shrubs, those found apparently growing wild being garden escapes. The plants contain cyanogenic glycosides and saponins. There have been no recent reports of poisoning in animals, but diarrhoea, contraction of abdominal muscles and stiffness of limbs in a horse, and abdominal pain, diarrhoea and shortness of breath in a cow have been reported.[1] Human poisoning, after ingestion of leaves and buds, has occurred, with clinical symptoms including nausea, vomiting and diarrhoea.[2]

HYPERICACEAE

St. John's Wort *Hypericum* spp (photo 22)

This large genus contains over 200 species, 10-15 of which are native in Britain, although some are rare or have very limited distribution. Several other species have been introduced and are common garden plants, and some of these have escaped and become naturalised.

Common St. John's Wort *Hypericum perforatum*

This is by far the most frequent *Hypericum* in Britain, being found throughout the country except for some parts of Ireland and northern Scotland. It is a perennial plant, usually 30-50 cm high but sometimes growing up to 90 cm. A smooth erect stem, with a woody base and two longitudinal ridges, grows from a thin underground rhizome. The leaves have no stalks and are in opposite pairs on the stem. They are elongated and elliptical, with pointed tips and 1-2 cm long. A characteristic feature is the presence of large numbers of translucent dots on the leaves, these being particularly clear when viewed against the light. Terminal and axillary clusters of flowers appear towards the top of the plant in mid to late summer. The flowers are up to 2 cm across and have yellow petals (usually five) and numerous prominent yellow stamens. The flowers turn brown and dry but remain on the capsule which contains numerous cylindrical pitted seeds.

The plant readily established itself in parts of the world to which it was introduced (e.g. New Zealand), and has become a serious agricultural problem, not only because of its harmful effect on livestock, but because its thick growth eliminates valuable pasture.

Poisonous principle St. John's wort and most other *Hypericum* species contain a red, fluorescent pigment called hypericin(e). Attempts to characterise this substance were made earlier this century, and several possibilities were proposed.[1] The pigment is now generally regarded as a naphthodianthrone derivative.

131

Poisoning in animals If plants containing this pigment are eaten, lesions may develop on unpigmented areas of skin exposed to bright sunlight. This effect, known as photosensitisation, occurs less frequently in Britain than in other countries where the sunlight is more intense, but may well be more common here than is generally supposed, and could be responsible for minor lesions on hairless parts of the skin, such as eyelids, muzzles and udders. Once an animal has developed a reaction to *Hypericum,* it remains sensitised, so that further eating of the plant and exposure to sunlight rapidly produces photosensitisation of increasing severity. The reaction produced by *Hypericum* is primary photosensitisation as it affects only the skin, on which the ultraviolet rays of the sun act directly, and does not involve metabolism of the pigment in the liver, in which case the skin lesions would be secondary. The reaction is most severe if the fresh plant is eaten, but photosensitivity can also result from eating the dried plant, although about 80% of the hypericin is lost with drying.[2] In severe cases the unpigmented areas of skin become oedematous and necrotic and may slough off, leaving painful lesions which are slow to heal.

The harmful effects of eating St. John's wort have been known for hundreds of years[3] and it is reported that the Arabs used to apply extracts of tobacco and henna to unpigmented areas of the skin of their animals to protect them from sunlight.[4] Under normal grazing conditions in bright sunlight, the skin reaction caused by eating *Hypericum* usually develops in 1-2 weeks.

Hypericum photosensitivity has caused serious illness and economic losses in New Zealand[5] and Australia[6] among sheep (affecting wool quality), in cows (reducing milk yield) and in horses. The carcasses of affected animals killed for meat are usually of poor quality. In addition to the skin lesions, affected sheep appear distressed, often shaking their heads, and may react to contact with water, so that crossing a stream or being dipped to remove parasites results in wild thrashing of limbs and convulsions.[5] This occurs only during the active phase of photosensitisation and not during the recovery period. In feeding experiments,[5] sheep given 100 g of the fresh plant daily developed the characteristic sensitivity to light, the effect being more severe when freshly extracted juice of the plants was given.

In cattle, feeding 0.5-0.6% of their body weight of the fresh plant (less than average daily consumption at grazing) was sufficient to induce photosensitivity.[7] When a single dose of an aqueous suspension of the finely ground dried plant (3 g per kg body weight), or an extract containing hypericin, was given by stomach tube to calves[2] which were then exposed to sunlight, their temperature and respiration rate began to rise 3-4 hours later. They passed soft faeces, became restless and licked the white areas of their body which became reddened. Calves given a single dose of 5 g per kg body weight of the dried plant had a more severe reaction. They shook their heads vigorously, and exudation and scabbing of the skin around the eyes and muzzle and on white areas of the body developed. The scabs subsequently dried and peeled off, but recovery was not complete for 30-40 days. Similar calves, given dried *Hypericum* but not exposed to sunlight, also passed soft faeces but there was no skin reaction.

Photosensitivity has been described in 17 pigs in Britain.[8] After being moved to rough ground where St. John's wort was growing in profusion, the white pigs and the white areas of Wessex pigs developed red patches which irritated; rubbing led to abrasions. A black sow was unaffected. In the shade of their sties the animals recovered.

Horses react in much the same way as sheep and cattle, but the effects tend to be more severe. The affected areas of skin irritate, and abrasion by the animals results in open lesions which may become infected. Loss of appetite, debility, staggering gait and coma have also been reported in horses.[6]

After feeding rabbits with fresh or dried *Hypericum*, some of the white ones died, while grey ones survived. In addition to skin lesions and necrosis of the ears, post-mortem examination revealed enlargement and cirrhosis of the liver and inflammation and necrosis of the kidneys.[9]

IRIDACEAE

Yellow Flag *Iris pseudacorus*

Yellow flag is found throughout Britain in marshes and wet ground at the edge of rivers, ditches and lakes.

The plant is an erect, slightly bluish-green perennial with long, narrow leaves in two opposite ranks sheathing the stem at the base, becoming flattened vertically in one plane and terminating in a point. They may be up to 50 mm wide and as long as, or longer than, the stem (up to 150 cm) which is stiff and bears 2-3 bright yellow flowers in early summer. They are 8-10 cm across and variable in shape, although all have outer segments (usually three), which are narrow at the base, but broaden before terminating in a point directed slightly downwards and away from the flower, revealing the inner segments and stamens and style, which are also yellow. The fruit is a green, elliptical capsule with a broad point at the tip and containing numerous light brown seeds.

Stinking Iris *Iris foetidissima* (photo 23)

This plant is native in Britain and is found in hedgerows, woodland and sea cliffs, usually on calcareous soils.

It is similar to, but smaller than the yellow flag, has darker green leaves, purplish-blue flowers, reddish-orange seeds and an unpleasant, pungent smell when bruised.

The unpleasant odour of *Iris foetidissima* makes it less likely to be eaten than *Iris pseudacorus,* but, although potentially poisonous, neither plant is eaten readily when growing undisturbed, and they are unlikely to be a danger to livestock. Both species have long been regarded as poisonous[1][2] and are still widely referred to as such,[3][4] although no recent cases of poisoning have been attributed to the plants.

Poisonous principles   The nature of these is not clear. In both species they have been described as a resin, a glycoside (iridin, irisin or irisine), myristic acid and an acrid compound. All parts of both wild and cultivated *Iris,* but especially the rhizomes, are poisonous.

Poisoning in animals   The chief clinical signs of *Iris* poisoning are irritation of the stomach and intestines, causing vomiting and diarrhoea, sometimes with bleeding.[5] Elevation of body temperature usually occurs.

Linnaeus, in the eighteenth century, referred to *Iris* as dangerous to cattle. More recently, a blue-flowered garden *Iris* was eaten by calves pastured on land where there was a flower border.[6] The animals became quiet and recumbent, with salivation and enlargement of glands in the head and throat. Irritating, encrusted lesions developed on the lips and muzzle. In two calves which died, there was acute abdominal pain; blood-stained faeces were produced. Post-mortem examination revealed inflammation of the stomach, and black areas, 1-15 cm across, in the intestines. The kidneys, liver and spleen were very dark. There were no further cases of illness when the *Iris* plants were removed. An outbreak of diarrhoea, with faeces containing blood in some cases, occurred in cattle in the West Highlands of Scotland[7] and was attributed to eating the underground parts of *Iris pseudacorus* exposed during drainage operations. The animals recovered when access to the plants was prevented. In the same area, hay often contains *Iris* leaves and it is suggested that the outbreaks of diarrhoea, common in housed cattle, may be caused by ingestion of the plant. Eating the rhizomes of *Iris pseudacorus* left on a canal bank after dredging caused diarrhoea, with haemorrhage, in eight pigs, two of which died. One sow aborted a few days after eating the plant.[8] Poisoning of horses, with recovery in a few days, has been reported.[5]

Human poisoning   Species of *Iris* are unlikely to be eaten by man, except mistakenly, but symptoms similar to those produced in animals were described[9] in the

134

USA in 1960. The sap of the plants can irritate the skin, sometimes causing blistering.[10]

JUNCACEAE
Rush *Juncus* spp

Several species of rush occur in Britain in marshy or muddy places on poorly drained soils where some areas, including pastures, may be dominated by the plants.

Rushes are erect plants with long, stiff, narrow leaves that are round in section or grass-like, and grow in tufts or from a creeping rhizome. In different species the leaves appear smooth, ridged or jointed and may be hollow or completely or partially filled with pith internally; some species have a sheathing leaf base. The inflorescence is terminal or lateral and composed of small, greenish or brown flowers in a compact or loose cluster.

Poisonous principles Some species of *Juncus* are said to have a high cyanide content, probably in the form of cyanogenic glycosides. However, there is very little recent information on the toxicity of rushes.

Poisoning in animals Poisoning of cattle by the joint leaf rush *(Juncus holoschoenus)* has been reported from Australia.[1] The incident involved three calves which ate rushes from a corner of a field and died a few hours later. Post-mortem examination revealed plants in the stomach. Rushes from the field were found to have a high cyanide content, but when tested again later, at the flowering stage, the concentration was much lower.

Species of *Juncus* have been incriminated in outbreaks of poisoning in South Africa in animals grazing areas of land that are sometimes waterlogged and may contain small streams or springs. Such areas are called 'vlci' and the term 'vlei poisoning' is sometimes used.[2] Various vlei plants have been tested for toxicity by feeding to experimental animals. The soft rush *(Juncus effusus)*, which dominates some areas of vlei, is considered a likely cause of the condition, in which rapid development of symptoms and sudden death, consistent with cyanide poisoning were reported. Rapid death is typical of acute cyanide poisoning, in which oxygen starvation of the central nervous system occurs as a result of inactivation of enzymes involved in tissue respiration.

There is very little known about the effects of eating *Juncus* on animals in Britain. The heath rush *(Juncus squarrosus)* is said to be grazed eagerly at times when the pasture is poor,[3] whereas the hard rush *(Juncus inflexus)*,

135

which is widespread on heavy soils, has been responsible for the loss of animals which sometimes appear to develop a taste for it, and eat it to the exclusion of other plants. It is said that its poisonous nature is not generally recognised,[3] although severe symptoms have been reported in cattle after eating the plant.[4] Irritation of the digestive tract, sometimes accompanied by diarrhoea developed initially, after which the animals lost condition rapidly and became nervous and partially blind. The disease was progressive, some animals becoming totally blind and developing convulsions; death from brain haemorrhages occurred in some cases. Although similar in some respects to magnesium deficiency, this condition was not improved by the injection of magnesium salts. Animals that recover remain nervous for several days, until their sight returns, but must be housed or kept away from pastures containing rushes or they will seek and eat the plants again and repeat the process. It is not stated which toxic constituents of the rushes are responsible for this syndrome.

JUNCAGINACEAE

Sea Arrow Grass *Triglochin maritima*

This robust, erect plant grows on salt marshes and grassy places on rocky shores wherever conditions are suitable around the coast of Britain.

The leaves, which grow from a stout rhizome, are long, narrow and thick, not flat as in true grasses. They are erect and, in Britain, may grow up to 30 cm long. The plant flowers from mid to late summer, the inflorescence being borne on a rather stiff stalk, often exceeding the height of the leaves. The flowers are small, green and crowded close to each other and to the stem. They develop into golden-brown fruits.

Marsh Arrow Grass *Triglochin palustris*

Although distributed throughout Britain, this species is found only very locally in marshy places. It is much more slender than sea arrow grass, having fine, almost thread-like leaves, often cylindrical almost to the tip, and a more delicate inflorescence on which the small flowers are not densely crowded together on the spike.

136

Poisonous principles   Although both of these plants are readily eaten by animals, they can cause poisoning, as hydrocyanic acid is released from them under certain conditions. A cyanogenic glycoside, tentatively named triglochinin, is thought to be the poisonous principle, although its exact nature has yet to be elucidated. The amount of the cyanogenic glycoside in the plant (sometimes called the cyanogenic potential) is variable, but increases under drought conditions, whether or not the plant is stunted. It is highest in the period of rapid growth which follows a retardation, such as wilting during drought or frosting. The rare occurrence of drought conditions in Britain may explain why animals are seldom poisoned by *Triglochin* in this country, while in other parts of the world, particularly the USA, it is well known as a potentially poisonous plant. In actively growing plants the green leaves are the most poisonous. Ensiling reduces, but does not eliminate the toxicity of arrow grass. Hydrocyanic acid is released by the hydrolytic action of enzymes liberated in the plant itself when crushed, and also in the stomach of animals which eat it.[1] Its release is hastened, in ruminants, by the favourable pH of the rumen and the activity of its bacteria which encourage enzymatic breakdown of the glycoside. Ruminants are therefore more susceptible to this type of poisoning than animals with a single stomach (like horses and pigs) in which the acidity of the digestive juices prevents enzymatic breakdown of the cyanogenic glycosides.[2] Hydrocyanic acid acts by inhibiting the utilisation of oxygen by cells. The blood remains highly oxygenated, and consequently bright red, while the tissues are lacking in oxygen; mucous membranes tend to become bluish (cyanosed). A cyanogenic glycoside content of 50 mg per 100 g of green arrow grass is considered lethal, even if an amount as small as 0.5% of the body weight of the animal is consumed.[3]

Poisoning in animals   There are no recent reports of poisoning by these plants in Britain, but clinical signs have been described for both sheep and cattle in the USA.[4][5] These include nervousness, trembling or jerking, erratic breathing, excess salivation and bright red blood which may be seen at the nostrils. Recumbency and convulsions may precede death which frequently occurs within an hour of eating the plants. In cases which survive for a longer period there may be vomiting, especially in pigs, and the mucous membranes may be bluish and the blood becomes dark,[6] due to lack of oxygen resulting from respiratory difficulties. Blood clotting may be impaired. The conditions under which poisoning may occur and the clinical signs in sheep have been examined in detail in animals fed experimentally with sea arrow grass.[7]

Post-mortem findings   These are similar in all animals. The bright red blood (especially in animals that die within an hour or two of poisoning) is characteristic, as is the smell of bitter almonds of the stomach contents. The muscles are usually dark and haemorrhages are common.

137

Treatment   The action of hydrocyanic acid is so rapid that it is often too late to treat a poisoned animal once the signs have been recognised. Several compounds have been tested as antidotes for cyanide intoxication[8] but the classical method of injecting an aqueous solution of sodium thiosulphate and sodium nitrite is still the preferred treatment. Intravenous injection gives quicker results, but intraperitoneal or subcutaneous injection may also be effective in saving an animal. Variations exist in the recommended concentrations of the sodium salts, but it is usual to inject a volume of a solution (usually 10-20%) which will give 0.5 g/kg body weight of sodium thiosulphate and 10-20 g/kg of sodium nitrite.[8] Sodium thiosulphate may be used alone, or in larger doses, but high doses of sodium nitrite should be avoided because of the risk of nitrite poisoning.

LABIATAE

Stinging Nettle *Urtica dioica*

This plant does not appear to be poisonous when taken internally. It has been recommended as a food plant,[1] and forms the basis of a traditional dish in Scotland. Experimental nutritional work on the stinging nettle revealed that it is a good source of protein, vitamins and fibre,[2] although it induced enlargement of the kidneys of guinea pigs and mice fed exclusively on the plant.

The leaf and stem surface of this nettle and some other *Urtica* spp. have stinging hairs which are readily damaged on contact. If touched, the hairs break and release into the skin substances which cause pain, reddening and itching and white weals which may coalesce. The reaction may be transitory, or persist for up to 24 hours. The active substances are histamine, acetylcholine and 5-hydroxytryptamine[3] and not formic acid, which formerly was believed to be responsible for the stinging action of the plant, but is now thought to cause only the initial pain.

Adverse effects after contact with *Urtica* rarely occur in animals, but there have been cases in hunting dogs in the USA. After massive exposure to the plants, clinical signs including trembling, vomiting, difficult breathing and weakness were reported; several animals died.[4]

Ground Ivy *Glechoma hederacea*

This plant is native in Britain, where it grows throughout the country in grassland, waste places and woods. In common with other Labiatae, ground ivy contains poorly characterised oils and a bitter substance.

The plant does not appear to have caused poisoning in Britain, but illness and death among horses and cattle which ate it have been reported in eastern Europe. After being fed with freshly cut lucerne from a field where clumps of *Glechoma hederacea* were growing, seven horses developed an accelerated weak pulse, difficulty in breathing, conjunctival haemorrhage, elevated temperature and dizziness.[5] Post-mortem examination of one old horse which died revealed enlargement of the spleen, dilation of the caecum and gastroenteritis. The disease was reproduced experimentally by feeding fresh or slightly wilted ground ivy to other horses. Poisoning in cattle was also recorded. In another outbreak, horses given freshly mown lucerne containing a high proportion of *Glechoma* developed forced, rapid breathing, and 15% mortality was recorded.[6] There was dilation of the air spaces in the lungs. With a change of feed and symptomatic treatment the other animals recovered.

Mint *Mentha* spp

Poisoning by mint rarely occurs, but the oils found in it (and in other members of the Labiatae) can cause inflammation, blistering and necrosis of the skin, cramps, increased urine production and damage to the central nervous system. Abortion has been induced experimentally by feeding mint, and occurred spontaneously in two cows which ate large quantities of horse mint *(Mentha longifolia)*.[7] Mint oils also stimulate the flow of bile and can produce allergic responses.

Stomach lavage, the use of emetics (if appropriate) and dosing with activated charcoal to adsorb residual oils are recommended for treatment.

Hemp Nettle *Galeopsis* spp

Hemp nettle is said to have caused poisoning of horses in Europe,[8] but no recent case reports have been found, except in Russia where 1.1-2.5% of seeds of red dead nettle *(Galeopsis ladanum)* were present as contaminants of feed given to horses and pigs.[9] Of 18 horses, two foals died and two adults had to be killed. The affected animals were weak and refused feed and water; sweating and muscle tremors occurred. Post-mortem examination revealed haemorrhagic inflammation of the stomach and small intestines. On a pig farm, 79 of 150 newly weaned pigs died. They refused feed, did not respond to touch, developed oedematous eyelids, red patches on the skin and were comatose before death. Jaundice, infiltration of gelatinous material beneath the skin, congestion of the liver and kidneys, and dark red coloration of the mucous membranes of the stomach and intestines were seen at post-mortem examination.

Lamium spp

Henbit *(Lamium amplexicaule)* and other dead nettles *(Lamium* spp*)* have been incriminated in cases of poisoning among livestock, but no recent cases have been recorded, although the plants are widely distributed throughout Britain and many other parts of the world.

LEGUMINOSAE

Groundnut *Arachis hypogea*

Other common names: Peanut; Earthnut; Monkeynut

Groundnuts are not grown commercially in Britain, but are imported, either as whole nuts (often for human consumption), or after oil extraction, when the residues are used as meal or cake for animal feeds.

The nuts themselves are not poisonous, but if infected with some fungi that produce toxic metabolites (mycotoxins) they can cause poisoning. Mycotoxin production can occur without visible signs of moulding, but moulding of feed does not necessarily indicate mycotoxin production, as only certain strains of fungi are involved. (For details of this type of poisoning, see pages 49-51).

Milk Vetch *Astragalus* spp

Other common names: Locoweed; Poison Vetch

There are many species and varieties of *Astragalus* and the taxonomy of the genus is confused. Most milk vetches are stout perennial plants or shrubs having compound leaves with elongated, round-tipped leaflets arranged in opposite pairs on the stalk. The flowers arise in compact spikes from the axils of the leaves, and are usually white, cream or pale purple. The fruit is a pod, often divided longitudinally into two compartments.

Although milk vetches occur in Britain they are rare or local in distribution and it is therefore unlikely that animals will be poisoned by eating them in this country. Some species of *Astragalus,* and the closely related *Oxytropis* (which occurs rarely in Scotland), are considered to be among the most poisonous plants available to livestock in the USA, although several other species appear to be harmless.

Some *Astragalus* species contain the glycoside of nitropropanol, called miserotoxin as it occurs in *Astragalus miser,* or glycosides of nitropropionic acid.[1] These organic nitrogen compounds can lead to acute poisoning of animals which develop difficulties in locomotion and breathing.[1] In addition, malformed foetuses may develop, particularly in sheep, when the ewes have eaten the plants during pregnancy.[2] The toxic principle responsible for this condition is not known. Some *Astragalus* plants accumulate selenium and animals eating these develop a staggering gait and may become blind.[2][3] There is, however, some doubt that this so-called 'blind staggers' is due solely to selenium intoxication.

Crown Vetch *Coronilla varia*

Crown vetch is not native in Britain, but has become well established, after its introduction, in several places scattered throughout the country.

Crown vetch is a straggling perennial plant with stems up to 60 cm long. The compound leaves have elongated, elliptical leaflets arranged in pairs on the stalk. The inflorescence arises from the leaf axil and consists of 10-20 white, pink or purple flowers. The fruit is a slender pod which breaks up, on ripening, into one-seeded sections.

Although it is used occasionally as a forage plant (not in Britain), *Coronilla* contains various poisonous principles, including several flavone C-glycosides[4] and also β-nitropropionic acid, which is a hydrolysis product of nitropropanoyl glucopyranoses. Experimental feeding of meadow voles, young pigs and chicks with crown vetch forage led to reduced feed intake, reduced activity, a hunched-up appearance, incoordination and, in some cases, death.[5] The glucopyranoses are detoxified by the action of rumen microorganisms, and crown vetch is therefore considered to be a suitable feed for ruminants.[6]

Goat's Rue *Galega officinalis*

Other common names: French Lilac; French Honeysuckle

Goat's rue is not native in Britain, but has become naturalised and established in some places. It is an erect, branched plant, which may grow as a woody shrub up to 1.5 m high. The compound leaves have 4-8 pairs of leaflets which are elongated but rounded at the base and tip, which terminates in a small point. The flowers are pale bluish purple (sometimes pink or white) and are borne on short stalks in an erect spike.

Poisonous principles   Several are said to be present in *Galega*. Toxicity varies with different plant populations, parts of the plant and stages of growth. Galegin(e) (isoamyleneguanidine) and hydroxygalegine are usually considered the most important toxins. Subcutaneous injection of mice with alcoholic extracts of *Galega officinalis*[7] revealed that the leaves are more poisonous than the seeds, although the seeds contain more galegine. It is assumed, therefore, that other toxic substances besides galegine are present, because the plant is especially poisonous at the flowering and fruiting stages (usually from mid to late summer). The poisonous principles are not destroyed by drying so hay containing the plant is also poisonous.

Poisoning   There have been sporadic outbreaks of poisoning by *Galega officinalis* since last century.[8] No cases have been reported in Britain but poisoning has occurred in France,[9] Romania,[10] and New Zealand.[11] Sheep eat goat's rue readily and are involved in most of the outbreaks of poisoning reported. In three separate outbreaks in 1979-80 in France, many sheep died after eating *Galega* at pasture or in cut forage or hay.[8] Occasionally cattle are also poisoned,[12] sometimes fatally, although they usually avoid the plant, possibly on account of its bitter taste. Clinical signs of *Galega* poisoning usually appear 18-24 hours after eating the plant, but may develop more rapidly and last for only a few hours. The signs may therefore not be noticed, affected animals often being found dead. Laboured breathing, oedema of the neck, frothy discharge from the nostrils, loss of balance, muscular spasms with the head thrown back and convulsions are reported consistently in poisoned sheep. Fluid accumulation in the thorax and abdomen and beneath the skin, congestion of blood vessels in the lungs and intestines, and haemorrhages beneath the skin, around the heart and in mucous membranes are typical post-mortem findings. It is often suggested that microscopic examination of plant remains in the stomach should be made to confirm diagnosis.[9]

Soya Bean *Glycine max*

Climatic conditions in Britain are not suitable for growing soya beans, although some varieties are being produced which could give fairly good crops in this country, and may be available commercially in the future. Because of their high protein content, soya beans are imported for incorporation into many animal feed mixes, and are used in human diets to replace, or supplement, animal proteins.

Poisonous principles Soya beans or meal (the residue after extraction of oil) should not be used untreated as, in common with other legume seeds, they contain various toxins. Among these are lectins (phytohaemagglutinins), enzyme (chiefly trypsin) inhibitors, saponic glycosides,[13] oestrogenic substances,[14] antithyroid factors[15][16] and ill-defined 'growth inhibitors'[17] whose presence is thought to account, at least partly, for the poor performance of animals on a diet containing soya beans, which are such a good source of vegetable protein that they are used as a reference with which other seeds are compared.[18]

Poisoning Extensive work has failed, so far, to link toxicity positively with any specific toxin, although trypsin inhibitors, associated with enlargement and degeneration of the pancreas, are often considered the main cause of death in experimental animals fed raw soya beans.[13] There are conflicting reports on the mechanism involving amino acid loss in this reaction.[19][20] The possibility of interaction between the toxins has been suggested.[13]

A commercial extraction method, now largely discontinued, using the solvent trichloroethylene, has been responsible for numerous outbreaks of poisoning.[21][22] Although the solvent itself is of low or doubtful toxicity to animals, even above the concentration used in the extraction process, the toxicity of soya bean residues after extraction is enhanced greatly. The extracted oil is usually considered harmless and useful for adding to animal feeds and for culinary use, but a toxic factor (chlorinated dibenzo-*p*-dioxin) released during some processing procedures has caused oedema, particularly around the heart, in chicks.[23] Since the most serious outbreaks of soya bean poisoning have involved residues from trichloroethylene-extracted seeds,[24] it has even been stated that soya beans themselves are not toxic.[24] This opinion is, however, not generally held. The apparent symptoms of poisoning by raw soya beans are confined mainly to depression of growth rate, which varies in different animal species and stages of their growth,[25] and may not readily be recognised in live animals. Post-mortem examination, however, often reveals changes in the liver, pancreas and thyroid gland. Congenital blindness in chicks hatched from eggs of hens fed raw soya bean meal has been reported.[26]

It should be emphasised that, when properly prepared (by commercial procedures or by household cooking involving boiling for at least 30

143

minutes, or pressure cooking), soya beans and food prepared from them are safe and nutritious.

Laburnum *Laburnum anagyroides* (photo 24)

Other common names: Golden Chain; Golden Rain

Laburnum does not grow wild in Britain, except occasionally in waste places as an escape from cultivation, but is often planted as an ornamental tree in gardens throughout the country.

Laburnum usually grows as a tree, 7-9 m high, with a trunk rarely exceeding 20 cm in diameter, but Scotch laburnum *(Laburnum alpinum)* is smaller and branches from near the base. Hybrids of the two species also occur and there are several commercial varieties recognised. The leaves have long stalks and bear three terminal leaflets, which are elliptical in shape, light green and minutely downy beneath. The conspicuous inflorescences develop in early summer and consist of long (up to 20 cm) pendulous clusters of bright yellow, pea-type flowers usually about 2 cm across. The fruits are pods, 3-8 cm long, depending on the variety. These are green and contain green seeds when first formed, but become pale brown and dry as they mature. When ripe the pods open explosively to reveal dark brown or black rounded seeds, usually about 0.5 cm in diameter. In most varieties the dry pods remain hanging on the tree throughout the winter.

Poisonous principles

All parts of the tree, but particularly the bark and seeds, contain a quinolizidine alkaloid, named cytisine, after the old name of the plant, *Cytisus laburnum.* It is said that the leaves become less toxic and the flowers and fruits more so as the latter develop.[27] The quantities of cytisine found in laburnum and said to be dangerous (or even fatal) vary greatly.

Poisoning in animals

In general, laburnum poisoning in animals is rare, but a few fatal cases have been reported. One horse fed with oats that had been spilled and then gathered up with a considerable amount of laburnum seeds and pods, and two others that ate leaves and pods of laburnum trees to which they had been tied, became uncoordinated, developed muscular tremors and slight abdominal pain, became comatose and died within four hours.[28] A pig became severely ill, with profuse diarrhoea, after eating lawn mowings containing laburnum leaves[29] and a cow lost condition and there was a fall in the yield of milk, which contained large yellow clots.[29] Other cattle which ate laburnum from a felled tree or branches left in their field during winter developed a stiff, unsteady gait and violent tremors.[30] Several animals went down and were unwilling to rise. If forced to do so they walked reluctantly, as if with sore feet. One animal died and twigs and pods of laburnum were found in the rumen. More recently, laburnum poisoning has been reported in dogs. One animal died in convulsions about 30 minutes after chewing a stick, subsequently found to be a piece of laburnum,[31] and two bitches were poisoned (one fatally) after chewing low hanging branches of a laburnum tree.[32] Post-mortem examination of stomach and intestinal contents of the dogs that died revealed bark of the tree in the first case, and a large quantity of pods in the second.

Human poisoning

There are many alarming and sometimes dramatic references to laburnum poisoning in human beings, but these appear to be based more on old accounts, with their descriptions of severe symptoms,[33] rather than on specific cases, in which poisoning is usually mild.[34] [35] Most cases of laburnum poisoning occur in children who eat the green pods whole, or open them and eat the seeds which they mistake for peas. The symptoms, which usually develop in less than an hour after eating laburnum, include burning of the mouth and throat, nausea, vomiting, abdominal pain, drowsiness, headache, dizziness, elevated body temperature, rapid pulse, mental confusion, cold clammy skin, difficult breathing and dilated pupils;[34] [36] diarrhoea is not a typical symptom, but has been recorded occasionally. It is even possible that some of these symptoms, attributed to laburnum, may be those of fear, induced by parental anxiety. In many cases the symptoms are limited to nausea, vomiting and mild abdominal pain and recovery is complete in 12-24 hours. The more severe symptoms attributed to laburnum, including hallucinations, convulsions, respiratory failure and coma, sometimes followed by death, are likely to occur only under exceptional circumstances and no actual account of such poisoning has been found. An unusual case is that of a paranoid schizophrenic man who died, apparently with no clinical symptoms, and in whom no abnormalities were revealed by post-mortem examination, except the presence of 23 laburnum pods in the stomach. Laburnum trees were growing in the hospital grounds. A diagnosis of cytisine poisoning was made,[37] based on toxicological analysis. It appeared that 35-50 mg of the alkaloid had been absorbed, but no precise figures are available for the fatal dose of cytisine in man.

Treatment

In cases of suspected laburnum poisoning in man it is recommended that vomiting be induced (if this has not already occurred) by using a suitable emetic, such as syrup of ipecacuanha. If referred to hospital, emetics and sometimes stomach lavage are usually given, followed by fluids and a purgative if necessary. Overnight admission is sometimes suggested, but is rarely necessary. Discharge for observation by parents, aided by a suitable instruction sheet, would seem sufficient in most cases.[38]

Vetchlings and Wild Peas *Lathyrus* spp

With the exception of the meadow vetchling *(Lathyrus pratensis),* which is common throughout Britain in hedges, field borders and grassy places, *Lathyrus* species have only a limited distribution in this country, and are not grown here as a fodder crop. The sweet pea *(Lathyrus odoratus)* is cultivated extensively in gardens.

Members of the genus are of different form, some being erect while others are scrambling plants with tendrils. The stems of most species are winged or angled and bear compound leaves with rounded or elongated leaflets, with or without prominent stipules. The pea-type flowers of most *Lathyrus* species in Britain are shades of pink or purple, but the meadow vetchling *(Lathyrus pratensis)* and the yellow vetchling *(Lathyrus aphaca)* have yellow flowers. Cultivated varieties of the sweet pea *(Lathyrus odoratus)* have large flowers, up to 4 cm long, of many different colours. The fruits of the plants are pods containing up to 20 seeds (usually less than 10) which are compressed or rounded, according to the species. The species whose seeds are eaten most frequently is the chick pea *(Lathyrus sativus).* This has many other common names including Indian pea, mutter pea, grass pea and chickling vetch. These names may cause confusion as some of them are also used for other leguminous plants, e.g. *Cicer arietinum,* which is also called chick pea.

Poisonous principles These are numerous toxic amino acids (lathyrogens)[39] and their derivatives. They occur in all parts of the plants but are present in highest concentration in the seedlings, pods and, particularly, the seeds. The amino acids include L-α,-γ-diaminobutyric acid, α-amino-β-oxalylaminopropionic acid and α-amino-γ-oxalylaminobutyric acid which are found in several *Lathyrus* species including the chick pea *(Lathyrus sativus),* and β-N-(γ-L-glutamyl) aminopropionitrile found in other species, including the sweet pea *(Lathyrus odoratus),* the caley (or kaley) pea or hairy vetchling *(Lathyrus hirsutus)* and the everlasting or wild pea *(Lathyrus sylvestris).* Sweet pea seedlings are said to be more toxic than dry seeds due to the presence of isoxazolin-5-one derivatives,[40] as well as the aminopropionitrile. Toxic amino acids have been found in several species of *Lathyrus* in many parts of the world, but the meadow vetchling *(Lathyrus pratensis),* the only common British member of the genus has not been recorded specifically as containing poisonous substances.

There is confusion, particularly in older literature, over many aspects of *Lathyrus* poisoning including the precise nature of the toxic principles, the plant species involved, the type of toxic reaction, and the possibility of contamination of *Lathyrus* seed with that of other plants, e.g. the common vetch *(Vicia sativa)* that are known to be toxic.

146

Poisoning The disease complex to which the name 'lathyrism'[41] was given in Italy in 1873,[39] was mentioned in works attributed to Hippocrates as early as 300 B.C. The complex has now been separated into two syndromes, osteolathyrism and neurolathyrism. Osteolathyrism, characterised by severe skeletal abnormalities and, in some animals, dilation and rupture of arteries, and damage to connective tissue, has been produced experimentally by feeding animals with β-aminopropionitrile or seeds of sweet pea *(Lathyrus odoratus)*.[42] [43] A separate name, 'odoratism', was suggested for this condition in 1951[39] but has not come into general use, and has caused some confusion.[44] [45] Osteolathyrism has not occurred in human beings and there are no conclusive reports of the condition in animals except as a result of experimental feeding. The syndrome called neurolathyrism, since the principal symptoms involve the nervous system, is the condition usually referred to simply as lathyrism.

As the seeds of the chick pea *(Lathyrus sativus)* are used for animal feed and human consumption more than those of other species of *Lathyrus*, they are the most frequently reported cause of lathyrism. However, the pods and seeds of several related plants also contain toxic amino acids[42] and some have been implicated in outbreaks of the disease.[42] Some of the species that induce osteolathyrism experimentally are also responsible for natural outbreaks of neurolathyrism, a paralytic condition which can affect animals and man. The disease is most likely to occur after a period of eating large quantities of chick peas, often when other feed is scarce. This form of lathyrism is characterised by weakness and paralysis of the hind legs and difficulty in breathing. The onset of symptoms may be rapid, the animals falling and being unable to rise. This effect can occur soon after eating *Lathyrus* seeds or may not develop for several weeks. Most animals recover within a few days, after a change of diet, but in others the disease may be progressive, with the forelimbs also becoming affected, and the respiratory problems leading to death. Horses are particularly susceptible to this condition,[46] although cattle[47] [48] and sheep[49] can also be affected. An outbreak in which 60 of 600 lambs died has been reported from New Zealand,[49] where *Lathyrus* does not usually cause poisoning.[50] The condition arose when the lambs were moved to a paddock, the edges of which contained a lot of everlasting or wild pea *(Lathyrus sylvestris)*.

Lathyrism has occurred in Britain in the past[46] as a result of feeding imported chick peas to domestic animals, but more recently some horses were poisoned and temporarily paralysed after eating hay containing a high proportion of grass vetchling *(Lathyrus nissolia)*.[51]

In man, lathyrism can result from eating large quantities of chick peas raw, cooked or ground into flour. This is most likely to occur in times of food shortage, such as during drought conditions in India, when these peas still grow while few other plants survive.[39] The neurotoxic symptoms are similar to those in animals, with paralysis usually confined to the legs but sometimes extending to the arms, bladder and bowel. There may be muscle tremors or rigidity of leg muscles. A variety of secondary symptoms may also occur, but these are resolved if the diet is corrected, whereas the paralysis is often permanent.[52] Lathyrism affects adults more than children and young men more than older men or women. Several theories have been put forward to explain this but none of them is conclusive. In the past, human lathyrism has occurred in several countries, including Britain, but it is now restricted to poorer parts of the world where famine conditions prevail. From time to time a ban has been placed on the sale of *Lathyrus sativus* seed because of its poisonous nature, but despite this, farmers continue to grow the plant when they lack alternative food sources.

Several methods for removing the toxins have been tried on both whole and dehusked *Lathyrus* seeds.[39] Hot water treatment of seeds, particularly when dehusked, greatly reduces the concentration of toxic amino acids but, in common with other water treatments, there is substantial loss of essential water-soluble nutrients, including vitamins. Attempts to produce a hybrid variety of *Lathyrus,* free of the toxic amino acids, are in progress.

It should be emphasised that when only relatively small quantities of chick peas are eaten, constituting part of a mixed diet, they are harmless and nutritious.

Birdsfoot Trefoil *Lotus corniculatus* (photo 25)

Other common name: Bacon and Eggs

Birdsfoot trefoil grows throughout Britain in pastures and grassy places where it sometimes forms a dense mat. The stems of the plant which are up to 40 cm long lie along the ground but often become erect near the tip. The compound leaves are usually less than 1 cm long, with paired oval leaflets which often have a blunt point at the apex. The flower stalks are less than 10 cm long and bear 2-6 pea-type flowers which are approximately 15 mm across and bright yellow, often streaked or tipped with red. The fruit is a pod which elongates up to 3 cm as it matures.

Poisonous principles *Lotus corniculatus* contains a cyanogenic glycoside, sometimes called lotusin(e), which is considered by some to be the same as linamarin, a cyanogenic glycoside also found in some other plants including linseed *(Linum usitatissimum).* Hydrocyanic acid is released when the glycoside comes into contact with hydrolysing enzymes present in the plant. This can occur when the plant is crushed or when broken down during digestion in the rumen. Natural populations of the plant contain both cyanogenic and non-cyanogenic plants, the difference being genetically determined. In some non-poisonous plants the glycoside may be present

148

but the enzyme absent. The amount of glycoside in the plant (cyanogenic potential) varies with climatic conditions, stage of growth and the part of the plant. Concentrations ranging from 5 to 51.5 mg % have been recorded.[53] These variations may well account for the contradictory reports that exist on the toxicity of this plant. It has a long-standing reputation for being poisonous, although there are few actual outbreaks reported and it is also claimed to be a harmless and useful fodder crop. In general the seed pods contain the least and the leaves the most glycoside, the amount increasing with the age of the leaves.[54] The glycoside is not destroyed by drying, so hay containing the plant is still toxic.[53] The seeds of the plant also contain saponins.[55]

Poisoning in animals

Evidence that hydrocyanic acid is a poisonous constituent of birdsfoot trefoil was obtained when juice pressed from freshly cut plants was introduced experimentally into the stomachs of sheep, which died in a few hours. No symptoms were produced in other sheep given juice from which the hydrocyanic acid had been removed.[56] Poisoning by *Lotus corniculatus*, in which the presence of hydrocyanic acid was confirmed, occurred in the USSR[57] in goats at pasture, and sheep given hay, containing the plant. The animals became restless, and muscular spasms, unsteady gait, progressive weakness and difficulty in breathing were reported. The milk from cows with symptoms of poisoning by the plant is reported to have a bitter taste and a yellow colour.[58]

Lupin *Lupinus* spp

Lupins are not native in Britain, but the tree lupin *(Lupinus arboreus)* has become naturalised in a few waste places and another species *(Lupinus nootkatensis)* is found beside rivers in some parts of Scotland. In other parts of Europe and in the USA and Australia, several varieties of lupins are grown for forage, but, although some attempts have been made to grow the plants for this purpose in Britain, they have been abandoned, largely because there are few areas with suitably sandy soil.[59] Many varieties of lupins, with a wide range of attractively coloured flowers, are cultivated. These are usually forms of *Lupinus polyphyllus* and may persist for a time in a semi-wild state after being thrown out from gardens.

Lupins are perennial plants, often 1 m high, with compound leaves, the elongated pointed leaflets radiating from the end of the stalk. The inflorescence is a terminal spike of closely packed flowers of a wide range of colours, those of wild lupins usually being white or shades of blue. The pods are elongated, constricted between the seeds and greyish brown and silky when ripe.

Poisonous principles   Lupins contain several toxic constituents, present in all parts of the plants, particularly the seeds; drying and storage do not eliminate the toxins. The most important toxins are alkaloids, some of which are named after the plant (lupinine, lupanine); others are named after different plants in the same family (anagyrine, sparteine). Other potentially damaging constituents of some species of lupin are enzyme (trypsin) inhibitors[60] and a substance called biochanin A, which has oestrogenic activity[61] and can give rise to reproductive disorders. Toxic metabolites (mycotoxins) produced by the fungus *Phomopsis leptostromiformis* that may infect lupin plants can have adverse effects on animals.

Poisoning in animals   Lupin poisoning can affect several animal species, but is of economic importance only in sheep and cattle. The so-called bitter varieties contain at least five toxic alkaloids.[62] To some extent animals are protected from eating these varieties by their bitter taste, but when they are eaten, nervous symptoms develop, including staggering, falling and convulsions. Affected animals may also have difficulty in breathing, and may froth at the mouth. Varieties with low alkaloid content, known as 'sweet' lupins, have been developed,[59] and the cultivation of bitter lupins is therefore declining. At least one alkaloid found in lupins (anagyrine) is teratogenic[63] and is the cause of a congenital condition in the USA called 'crooked calf disease'.[64] Calves with leg deformities, spinal curvatures and sometimes cleft palate are most likely to occur if cows have eaten lupins containing the alkaloid between 40 and 70 days of pregnancy. The presence of anagyrine has been reported in milk 10 and 24 hours after feeding a goat with 2-3 g of toxic lupin.[65]

Another type of poisoning that may result from eating lupins is called lupinosis. In the past this condition was also usually attributed to alkaloids, although it occurred after eating both sweet and bitter lupins. Lupinosis is now known to result from fungal infection of the plants, and several fungi found on the plants have been suspected. The original toxic fungal isolate, from lupins involved in an outbreak of lupinosis in the Cape Province of South Africa in 1969, was tentatively named *Cryptosporium leptostromiforme*. It has also been referred to as *Cytospora* sp,[66] but further taxonomic work has established that the fungus is *Phomopsis leptostromiformis;*[67] *Phomopsis russiana*[68] is one of several synonyms under which this fungus is described. A mycotoxin (phomopsin A) produced by the fungi is the toxic principle. It is of interest that more than 100 years ago a possible connection between fungal infection and lupin poisoning was suggested.[69] Detailed symptoms and post-mortem findings in affected sheep were described in Germany in 1879, as were various fungi seen on the plants. However, experimental feeding of sheep with lupins infected with fungi failed to reproduce the condition. It has been suggested subsequently that the lupins may have been infected with fungi other than those that produce the mycotoxins responsible for lupinosis. Lupinosis is characterised by damage to the liver

150

and is accompanied by jaundice, depression and loss of weight and condition. In Australia, two distinct forms of liver disease are seen in cattle affected by lupinosis.[70] The commoner form occurs in late pregnant or recently calved cows, and is characterised by fatty liver. This may be a nutritional disorder, secondary to loss of appetite resulting from lupinosis toxin. The other form of the disease affects all classes of cattle and appears to be a direct result of lupinosis toxin. Mortality from this form is lower and the livers are not fatty but cirrhotic, with extensive damage to cells and development of fibrous tissue. Sensitivity of the skin to light (photosensitivity) may also occur and give rise to skin lesions.

Human poisoning The only likely cause of lupin poisoning in human beings is the consumption of green, unripe seeds or pods of garden lupins, mistaken for peas or beans, or of ripe seeds, the pods of which are attractive to children because of their covering of silky hairs. The effects are similar to those of laburnum, but not as severe, and include nausea, vomiting, dizziness, headache and abdominal pain.[71] There may be respiratory depression and slowing of the heart.[72] Treatment is symptomatic and supportive, although this is rarely required.

Lucerne *Medicago sativa*

Other common name: Alfalfa

This plant is not native in Britain, but has become naturalised and is fairly common, especially on calcareous soils in some areas of south-east England. It is an important forage crop in many parts of the world, including Britain,[73] where it is often sown with a grass.

Lucerne is a deep-rooted perennial plant, the forage varieties of which are mainly erect in habit and up to 1 m high. The leaves are compound and composed of three radiating, elongated oval leaflets all attached to the end of the stalk. The flowers are purple, and borne in the axils of the leaves. The fruit is a pod which splits longitudinally, on ripening, into two spirally twisting portions.

Some of the conditions that result from eating clovers *(Trifolium* spp.) may also occur in animals fed lucerne. These include reproductive failure, due to the oestrogenic substances in the plant, and photosensitivity, with consequent dermatitis. Other species of *Medicago,* including hairy medick *(Medicago hispida)* and burr trefoil *(Medicago denticulata)* which are both now placed in the *Medicago polymorpha* group, have caused photosensitivity. Loss of condition and reluctance to move were associated with soreness of the skin in young pigs which ate lucerne and medick.[74] All animal species are said to be susceptible to this type of poisoning, but there are few reported cases. Prolonged blood coagulation time has been recorded during experiments on calves grazing lucerne.[75]

Sweet Clover *Melilotus* spp

Other common name: Melilot (used preferentially in Britain)

The common or ribbed melilot *(Melilotus officinalis)*, the white melilot *(Melilotus alba)* and the tall melilot *(Melilotus altissima)* are not native to Britain, but have become naturalised in fields and waste places, particularly in southern England.

The three plants are similar in appearance, being branched, usually erect, biennials (sometimes annual) with compound leaves having elongated, elliptical leaflets, pointed at both ends. The inflorescences are loose, slender clusters of small pea-type flowers. Those of the common melilot are yellowish, those of white melilot are white and those of tall melilot are yellow. The pods are up to 5 mm long and brown when ripe (black in tall melilot).

Poisonous principles
Melilots are safe for grazing, but in hay or silage natural constituents of the plants (coumarins) may be changed by the action of moulds into dicoumarol (3,3'-methylene-bis-4-hydroxycoumarin) which impairs blood clotting.[76][77] This characteristic has been utilised in the development of anticoagulant preparations, used extensively as rodenticides. The conversion of coumarins to dicoumarol is not associated with any particular fungus, and a variety of fungi (which are almost inevitably present) can render the plants toxic. The concentration of coumarins varies in different strains of the plants, and the toxicity of a sample is not related to the extent of spoilage by moulds.

Poisoning in animals
Sweet clover poisoning is unlikely to occur in Britain, because *Melilotus* is not grown as a fodder crop, but it is a problem, particularly in North America. It primarily affects cattle[77] but has occurred very occasionally in horses and sheep. Haemorrhages, resulting from failure of blood to clot, may be internal or external, and are extensive and often fatal. The course of the disease is rapid, with subcutaneous haemorrhages being visible as swellings, usually on the back of the animals. This is associated with pale mucous membranes, weakness and rapid heartbeat just before death, which usually occurs after about three days. At post-mortem examination, the tissues appear bruised and there are haemorrhages of varying severity throughout the body.[76]

Menadione (synthetic vitamin K) is used for treating sweet clover poisoning.[78] Although not so effective as the naturally occurring vitamin, it is less expensive.

152

The small-flowered melilot *(Melilotus indica)* that has become naturalised in some fields and waste places, mainly in southern parts of Britain, is said to taint milk and dairy products if eaten by cows, and flour if harvested with wheat. There are sporadic reports in old literature of poisoning in animals after eating the plant, but no reports of recent outbreaks have been found.[78]

Beans *Phaseolus vulgaris*

Other common names: Black Bean; French Bean; Haricot Bean; Navy Bean; Pinto Bean; Red Kidney Bean; Wax Bean; White Bean; and many others.

In this diverse species there are many varieties, distinguishable morphologically and varying considerably in the constituents of their seeds. Those constituents of nutritional and toxicological importance have, understandably, received the most attention.

Poisonous principles It has long been known that the raw seeds of some members of the Leguminosae can cause poisoning. A variety of constituents have been claimed to be at least partly responsible for this toxicity. These include enzyme inhibitors, lectins, amino acids, cyanogenic glycosides, saponins, globulins, oestrogens, goitrogens and ill-defined 'growth inhibitors'.[79] [80] Of these, the two most seriously considered as the main toxic constituents are the enzyme (chiefly trypsin) inhibitors and the lectins. There is evidence in favour of the trypsin inhibitors being involved,[80] but more recent work claims that the lectins are the main toxic principles.[81] [82] However, as there is a considerable amount of work in progress on both the nutritional and toxic constituents of legume seeds, it may well be that even current thinking will need revision in the future.

Many plants contain lectins which are phytohaemagglutinins, with the ability to agglutinate red blood cells *in vitro*. Several different lectins often occur together in seeds and not all are poisonous. The lectin content of different varieties of beans varies considerably and could account for the conflicting reports on the toxicity of these seeds. The mechanism of lectin toxicity is still not clear, and is probably not related to the effect on red blood cells. It is known to involve depression of protein absorption as a result of damage to the cells of the intestinal walls. Nitrogen is present in abnormally large amounts in the faeces and urine (as urea) of animals poisoned by legume seeds, or, experimentally, by pure lectin. The excess nitrogen may also result from a systemic effect of lectin toxicity involving increased tissue catabolism (chemical breakdown of complex compounds).

153

The action of the lectins is often said to be similar to that of ricin, the toxic constituent of the castor bean *(Ricinus communis)*. However, the phytohaemagglutinins of *Ricinus* are not toxic, ricin being a simple protein, a heat-stable toxalbumin. The toxin of legume seeds is still often referred to as a toxalbumin, under the name phasin, first used early this century. Both lectins and trypsin inhibitors are destroyed by heat, which may account, partly, for each of them being considered as the toxic factor of the beans. It is essential that sufficient heat be applied to denature the lectins, as undercooked beans (for example those cooked in an electric slow cooker for human consumption)[83] retain at least some of their toxicity.

Poisoning   From last century onwards there have been sporadic references to poisoning by legume seeds, but recent reports in the medical press,[83][84] concerning raw and inadequately cooked red kidney beans, have received considerable attention. Mice, rats, chicks and quails have been poisoned experimentally by beans or their extracts,[85] the severity of the toxic reaction varying with the type and strain of animal used. The symptoms of lectin poisoning, common to animals and man, are nausea, vomiting (where possible) and diarrhoea,[83][85][86] which is usually very watery and may contain blood. The body temperature is low, the heart rate high and there may be abdominal pain. Recovery is usually rapid and treatment is rarely necessary, although attention should be given to replacing lost fluids.

The current trend in increased production of plant protein to supplement (or replace) the more expensive animal protein in the human diet could lead to an increase in poisoning by legume seeds in both human beings and animals, which are often given seeds considered unfit for human consumption. It should, however, be emphasised that legume seeds are safe and highly nutritious foods when properly heat treated (e.g. by boiling for at least 20 minutes). Badly stored, damp beans may become contaminated by moulds and therefore be poisonous, due to the presence of mycotoxins produced by the fungi.

The toxins of legumes have been utilised medically to destroy malignant cells and also as pesticides in agriculture. Concern has been expressed that, by selective breeding to eliminate toxic constituents for the food industry, the natural defences of the plant against insects will be undermined.[79]

Pea *Pisum* spp

Pea plants *(Pisum sativum)* are grown on a large scale in many countries, including Britain, for the production of their fresh green seeds that are used mainly for human consumption. Field peas *(Pisum arvense)* are grown, chiefly on light calcareous soils, in this country and are cut green for direct feeding to animals or for silage. Both the seeds (peas) and the plants (vines) sometimes produce adverse effects if fed to animals. There have been some reports of lameness in pigs that grazed *Pisum arvense*.[87] When ten experimental pigs were placed in the pea pasture, the plants were refused initially, then eaten readily. Muscular incoordination and weakness, particularly of the hind legs, developed, with varying severity, in all of the animals. A staggering gait was observed and eventually two of the animals were unable to stand.[87] Incoordination also occurred in the lambs of ewes fed pea vine silage and pods from canning peas *(Pisum sativum)*.[88] Affected animals were tense and tended to run, walk backwards, then collapse. This was repeated after rest or if forced to move. Growth inhibitors are present in raw peas, as in several other legume seeds. Depression of growth occurred in chicks,[89] and two factors present in the peas were thought to be responsible. Neither was identified, but one was inactivated by heat (autoclaving), and the other interfered with zinc utilisation. Pea vine silage is a good cattle feed, but has a strong odour. If fed to cows after milking, however, there is no taint in the milk.[90]

Acacia *Robinia pseudoacacia*

Other common names: Black Acacia; Black Locust

This large, deciduous tree, which often grows 25-30 m high, is not native in Britain but has become established after its introduction from North America; it is often planted as an ornamental tree or in thickets.

The trunk and older branches are deeply fissured. The leaves are compound, consisting of elliptical leaflets arranged in pairs in one plane on the stalk, at the base of which there are often persistent spines. The fragrant flowers are white (occasionally pink) and hang in drooping clusters. The fruits are flat pods containing numerous seeds.

Poisonous principles These are not fully known but are thought to include toxic proteins, similar to ricin in the castor oil plant *(Ricinus communis)*, but far less toxic. These proteins are usually referred to as toxalbumins named robin(in) and phasin. A glycoprotein which agglutinates red blood cells (a phytohaemagglutinin) has also been extracted from the plant, but it is not clear whether this is robinin or another substance. All parts of the tree, except perhaps the flowers, are said to be poisonous; the bark is usually considered the most toxic.

Poisoning This has not been reported in Britain, but the tree should be regarded as potentially poisonous as it has caused illness and sometimes death in horses, cattle, sheep and poultry.[91] Clinical signs are similar in all animal species and include staggering, incoordination, paralysis and gastrointestinal disturbances, which may be severe. In addition, laminitis was recorded in one of nine horses that suffered severe colic after chewing bark from acacia fence posts.[92] Post-mortem examination reveals intense irritation and inflammation of the mucous membranes of the digestive tract. A phytohaemagglutinin extracted from the plant caused fatty degeneration of the liver and death in chick embryos[93] at doses of 0.25-2.0 mg per egg.

Poisoning in human beings is characterised by lassitude, nausea, vomiting, dilation of pupils and, in severe cases, stupor.[94]

Broom *Sarothamnus scoparius*

This much branched shrub is generally distributed throughout Britain on heaths and waste land, but is restricted to acid soils. The branches are flexible, angled and green throughout the year. The leaves consist of 1-3 elongated leaflets usually less than 1 cm long. The flowers are bright yellow and the fruits are pods which become dry and dark brownish-grey when ripe. The seeds are blackish brown and are shed explosively as the pods open with a characteristic snap. The cultivated Spanish broom *(Spartium junceum)* is common in gardens throughout the country and sometimes grows wild, as a garden escape. This shrub is usually larger than the common broom and the flowers are of various colours.

Broom contains small amounts of the toxic quinolizidine alkaloids sparteine and isosparteine. Cytisine, genistein, lupinidine and sarothamnine are also said to be present,[95] although some of these names may refer to the same compound. The alkaloids can depress the heart and nervous system, sometimes with paralysis of motor nerve endings. Sparteine sulphate has been used medicinally[96] in small doses, and acts as an antidote to some poisons, including snake venom. It is doubtful that the plant itself could cause poisoning, except in very unusual circumstances, as insufficient amounts of the alkaloids are present, and the small leaves and somewhat wiry stems make it unattractive as a food plant. No reports of specific cases have been traced, but reference is still made to broom as a poisonous plant and a statement that the average poisonous dose for a horse would be over 11 kg (25 lbs)[97] is widely quoted.

Clover *Trifolium* spp

Several clovers are native and widely distributed as wild plants in Britain, and a range of cultivated varieties is grown for grazing or hay or to be ploughed in to increase soil nitrogen.

Red Clover *Trifolium pratense*

This plant is generally distributed in grassy places throughout Britain. It is perennial and may be erect or prostrate in habit. The leaves are formed of three radiating leaflets, all attached at the end of the stalk. The leaflets may be slightly toothed at the edges and, with the exception of some uniformly green cultivated forms, have a white crescent-shaped area near the base. The pinkish-purple flowers form in a dense terminal head which is spherical at first but elongates slightly to become ovoid.

White Clover *Trifolium repens*

Other common names: Dutch Clover; Ladino Clover (a large-leaved cultivated form).

White clover is a perennial plant that grows in grassy places throughout Britain. It is basically similar to red clover *(Trifolium pratense)* but is a creeping plant, rooting at the nodes. The leaflets have a whitish band towards the base and the flowers are white (occasionally pale pink).

Alsike Clover *Trifolium hybridum*

This clover is probably not a native British plant, but has become naturalised, often beside roads, throughout the country. Alsike clover is a white-flowered perennial similar to white clover *(Trifolium repens)* but it is not creeping.

Subterranean Clover *Trifolium subterraneum*

Other common name: Subterranean Trefoil

This plant is native in Britain, but occurs only locally in sandy and gravelly pastures, in the southern part of the country. It is a hairy, prostrate annual, with sparsely flowered heads bearing both fertile cream-coloured flowers and sterile flowers. The calyx enlarges to cover the seed pod which burrows into the soil as it matures.

Poisonous principles Clovers may contain a number of compounds that can have adverse effects on animals. These include oestrogens, cyanogenic glycosides, goitrogens, nitrates and substances that can cause bloat, laminitis, blood coagulation disorders or photosensitivity. Diseases can also arise from ingestion of toxic metabolites (mycotoxins) of fungi that infect clover.

Poisoning in animals Clovers have poisoned animals in many parts of the world and should therefore be regarded as potentially poisonous in Britain, although, for a variety of reasons including climate, agricultural methods[98 99] and possibly the strains of the plant present, they cause few problems in this country.

Oestrogens Many clovers contain oestrogenic substances called phyto-oestrogens (isoflavones) such as genistein and formononetin, that can cause reproductive problems in animals that eat them. Female animals may develop swelling of the external genital organs, milk production without pregnancy, temporary or permanent infertility, and abortion; wethers (castrated male sheep) may develop swelling of the teats and the rudimentary mammary glands may be stimulated to produce milk. These conditions are associated particularly with subterranean clover *(Trifolium subterraneum)* in Australia.[100] White clover *(Trifolium repens)* can become oestrogenic[101] if infected with various fungi that cause leaf-spot diseases in the plants. It has been suggested that 'ringwomb', a condition occurring in ewes in Britain, and associated with difficult birth due to incomplete dilation of the cervix, may be caused by clover oestrogens.[102] Ruminants can detoxify some phyto-oestrogens, but not others.

Cyanogenic glycosides Some strains of white clover *(Trifolium repens)* can cause hydrocyanic acid poisoning as they contain both cyanogenic glycosides and an enzyme (β-glucosidase) which releases the toxin from the glycosides. These glycosides include lotaustralin and linamarin, and the enzyme is sometimes called linamarase. Cyanogenic potential may be linked to plant damage caused by heavy grazing,[103] possibly indicating that the cyanide toxicity of clover is a natural defence mechanism of the plant. In general, clovers do not contain enough cyanogenic glycosides to cause severe poisoning, but typical symptoms, including shortness of breath, muscular contractions and initially, bright red mucous

158

membranes, have been seen occasionally in cattle as a result of eating white clover. The condition has been reproduced experimentally in cattle given minced white clover through a stomach tube.[104] The animals become prostrate, with rigid limbs, distressed breathing, increased heart rate and, finally, cyanosis of the mucous membranes, indicating oxygen shortage in the tissues, which occurs when death from cyanide poisoning is delayed.

Goitrogens   Consumption of some clovers by pregnant ewes has led to goitre in their lambs. This goitrogenic activity has been attributed to oestrogens, cyanogenic glycosides and another, as yet unidentified, substance.

Nitrates   Bacterial action in the root nodules of leguminous plants results in their having a high nitrogen content. Nitrates eaten in forage are converted in the rumen to nitrites; these combine with haemoglobin in the blood to form methaemoglobin, a stable substance that does not combine with oxygen. Typical symptoms are bluish mucous membranes, laboured breathing, staggering and vomiting (where possible). Nitrite poisoning may occur, with or without other types of poisoning attributable to clovers.

Bloat   Excessive intake of clovers may result in bloat, a condition in which the rumen is distended because the gases resulting from ruminal digestion become trapped in a stable foam produced by foaming agents from the plants. The various factors which lead to bloat are still not fully understood, but it is considered to be a metabolic disorder rather than poisoning.

Laminitis   This condition, characterised by tenderness, swelling and inflammation around the hooves, is seen most frequently in horses and usually results from overfeeding with grain. However, severe laminitis has been reported in Britain among cattle pastured on white clover that had seeded, the seeds having sprouted again in the seedheads.[105] The feet of affected animals developed bony outgrowths and there was separation and sloughing of skin.

Blood coagulation disorders   Preliminary studies have revealed that the clotting time of blood is prolonged in animals fed legume forage.[106] This has been demonstrated experimentally in calves grazing lucerne and in sheep fed white clover. No haemorrhagic disease or other adverse effects have been described in live animals, but this condition is of importance in the meat industry where undesirable 'blood splash' from the meat of such animals is encountered.

Photosensitivity   Some species of *Trifolium*, particularly white and Alsike clover, can, under certain weather conditions, lead to photosensitive reactions with severe necrosis of unpigmented skin of animals that eat them.[107] [108] This condition, sometimes called 'trifoliosis' or clover disease, may be primary photosensitivity (a direct effect on the skin, without involvement of the liver) but secondary photosensitivity resulting from liver damage may also result from eating these plants. In addition to this skin reaction, other symptoms including dullness, staggering, blindness, jaundice and gross enlargement of the liver have been attributed to the consumption of clover. There may also be gastrointestinal disturbances and, in cows, a fall in milk yield. Horses appear to be particularly susceptible to clover-induced photosensitivity, which has been called 'big liver disease'[109] (chronic hypertrophic cirrhosis). Liver disease has been reproduced experimentally by feeding Alsike clover to horses.[109] Individual animals vary in their susceptibility to the effect of clover disease, some recovering in a few days while others develop a chronic condition from which recovery is slow.

Mycotoxins   Most reports of 'trifoliosis' are from Australia and the USA and are not recent. Some of these old reports, particularly those in which the skin reaction is limited to the muzzle of the animal, probably refer to conditions resembling facial eczema,[110] a sheep disease occurring in New Zealand and to a limited extent in Australia and South Africa. It is now known to be caused by contamination of pasture plants with spores of the fungus *Pithomyces chartarum*, which produces the mycotoxin sporidesmin. From descriptions of clinical signs, it seems possible that some other skin conditions, perhaps including those attributed to photosensitivity, may also result from toxins produced by fungi infecting clovers rather than from the plants themselves.

Vetch *Vicia* spp

Other common name: Tare

Several vetches have caused poisoning in animals under natural conditions and in experimental work. These include the common vetch (*Vicia sativa*) and its cultivated form (*Vicia sativa* var. *sativa*), the narrow-leaved vetch (*Vicia sativa* var. *angustifolia*), the hairy tare (*Vicia hirsuta*) and the hairy vetch (*Vicia villosa*). There have been changes in the classification of vetches; some plants previously given the rank of species, for example *Vicia angustifolia*, now being considered varieties or subspecies. There is considerable variation even among these, and there are many intermediate forms.

Common Vetch *Vicia sativa*

This vetch is generally distributed as a wild plant in hedges and grassy places throughout Britain, and its cultivated form is grown in this country, usually on moderately calcareous soils, for animal feeding, either freshly cut or as hay or silage.[111]

Common vetch is a trailing or climbing plant, and when cultivated, is often sown mixed with another plant, usually a grass, for support. It climbs by means of fine tendrils and the stems of wild plants may be up to 120 cm long. The leaves have paired, elongated oval leaflets 1-2 cm long, and pointed stipules that often have a dark spot. The pale purple flowers are borne singly or in pairs and are up to 2 cm long. The fruit is a beaked pod, up to 7 cm long, containing 4-10 seeds.

Poisonous principles
There is confusion over the nature of these in vetches. It is usually stated that they contain cyanogenic glycosides and the names vicianin, vicine, divicine and convicine have been given to them. The release of hydrocyanic acid from the glycosides is dependent on the action of enzymes in the plant (when crushed) or, to a smaller extent, in the digestive system of animals. The apparently contradictory reports on the toxicity of vetch plants and their seeds under natural conditions and in experimental work[112] may relate to the presence or absence (in toxicologically significant quantities) of the glycosides or the enzyme in different species, varieties or plant populations. It has been reported, for example, that the common vetch *(Vicia sativa)* does not contain cyanogenic glycosides, but that they are present in the narrow-leaved vetch[113] (now usually classified as *Vicia sativa* subsp. *angustifolia,* but often still referred to as *Vicia angustifolia).* It is also stated, however, that the seed of *Vicia sativa* has cyanogenic potential.[114] No conclusive reports typical of hydrocyanic acid poisoning of animals after eating vetches have been found.

Some vetches contain a toxic amino acid β-cyano-L-alanine[115] that may be at least partially responsible for the paralytic disease, neurolathyrism, associated with species of *Lathyrus.* It has even been suggested that neurolathyrism occurs, or is more severe, when *Lathyrus* seeds are contaminated by those of vetches. However, some species of *Lathyrus* are poisonous alone, and no reports of poisoning by vetches involving the nervous system and definitely attributed to this amino acid have been traced.

Poisoning in animals
Various vetches have undoubtedly caused poisoning, although this has not necessarily been linked with any specific poisonous substances present in the plants. No reports have been found of poisoning of animals by vetches in Britain, but as they grow in this country, and can be toxic, they are included. In the old literature, poisoning by the common vetch has been described in horses, pigs and cattle,[116] with symptoms including skin

161

lesions with hair loss, digestive disturbances and weakness and sometimes loss of use of hindquarters. Post-mortem examination often revealed enlargement of the liver. Experiments on poultry given feed containing 30-80% of seeds of *Vicia sativa* and/or *Vicia villosa*[117] [118] resulted in 20-40% mortality in chicks. Clinical signs included loss of weight and condition, excitability, incoordination, difficulty in breathing and sometimes violent convulsions. The signs were more severe, and death was more rapid, with common vetch seeds.

In cattle, three apparently different disease syndromes have been recognised after eating *Vicia villosa*. Acute illness and death occurred in five of six cattle that ate hairy vetch seed from a sack.[119] The animals were extremely restless, appeared to be in severe pain, and convulsions occurred when handling was attempted. The second type involves skin lesions, cough and respiratory distress and general weakness, followed by death in some animals after about two weeks.[116] Post-mortem examination reveals inflammation of the forestomachs, severe bronchitis with pneumonia, and a yellowish brown liver.[116] The third type is also characterised by a rough coat and necrotic skin lesions on both pigmented and non-pigmented skin, but is otherwise similar to a photosensitisation reaction. Soreness of the eyes (conjunctivitis) and severe diarrhoea, accompanied by progressive weight loss and 50% mortality, were recorded among the clinically ill cattle in 23 herds in the USA.[120] Similar clinical signs, with dermatitis spreading from the tail and neck to the whole body of black-coated (Angus) cattle have been recorded recently;[121] some animals became emaciated and died.

Broad Bean *Vicia faba*

Other common names: Horse Bean; Fava Bean

This plant has been cultivated since prehistoric times in the Mediterranean area[122] and its large seeds are used in many countries for human and animal consumption. The plant is an erect, pale green, square-stemmed annual, ranging from about 50 cm to over 1 m in height, according to the variety. Occasional plants may persist in a semi-wild state for some years after planting. The compound leaves have several pairs of oval leaflets. The inflorescences are axillary clusters of white, pea-type flowers with a blackish-purple blotch. The fruit is a fleshy pod, up to 20 cm long, containing large flat seeds, 2-3 cm long. Both the pod and the seeds become light brown and hard when dry; the seeds usually have a prominent black scar.

Poisonous principles Although broad beans can have adverse effects on animals, no specific constituents of the plants have been incriminated.

Poisoning in animals   Broad beans are not usually considered poisonous to animals, and many varieties are used for animal feed, either in silage, when the whole plant is eaten, or when the beans are added to mixed feed. In experimental work with pigs, a slight reduction in growth rate occurred with increasing proportions (up to 25%) of broad beans in the diet,[123] compared with similar pigs given other sources of protein, but there was no evidence of toxicity. However, during an economic crisis in Poland, poisoning occurred in pigs given broad beans as approximately one third of their diet.[124] In this outbreak 25% of the animals died and a further 25% were slaughtered. The clinical signs appeared in three to five days and included depression, reduced activity, loss of appetite, flatulence, constipation and a hunched appearance indicative of abdominal pain. Post-mortem examination revealed inflammation of the alimentary tract, pale yellow liver and kidneys. The blood vessels of the intestinal mucous membranes, lungs and urinary bladder were congested. It was noted that the feed had not been mixed thoroughly, so that some animals would have eaten more beans than others.

Human poisoning   Broad beans are not poisonous, in the conventional sense, to human beings but they may cause favism in susceptible individuals. This disease, also called fabism or fabismus,[125] is characterised by haemolytic anaemia of varying severity, and it can occur after inhaling the pollen or eating the seeds of the plant, particularly when raw or partially cooked. Favism is prevalent only in some islands and coastal regions of the Mediterranean, with its highest frequency in Sardinia. Susceptibility to the condition is dependent on a genetically transmitted, male sex-linked deficiency of the enzyme glucose-6-phosphate dehydrogenase. It is therefore determined racially rather than geographically, and cases that occur outside the endemic region, involve individuals who originated there.[126]

The nature of the causative agent of favism has not been established with certainty, although several suggestions have been made. These include derivatives of toxic glycosides (vicine and convicine),[125] breakdown products of amino acids, and insect damage. It has been suggested in the past[127] [128] that beans that have caused poisoning in animals or man may have been contaminated with fungi, but this has not been proved.

The symptoms of favism include vomiting, abdominal pain, dizziness and elevated body temperature. In more serious cases there may be severe anaemia with associated jaundice and dark or blood-stained urine; collapse may occur. Environmental conditions and variations in the toxicity of different samples of beans can influence the severity of the disease. Except for individuals of susceptible races, broad beans are safe and good to eat.

Wisteria *Wisteria* spp

Wisteria occurs in Britain only as an ornamental plant in gardens. It is grown occasionally as a specimen tree, but is more often trained on walls, against which it grows as a woody climber, with intertwining branches. The leaves have paired, oval leaflets, pointed at both ends. The inflorescences are pendulous clusters of fragrant, pea-type flowers that are usually bluish or purple, but may be pink or white according to the variety. The fruit is a flat pod which dries on ripening and splits open to reveal dark, rounded seeds.

Poisonous principles
Little work appears to have been done on the nature of the poisonous principles of *Wisteria,* but these are generally thought to be a glycoside (wistarin) and a resin.

Poisoning
It is sometimes stated that wisteria has been found only recently to be poisonous, but its toxic nature was known in the 1880s and symptoms produced in man were described in detail.[129] About the same time experimental feeding of animals failed to produce symptoms[130] and it appears that reports claiming the plant is not poisonous are based largely on these old experiments. The toxicity of *Wisteria* in animals is still not proven, but is well documented in man. Poisoning has resulted from chewing wisteria twigs,[129] but is most common in children who have eaten the pods and seeds, mistaking them for peas. Even one or two seeds may produce a reaction.[131] *Wisteria* acts as a digestive system irritant and can cause nausea, abdominal pain, vomiting and, sometimes, diarrhoea,[132] but even in severe cases, recovery is usually complete in 24 hours.[133]

Emesis should be induced or stomach lavage carried out; otherwise only supportive treatment is required.

LILIACEAE

Meadow Saffron *Colchicum autumnale* (photo 26)

Other common names: Autumn Crocus; Naked Ladies

Meadow saffron grows in several isolated areas of England and Wales in damp meadows and woods. It is often locally abundant. The plant has been introduced to some parts of Scotland. The alternative common name, autumn crocus, sometimes causes confusion with *Crocus nudiflorus*[1] which is also called autumn, or autumnal, crocus but which belongs to a different family (Iridaceae).

Colchicum is a perennial which grows from a corm 3-5 cm in diameter. The plant has glossy, bright green, parallel-veined leaves which grow up to 30 cm long and 4 cm wide. These are produced at the base of the plant in spring and die before the flowers appear. The flowers which, when open, resemble superficially a spring-flowering crocus, are pale purple (sometimes almost white) and appear, one or more from each corm, in late summer or autumn. The basal part of the flower is narrow, tubular and up to 20 cm long. The flowers die down soon after they have opened, and an oval fruit, 3-5 cm long, is formed at the base of the flower tube, close to the soil, where it remains until the following spring when the flower stalk elongates so that the fruit appears above the leaves and opens when ripe, to reveal numerous small seeds.

Poisonous principles

These are two structurally similar alkaloids, colchicine and colchiceine, of which the former is the more toxic. Both are able to withstand drying, storage and boiling without losing their toxic properties. Colchicine affects the nervous system, paralysing peripheral nerve endings and blocking neuromuscular connections; it also prevents normal cell division. Because of the last property, colchicine has been used in experiments on plant genetics, and the possibility of its use against cancer has been investigated. Colchicine has been used medicinally in the treatment of gout and rheumatism.

All parts of the plant are poisonous, particularly the corm (colchicine content 0.03-0.06%) and the seeds (colchicine content 0.02-0.04%). The highest concentration is present in the plant during the summer.[2,3] The lethal dose has been estimated as 8-16 g of fresh leaves per kg of body weight for cattle,[2] 6.4 g/kg for lambs aged 2-3 months and 12 g/kg for adult guinea pigs.[4]

Poisoning in animals

As the plant grows in meadows, the domestic animals most likely to be poisoned by *Colchicum* are cattle and sheep. Poisoning has been reported in cattle,[2,3,5,6] sheep,[2,3,4,7] horses,[2,3] pigs[3,8] and goats.[3] Poisoning due to colchicine has also been reported in man[3,8] and dogs,[3,9] and laboratory animals have been poisoned when fed with either colchicine or *Colchicum*.[3,7]

Colchicine is absorbed slowly into the body, and signs of poisoning may be delayed for several (12-48) hours.[2] Excretion of colchicine by the kidneys and in the milk of lactating animals in also very slow, so that there is a gradual increase in concentration of colchicine which may reach a toxic level. As colchicine is excreted in milk, young animals and human beings that drink the milk are liable to be poisoned.[8] Cattle, and to a lesser extent sheep and goats, can develop a tolerance and even complete resistance to *Colchicum*.[8] In most animals, *Colchicum* poisoning produces abdominal pain, salivation, severe diarrhoea, grinding of teeth, coldness of the extremities, depression, apathy, incoordination, decreased milk production, collapse and death through respiratory or circulatory failure. Colchicine given to dogs (4 mg daily for 14 days) interfered with gastrointestinal absorption of some sugars and fat.[9]

Colchicum poisoning is seldom reported in Britain, but in northern Germany (GDR) an outbreak was recorded which affected 30 of a herd of 96 cattle[5] after their first introduction to spring pasture. They developed salivation, depression, unsteady gait, abdominal pain, greenish diarrhoea with mucus, and a sudden decrease in milk production. Three of the cows died. A high annual incidence of poisoning has been reported among lambs during May-July in the highlands of central Tien-Shan in Kirghizia (USSR).[4] Clinical signs in the lambs were abdominal pain, followed by salivation, diarrhoea and later depression, apathy and collapse. Post-mortem examination revealed acute gastrointestinal inflammation. The myocardium appeared flabby, with small haemorrhages; the liver and spleen were congested and enlarged, the lymph nodes were oedematous and haemorrhagic, the lungs and kidneys were congested, and the mucous membranes of the intestine were thickened and covered with mucus. The main histological changes were congestion of organs, haemorrhages and destruction of lymphocytes in the lymph nodes, spleen and lymphoid follicles of the large intestine.[7]

Colchicum poisoning can be diagnosed by identifying leaves or seeds in stomach contents, although it is difficult to recognise flowers ingested in autumn. The presence of colchicine in ruminal fluid can be detected by thin layer chromatography.[10]

Human poisoning This can occur if children eat the flowers, or if the leaves are mistaken for those of an edible plant, or the bulbs for onions. Drinking milk from poisoned animals can also cause poisoning.[8] Symptoms are burning of the mouth and throat, nausea, abdominal pain, violent vomiting and diarrhoea, shock due to fluid loss, and collapse. Scanty and blood-stained urine indicates kidney damage. Fluid therapy, and analgesics to relieve pain, are recommended.[11] [12]

Bog Asphodel *Narthecium ossifragum* (photo 27)

Bog asphodel is found throughout Britain in bogs, wet moors and heaths. It is a summer-flowering plant with a creeping underground stem (rhizome) and many fibrous roots. Stiff, narrow leaves (5-30 cm long and 2-5 mm wide) arise at ground level. Their basal sheaths are flattened in one plane, and the tips of the leaves tend to curve downwards. The flower stalk is stiff and erect (5-40 cm high) and bears a few leaf-like bracts that clasp the stalk and rarely exceed 4 cm in length. The inflorescence is a terminal cluster of yellow flowers with prominent, bright orange centres. After flowering, the ovaries and top of the stem become uniformly orange.

Poisonous principles

The precise nature of these has been elucidated only comparatively recently,[25] although saponins have been suspected for many years. A major saponin, narthecin, and a minor one, xylosin, have been identified. These are spirostanol saponins, derived by hydrolysis from furostanols, the form in which the saponins exist in the plant.

Poisoning in animals

The specific name 'ossifragum' refers to the belief of former times that the plant predisposed to fracture of the bones of animals which ate it. Although *Narthecium* has long had the reputation of being poisonous, references to its toxicity were rarely seen until the 1950s. Since then, increasing numbers of reports of liver disfunction and photosensitisation, associated with sheep grazing *Narthecium*, have been recorded, chiefly from Norway, where the disease was first described, and the name 'alveld' (elf fire) given.[26] The disease occurs mainly in lambs up to about five months of age.

The photosensitisation is of the secondary (hepatogenous) type, the saponins in the plant causing liver damage and interfering with the excretion in bile of the photosensitive substance phylloerythrin, a normal breakdown product of chlorophyll. The phylloerythrin accumulates in the circulating blood of animals that have eaten *Narthecium*.[26] When exposed to bright sunlight the poorly pigmented areas of skin, particularly those with least wool, develop clinical signs of photosensitisation. These include oedema and reddening of the skin, initially of the ears which become hot and drooping. The whole head is usually involved and the effects sometimes extend along the back and to the forelegs. This is followed by itching, pain, exudation of fluid from broken skin that may become infected, and sloughing of dead tissues, sometimes including the tips of the ears; in severe cases there may be blindness.[27] It has been noticed that affected animals often seek shade. Mortality rates of 25-50% have been recorded in lambs in Norway.[27] Jaundice, resulting from damage to the liver, is often, though not necessarily seen. This may occur in black lambs that do not suffer from photosensitisation.[27] The disease has been reproduced experimentally by administration of saponin extracts from the plants,[27] and in lambs placed on pastures containing *Narthecium*.[28] Although the association between *Narthecium* ingestion and these clinical signs has been studied extensively mainly in Norway, some outbreaks of animal disease in Britain are thought to involve the plant. Loss of ears and death in lambs on Dartmoor have been attributed to bog asphodel.[29] It appears that only white-faced lambs in their first year on moorland pasture are affected. A similar condition, known locally as 'heddles' or 'hard lug' has been known for many years to farmers in the Antrim Hills in

Ireland;[30] photosensitisation after eating *Narthecium* has been suspected as the cause. In this area feeding lambs exclusively on bog asphodel failed to reproduce the disease, but there were no alternating periods of showers and bright sunlight (weather conditions associated with the disease) during the four days of the experiment; the animals may have had some reaction, however, as they remained in the shade. Photosensitisation, with skin lesions developing particularly on the ears but also on other white areas of the head and legs, has occurred annually in sheep of the Blackface breed on farms in Perthshire.[31] Swelling of eyelids and consequent closure of the eyes led to the death of some animals that wandered aimlessly into bogs and streams. Known locally as 'plochteach', the disease affects up to 10% of young lambs in May and June; severe jaundice is also present in some cases. Lambs with this condition were studied over three consecutive years[31] and high phylloerythrin levels in blood were found consistently. It was suggested that *Narthecium* may be involved, mainly because of the similarities to alveld disease in Norway. Diseases in sheep described as 'yellowses' or 'head greet' in Scotland and 'saut' in Cumbria have been recognised for many years,[31] and bog asphodel was thought to be the cause.

It was suggested, although not verified, that bog asphodel caused the death of 15 ponies on Dartmoor in 1977.[32]

Lily of the Valley *Convallaria majalis*

This spring-flowering woodland plant is native in Britain, especially in eastern parts of the country, where it is widespread, but local in its distribution. It is widely cultivated and often occurs as a garden escape.

The plant is a perennial with a creeping rhizome, and leaves 8-20 cm long, pointed at the tip, widening up to 5 cm then narrowing into a stalk which sheaths the stem at the base. The flower stalk rarely exceeds 10 cm in height, has no leaves, and bears a terminal cluster of 6-12 fragrant white, bell-shaped flowers about 8 mm across.

Poisonous principles All parts of the plant are said to be poisonous, but there is some confusion about the toxic compounds present in the plant. The three most frequently named are the glycosides convallarin, convallamarin and convallotoxin, the last being one of the most toxic naturally occurring substances which affect the heart. All *Convallaria* glycosides cause irregularities of the action of the heart, and some of them are saponins which, together with volatile oils also present in the plant, act as gastrointestinal irritants.

168

Poisoning in animals The plant is said to be dangerously poisonous to animals and birds, although, with the exception of reported poisoning in poultry (of which no details are given) there is a lack of evidence to substantiate this. However, because of the nature of its toxic constituents and its known toxicity to man, the plant should be regarded as potentially poisonous to livestock.

Human poisoning In the USA in 1959-60, cases reported of lily of the valley being eaten included four children, aged eight months to two years, who ate the fruit (berry) or seeds of the plant.[13] [14] Children have also been poisoned, some fatally, by chewing the growing plant, eating berries or by drinking water from vases containing poisonous plants, including *Convallaria*.[15] When lily of the valley leaves were mistaken for those of wild garlic, and made into soup, those eating it became hot, flushed and tense and developed headache and hallucinations; red skin patches also occurred.[16] Symptoms of *Convallaria* poisoning in man include excess salivation, nausea, stomach pains, vomiting, headache, dilated pupils, cold clammy skin and slow irregular heartbeat, sometimes leading to coma and death from heart failure.[17] [18] Treatment with emetics, or stomach lavage is recommended, in addition to a cardiac depressant, such as quinidine, to control cardiac rhythm.

Bluebell *Endymion nonscriptus*

Other common name: Wild Hyacinth

Bluebells are common throughout Britain in woods and shady places, but rarely grow in pastures. Linear leaves, 20-45 cm long and about 1 cm wide develop in early spring from the white, oval bulb. The single flower stalk appears a few weeks later and bears 4-16 drooping, blue, bell-shaped flowers.

Poisonous principles All parts of the plant contain glycosides, generally termed scillarens, which are similar in chemical structure to the cardiac glycosides of *Digitalis*.

Poisoning in animals In a horse which had eaten bluebell bulbs,[19] clinical signs appeared after about six hours, when the animal appeared to be choking. There was some abdominal pain and intermittent attempts at vomiting; the pulse was slow and weak and the temperature low, the skin was cold and clammy. About ten hours later there was dark-coloured diarrhoea with a considerable amount of blood; urination ceased altogether. The horse was acutely ill for two days, then slowly recovered but continued to pass blood-stained urine for several days. In early spring in Britain, when feed was scarce, an area of bluebells with closely cropped leaves was seen adjacent to pasture where a group of Hereford cows and calves were grazing. Within the next few days, the animals became dull and lethargic, chewed only intermittently and produced hard, dry faeces. Body temperature and respiration rate decreased and heart beat was erratic. Lactating cows became dry. The animals recovered slowly when removed from the area and given extra feed. Bluebell poisoning was considered to be the cause of the condition.[20]

Human poisoning Bluebell bulbs have caused poisoning when eaten in mistake for onions. The fruits of bluebell have also caused poisoning, an 18-month-old child developing diarrhoea after eating 6-10 pods with seeds.[16] The sap of the plant can cause dermatitis.[21]

Hyacinth *Hyacinthus orientalis*

This cultivated plant is similar to, but larger than the bluebell *(Endymion nonscriptus)*, and has white, blue, pink or occasionally yellow flowers. Feeding of bulbs during war-time feed shortage in the Netherlands was suspected to be the cause of severe purgation in cattle.[22] Hyacinth bulbs have been mistaken for onions and, when eaten, they can cause stomach cramps, vomiting and diarrhoea.[23] Stomach lavage or the use of emetics is recommended. The sap of the plants can cause dermatitis in man.[24]

Star of Bethlehem *Ornithogalum umbellatum*

This plant is thought to be native in eastern England, but is found throughout Britain where it and other *Ornithogalum* species have become naturalised locally. Characteristics of the plant are the pale green or white midribs of the long narrow leaves and the 6-pointed, star-like flowers which have a green stripe on the back of each segment. It is stated that alkaloids found in the bulbs and above-ground parts can cause nausea and intestinal disorders.[23] Children have been poisoned by eating the flowers and bulbs. Stomach lavage or the use of emetics is recommended.

Other species of *Ornithogalum*, several of which share the common name chincherinchee, are grown only as ornamentals in Britain. These are highly toxic and are responsible for permanent blindness, and sometimes death in cattle in South Africa.[33] They can also cause dermatitis in man. This is a potential hazard in the cut-flower trade, as chincherinchees are imported from South Africa.

16b

16   White Bryony (*Bryonia dioica*) (a) flowers
(b) fruit
HCB

17   Black Bryony (*Tamus communis*) (a)
flowers (b) fruit. The berries are red
when ripe
HCB

16a

17a   17b

18

18 Rhododendron (*Rhododendron ponticum*)
HCB

19 Sun Spurge (*Euphorbia helioscopia*)
HCB

20 Dog's Mercury (*Mercurialis perennis*)
JH

21 Oak (*Quercus robur*)
HCB

19

20

21

Tulip *Tulipa* spp

Tulips are not native in Britain, but many species and varieties are cultivated. These vary in size, and there is a wide range of flower colours. The plants grow in spring from a bulb with a thin, brown papery skin. The leaves are smooth, broad, somewhat fleshy and taper to a point; the flowers are borne singly on a cylindrical stalk, the coloured flower segments overlapping each other to form a straight-sided, cup-shaped flower held vertically on the plant.

Poisonous principles Tulips contain substances named as tulipalin A and B, but they have not definitely been linked with the toxicity of the plant. The acylglucoside tuliposide A is an allergenic component.

Poisoning The few outbreaks reported all refer to human ingestion of tulip bulbs either to supplement food, as occurred in the Netherlands in the Second World War,[23][34] or when used in mistake for onions.[16] In one recent outbreak in Yugoslavia,[34] five tulip bulbs were used in place of onions in a goulash eaten by all six members of a family. The dish had a bitter taste and within ten minutes, symptoms including nausea, sweating, increased salivation, difficult breathing and palpitations were experienced. Vomiting occurred in some, and weakness persisted for several days in all cases. A dog that ate some of the goulash vomited many times and thereafter ate nothing for three days.

LINACEAE

Linseed *Linum usitatissimum*

Other common name: Flax

Flax was cultivated formerly in Britain both for the fibre in its stem and for its seeds (linseed). In recent years the plant has not been grown, except occasionally in Ireland, but linseed is imported either as such, or as a constituent of prepared oilseed cake or meal for animal feed.

Poisonous principles Linseed contains the cyanogenic glycosides, linamarin and lotaustralin, from which hydrocyanic acid is released by hydrolysis involving the enzyme β-glucosidase, sometimes called linamarase. Hydrolysis may take place in the plant itself, if crushed or bruised, or in the stomach of animals after ingestion of the seeds.[1] The severity of poisoning depends on the cyanogenic glycoside content of the plant (which varies considerably with

171

genetic strain, climate, season and soil type), the activity of the enzyme, and the rate of release of the hydrocyanic acid (which is influenced by the amount of water present, drinking water resulting in rapid release of the toxic substance).[2] If the toxic material is eaten slowly, enzymatic detoxification of the cyanide occurs. Another component of linseed, a dipeptide named linatine (or linatene) is a vitamin B_6 antagonist. Marginal deficiency of the vitamin developed in pigs fed 300 g/kg body weight of linseed meal.[3] Because of the growth-inhibiting effect of linatine, linseed is not recommended for inclusion in poultry feed.[4]

Poisoning in animals
Hydrocyanic acid prevents the utilisation of oxygen by cells. The blood, therefore, retains oxygen and remains bright red, and it is oxygen deficiency in brain cells that leads to death. Most cases of hydrocyanic acid poisoning after consumption of linseed cake or meal are in older literature. Modern methods of extraction of linseed oil involve heat treatment, during which the enzyme responsible for the release of hydrocyanic acid from the glycoside is inactivated.

Poisoning has been reported in cattle given linseed cake containing 0.4% hydrocyanic acid or a hot water extract of cake which contained 0.8% hydrocyanic acid.[5] Salivation, staggering and somnolence resulted from eating the cake, while drinking the extract produced more severe symptoms, the animals trembling, gasping, falling and having convulsions before death which occurred within an hour. In other cases of linseed cake poisoning in cattle,[6] prostration, depression, dilated pupils and rapid pulse were reported. Similar symptoms and some deaths were reported in sheep[7][8] given linseed cake and in lambs, as a result of being suckled by poisoned ewes. Occasionally animals die so quickly that no symptoms are seen. Reference is often made to the laxative effect of linseed oil feeds[9] and gastrointestinal inflammation has been found at post-mortem examination. No reference to the substance(s) responsible for this effect has been found.

Treatment
For poisoning by hydrocyanic acid, intravenous injections of sodium thiosulphate and sodium nitrite are recommended. Oxygen may also be beneficial.

Purging (or fairy) flax *(Linum catharticum)* is a common annual plant found throughout Britain, often as a weed of cultivation. Purging flax also contains linamarin, but the plant has not been incriminated in cases of poisoning. If eaten in sufficient quantity it may cause diarrhoea.[10]

LOBELIACEAE

Lobelia spp

Acrid lobelia occurs occasionally as a wild plant in Britain, where it is said to be uncommon, but increasing in frequency. Several *Lobelia* spp. are cultivated in gardens. The plants contain an alkaloid, or mixture of alkaloids, named lobeline.

Acrid lobelia *(Lobelia urens)* was reported in early literature[1] to cause inflammation if applied to the eyes, and symptoms similar to poisoning by deadly nightshade *(Atropa belladonna),* with inflammation, if taken internally. No evidence of such poisoning has been found in later literature. Other species of *Lobelia* have been implicated in cases of poisoning in animals abroad. After an outbreak of poisoning in cattle that had been grazing pasture in which *Lobelia berlandieri* was one of the dominant species, feeding trials with the plant were carried out on sheep.[2] Clinical signs including dilated pupils, sluggishness, loss of appetite and diarrhoea developed initially, followed by nasal discharge and ulceration of the mouth; coma preceded death. In man, *Lobelia* can irritate the skin.[3]

LORANTHACEAE

Mistletoe *Viscum album*

Mistletoe grows as a parasite, almost exclusively on deciduous trees, and is common in southern England and parts of the Midlands, but infrequent elsewhere and absent from Scotland.

The plant is much branched and woody and readily recognised by its dense, twiggy, compact appearance on host trees. The stems, which may grow up to 1 m in length, bear thick, tough, evergreen leaves, 5-8 cm long, and up to 2 cm across. They have clearly parallel veins, are rounded or bluntly pointed at the tip and narrow into a short stalk at the base. In spring, small compact clusters of yellowish-green flowers, which are usually unisexual, grow on very short stalks at the tips of branches or in the axils of the leaves. The fruits remain until the winter and are white, slightly translucent berries containing viscous juice and a single seed.

There are few reported cases of poisoning by *Viscum,* but other mistletoes *(Loranthus* and *Phoradendron),* which are not native in Britain, are considered highly toxic.

Poisonous principles	The leaves and berries of the plant contain toxic basic proteins, named viscotoxins, which are a mixture of several closely related polypeptides.[1] The amino acid composition of two of these, viscotoxins A and B, has been studied in detail.[2]
Poisoning in animals	Symptoms of poisoning by berries of *Viscum album* have been described for dogs and horses. A small dog (griffon) which ate part of a spray of mistletoe with berries[3] developed nervous symptoms, including constant nodding of the head and incoordination of the hindquarters. Later the animal was unable to stand, and handling produced muscular twitching. There was slight salivation, frequent production of dark coloured urine, a progressive decrease in body temperature and strength of pulse, and the animal died 50 hours after eating the mistletoe. Another dog which ate *Viscum* experienced prolonged periods of excitation, was sensitive to its abdomen being touched, had dilated pupils and a slow respiratory rate, but recovered after 24 hours.[4] Post-mortem examination of the dog which died revealed slightly increased amounts of blood (hyperaemia) in the intestines, liver and brain, and oedema of lymph nodes, lungs and around the brain and kidneys, which were pale in colour. Microscopic examination revealed some fatty changes in the liver.[3] Symptoms described in the horse include incoordination, abdominal pain and difficult breathing.[5] Severe cases may be fatal.
Human poisoning	Both in man and domestic animals, mistletoe poisoning is most likely to occur around Christmas time when the plant, normally inaccessible at the top of tall trees, is brought indoors. Most human cases involve children, who have eaten the berries. An early report of poisoning in a child[6] gives symptoms including pale lips, inflammation of the eyes, dilated pupils, slow pulse, laboured breathing, hallucinations and coma. Induced vomiting revealed mistletoe berries. The severity of symptoms varies with the number of berries eaten and the age of the child. As few as 3-4 berries may produce mild symptoms, and gastroenteritis may result if large numbers are consumed.[7] Treatment of cases of mistletoe poisoning is symptomatic. The induction of vomiting, using a suitable emetic, such as syrup of ipecacuanha, is recommended where possible.

Mistletoe is a possible toxic agent in some herbal remedies and has been suspected of causing hepatitis in individuals who have taken them.[8] [9]

MALVACEAE

Mallow *Malva* spp

There are several native species of mallow in Britain, including the common mallow *(Malva sylvestris)* and the dwarf mallow *(Malva neglecta)*. The marsh mallow *(Malva parviflora)* has been introduced to this country and has become established locally. It is this species that is recognised as a poisonous plant abroad, mainly in Australia[1][2] and South Africa,[3] but also in the USA. Even in these countries, however, outbreaks of poisoning are recorded only in older literature. The conditions under which poisoning occurs in different countries appear to vary as, in the USA, a sheep fed experimentally with cut, dried mallow for 11 days increased in weight and was apparently unaffected.[4]

Poisonous principles
The plants contain nitrates (readily converted to nitrites that combine with haemoglobin to form methaemoglobin, thus preventing adequate uptake of oxygen). A fatty acid now often called malvalic acid, but referred to previously as Halphen acid, is also present.

Poisoning in animals
Sheep are most often affected and develop clinical signs including staggering, incoordination, trembling, arched back, extended head and laboured breathing;[1][2] severely affected animals may fall and die. It has been noted on several occasions, and verified experimentally, that staggers develop when the sheep are driven.[1] Staggers in lambs has resulted from sucking the milk of ewes that have eaten mallow.[1] A similar condition occurs, though much less frequently in horses and cattle.[5] In addition to the staggering characteristic of mallow poisoning, profuse sweating and rapid breathing have been seen in horses.[1] It is unlikely that sufficient mallow would be found and eaten by animals in Britain for such severe poisoning to occur, although the plant appears to be increasing in some waste places and areas previously kept weed-free by herbicides.

Later reports on the adverse effects of mallow have been in poultry, the biologically active fatty acid in the plants[6] having been implicated as the cause of a pinkish colouration of the whites of eggs,[7] particularly after storage.[8] There have been no reports of this occurring in Britain.

OLEACEAE

Ash *Fraxinus excelsior* (photo 28)

Ash is a tall, deciduous tree with spreading branches, growing up to 25 m high, in mixed woodland, scrub and hedges throughout Britain, but especially in wetter parts of the country on calcareous soils.

The trunk of the tree is grey and sometimes fissured, the buds are large (up to 10 mm) and have a sooty appearance. The leaves are compound, bearing 7-13 oval leaflets which have slightly serrated edges and are pointed at the tip. Small flowers appear in bunches, before the leaves, and are reddish-purple, due to the colour of the stamens, there being no sepals or petals. The winged fruits (keys) are 3-4 cm long and hang in clusters in autumn, often persisting into the winter after the leaves have fallen.

Poisonous principles These have not been determined fully, but are probably glycosides, including the lactone glycoside aesculin, which also occurs in *Aesculus* species.

Poisoning Although a rare occurrence, ash poisoning is a potential problem where animals graze near these trees. Eating fallen leaves in autumn can cause impaction of the rumen in cattle, a condition formerly known in the Midlands as 'wood evil'. The symptoms are acute indigestion with cessation of rumination, distension and hardness of the rumen, the passage of small amounts of hard faeces or no defaecation, grunting and reduced milk yield.[1] Drowsiness, abdominal pain, incoordination and collapse were also seen in two cows[2] which stripped leaves and fruits from a branch of ash which fell in a storm. In these animals there was pronounced oedema of the ribs, flanks and udder and purple discoloration of the perineum. Treatment should include attempts to stimulate resumption of rumination, but may necessitate rumenotomy.[1] Ash has caused dermatitis in man.[3]

Privet *Ligustrum* spp

Common privet *(Ligustrum vulgare)* is a native shrub of southern England, where it is found chiefly on calcareous soils. An introduced species, oval-leaved privet *(Ligustrum ovalifolium)*, is common throughout the country as a cultivated hedging plant, and many yellow and variegated types are grown as ornamentals. Common privet is deciduous, but the cultivated varieties may keep some of their leaves throughout the winter and be classified as evergreen.

Common privet can grow up to 5 m in height, has smooth bark, slender branches and young shoots with a light covering of small, soft hairs. The leaves are 3-6 cm long, have short stalks and are bright green and shiny when young, becoming dull later. They are 1-2 cm wide and taper gradually to a point at the tip and towards the stalk. Clusters of small, creamy-white flowers appear in summer. They have a tubular base, extending into a flattened expanded portion, 4-5 mm in diameter. The fruits are black, shining berries, 6-8 mm in diameter. Oval-leaved privet is very similar except that the shoots are hairless, the leaves more oval or elliptical in shape and the flowers are longer.

Poisonous principle

The precise nature of this is not known, but it is generally referred to as a glycoside, ligustrin. The berries are usually considered the most toxic, but all aerial parts of the plant have been involved in poisoning.

Poisoning in animals

Poisoning by privet is rare, but when it does occur it is often severe or even fatal, and the plant should be considered potentially dangerous. Most cases involve hedges or their trimmings rather than the wild plants. Death has occurred in horses from 4-48 hours after eating the plant. Clinical signs of colic and unsteady gait preceded death in two horses which had eaten material from a neglected hedge which was in flower;[4] five horses died after eating twigs with leaves from an untrimmed hedge in an earlier incident in Britain.[5] Some animals were staggering, while others were down and unable to rise and appeared to have paralysis of the hindquarters. The pulse was rapid, the visible mucous membranes were congested and the pupils dilated. In New Zealand, five heifers died and others became ill after grazing a privet hedge at the berry stage.[6] Eating trimmings from a privet hedge caused the death of sheep in Maryland, USA.[7]

In all of the post-mortem examinations described, the presence of privet in the stomach and intense gastrointestinal irritation and inflammation were the only findings.

Human poisoning

Privet berries are often stated to be a cause of poisoning, particularly in children. Vomiting and diarrhoea were reported in two children[8] who ate privet berries, and in an intoxicated man[8] who ate the leaves. There are, however, very few actual reports of human poisoning by this plant, but its toxicity should not be underestimated, and it is said to have caused fatal poisoning. Privet can cause dermatitis[9] and in one case a severe skin reaction occurred in a boy working on a privet hedge.[7]

OROBANCHACEAE

Broomrape *Orobanche* spp

Several species of *Orobanche* are native in Britain, where they parasitise the roots of other plants to which they are attached by underground tubers. From these tubers arise fleshy, aerial, flowering shoots, devoid of chlorophyll, and usually yellowish in colour although often tinged with russet brown, red or purple. Depending on the species, the shoots may have a few or many scales at the base. The two-lipped flowers form in densely packed terminal clusters and may be lobed. At least part of the flowers is usually purple. The parasitic nature of broomrapes renders them undesirable in crops, and in former times it was even considered necessary to stop growing certain clover crops because of this parasitism.[1] Broomrape is not now a problem in crops in Britain, but can still be found parasitising wild plants.

Poisonous principles These are said to be glycosides, resins and tannins,[2] but little is known about them.

Poisoning There are references in old literature[1 3] to the noxious effect of broomrape on domestic animals, in which gastrointestinal disturbances occurred, but there are few reported cases of poisoning, possibly because the plant is unattractive to animals. However, poisoning has been demonstrated in feeding experiments with lesser broomrape *(Orobanche minor)* using either the plant itself or extracts of it.[2] Reduced appetite and rumination, depression, prostration and thirst were reported in four goats, two of which died. Dose-related symptoms of poisoning also occurred in dogs. A diuretic effect of broomrape was demonstrated by increased urine production in experimental animals.

OXALIDACEAE

Wood Sorrel *Oxalis acetosella*

Other common name: Sleeping Beauty

The common name of this plant can cause confusion with other sorrels which are *Rumex* species and in a different family (Polygonaceae). *Oxalis acetosella,* the only member of the large genus native in Britain, grows in woods and shady places where it may be the dominant ground cover plant. It has yellowish-green, compound leaves divided into three more or less

178

equal, bluntly rounded leaflets (similar to clovers) and bears white flowers, veined with lilac, on slender stalks up to 15 cm long.

Poisonous principles   *Oxalis* contains oxalic acid and oxalates which can cause poisoning. It is unlikely that enough of the plant would be eaten to cause poisoning in Britain, but procumbent yellow sorrel *(Oxalis corniculata),* an introduced species in this country, has caused poisoning, particularly of sheep in Australia where it is a troublesome weed. A total oxalate content of 7% has been estimated in air-dried plants.[1]

Poisoning in animals   Sheep and ruminants can detoxify considerable quantities of ingested oxalates. The nutritional status of the animals before eating plants containing oxalates is an important factor in determining the severity of the toxic reaction. If eaten in sufficiently large quantities over a relatively short period, plants containing oxalates can cause severe calcium deficiency (hypocalcaemia), as the oxalates ingested combine with blood calcium to produce insoluble calcium oxalate. As little as 600 g of the plant fed to sheep can cause hypocalcaemia.[1] Severely affected animals develop muscular twitching, trembling and staggering, and may die suddenly. Ingestion of smaller quantities of the plant over a long period results in the formation of calcium oxalate deposits in the kidney tubules, sometimes leading to kidney failure and death. In one outbreak of poisoning by *Oxalis corniculata,* sheep walked with a stiff gait, paralysis of the hind limbs developed and the animals dragged themselves along on their knees.[2] In Australia, more than 10% of nearly 3000 sheep died after eating *Oxalis* which grew in abundance on the route along which they were being driven; affected animals lay on their briskets, with outstretched necks.[3] Post-mortem examination revealed congestion of the intestines and kidney degeneration. Injection of soluble calcium may prevent death if given in the early stages of poisoning.

Early this century it was stated that milk from cows poisoned by *Oxalis* is difficult to churn into butter,[4] but there is no recent report of this.

PAEONIACEAE

Peony *Paeonia* spp

Peonies are not native British plants, but an introduced species has become naturalised locally in an area of south-east England. There are many species and varieties cultivated in gardens. Simple, leafy shoots grow annually from the perennial tuberous stock of the plants. The leaves are smooth, dark-green and divided into pointed leaflets; the flowers are produced terminally and are large (up to 10 cm across) and conspicuous, having many slightly incurved dark red, pink or white petals. The fruits, which grow up to 2 cm long, are pale green at first and covered with downy hairs. They contain smooth round seeds which change from red to dark blue and finally black as they ripen.

Poisonous principles Information on the nature of these is confusing. A glycoside, peonin, responsible for the deep purple coloration of the flowers, is also said by some to be present throughout the plant and to be toxic. Others state that alkaloids are the toxic factors.

Poisoning An unidentified substance isolated from peonies is said to cause difficulty in swallowing, coldness and loss of sensitivity of extremities, constriction of blood vessels in the kidneys and inflammation of intestines and kidneys.[1] Species of *Paeonia* have long been suspected of being poisonous plants and are included in lists of such plants from the 18th century. There is, however, little evidence to substantiate this, although it seems likely that the plant does contain at least a gastrointestinal irritant. A case is reported of an 8-month-old girl who vomited an hour after eating 3-4 peony flower petals.[2]

PAPAVERACEAE

Field Poppy *Papaver rhoeas*

Other common names: Red Poppy; Corn Poppy

This plant, the only *Papaver* species native in Britain, is still common, particularly in the south, where it is often seen in waste places and beside roads and railways. Its occurrence in arable land has been greatly reduced by herbicides.

The erect stems of the plant grow up to 60 cm in height and bear stiffly hairy leaves with deeply indented or toothed edges. The flower buds are pendulous, but the flowers, which develop in summer, are erect and have delicate scarlet petals (rarely pink or white) that often have a dark blotch at the base. The fruit is a firm, smooth capsule with a flattened top on which are dark radiating lines (stigma rays). The seeds are very small, numerous and golden brown. The form of the plant is variable.

Poisonous principles All parts of the plant are said to be poisonous, and it is generally considered to have an unpleasant taste. Various alkaloids, one of which is rhoeadine, are contained in the plant.

180

Poisoning in animals Symptoms described in cattle in early literature[1] are consistent with those described more recently for other *Papaver* species. However, no recent cases of poisoning by the British poppy *(Papaver rhoeas)* have been described, although the plant should be considered as potentially toxic.

Opium Poppy *Papaver somniferum*

Other common name: White Poppy

Opium poppies are not native in Britain but are sometimes grown as ornamentals. They occur occasionally as wild plants when they are garden escapes or relics of former cultivation. Legislation to control the growing of opium poppies, in an attempt to limit the availability of the narcotic drug, opium, has been made in some countries. *Papaver somniferum* grows up to 100 cm tall, is smooth and uniformly bluish green. The lobed leaves have undulating margins; the flower petals are white or pale lilac, with or without a darker basal blotch. The fruit is a spherical or oval capsule and the numerous, small seeds are black or white. The plants are very variable in form and numerous subspecies have been defined.

The seeds of the plants are generally considered harmless and are sometimes used as condiments, and for decorating bread. An edible oil can be obtained by pressing the seeds and there was a revival of the cultivation of the poppy for this purpose in France during the Second World War.[2] However, the residues left after pressing caused many cases of poisoning when fed to cattle.

Poisonous principles These are found in the crude resin, opium, which is present in the whole plant but mainly in the unripe seed capsule, the milky sap of which is released by cutting and then allowed to dry before collection. Medicinal drugs, such as morphine and codeine, are constituents of opium as are many other alkaloids, including papaverine, laudanine, narcotine, narceine, amurine, nudaurine and protopine. It is highly probable that individual alkaloids, described over the years, have been referred to by more than one name.

Poisoning in animals This has been recognised for many years.[1] The plant is seldom eaten while growing, but, when stalks with seed capsules[3] or seed residues after oil extraction[2] were fed to cattle, they became restless within a few hours and moved, turned or ran about constantly. When tied to prevent this, the animals moved their feet continuously, scraping the ground and injuring themselves by abrasion. Continuous lowing was also a characteristic sign.

181

Feeding, rumination and lactation ceased, and the animals produced excess saliva; their body temperature decreased and the rate of breathing increased. Finally the animals went into a deep sleep. Poisoning by opium poppies is rarely fatal, but affected animals are often an economic loss as they are very slow to recover, and the milk yield of lactating animals rarely returns to normal. Post-mortem examination revealed inflammation of the intestines and kidneys, increased blood in the blood vessels of the brain and yellowing of the liver.

Iceland Poppy *Papaver nudicaule*

This plant has leaves in a basal rossette and flowers (3-8 cm across) with yellow, orange or reddish petals. Iceland poppies are grown only as ornamentals in Britain but are of some importance, as incidents of poisoning have occured when animals have had access to garden rubbish containing the plants.

As with other *Papaver* species, Iceland poppies contain a variety of toxic alkaloids. Poisoning has been recorded in horses,[4] cattle[5] and sheep.[6][7][8] In most cases poisoning has resulted from cut flowers or discarded plants being thrown to animals; there are no records of animals having eaten the growing plant. The clinical signs are similar in all animal species and include initial restlessness and excitation, followed by incoordination, stiffness, muscular twitches and spasms of limbs, falling and inability to rise and, in some cases, distension of the abdomen (bloat). Iceland poppy poisoning is rarely fatal, but affected animals may take many months to recover and, in lactating animals, milk yield remains depressed.

Yellow Horned Poppy *Glaucium flavum*

Other common name: Sea Poppy

This plant, which has large, coarse, deeply serrated, divided leaves, and flowers (6-9 cm across) with rounded, yellow petals, grows chiefly on shingle banks around the coast of England and southern Scotland.

No actual cases of poisoning by this plant in its wild state have been recorded, but it should be regarded as potentially toxic as it contains poisonous alkaloids, named as glaucine, protopine, chelerythrine and sanguinarine.[9]

Other poppies which occur in Britain and have been recorded as causing poisoning in animals in other countries are the long-headed poppy

22

23

22 St. John's Wort (*Hypericum perforatum*)
HCB

23 Stinking Iris (*Iris foetidissima*)
HCB

24 Laburnum (*Laburnum anagyroides*)
unripe fruits: the flowers are shown
on the cover
HCB

25 Birdsfoot Trefoil (*Lotus corniculatus*)
JH

24

25

26

27

26 Meadow Saffron (*Colchicum autumnale*)
JH

27 Bog Asphodel (*Narthecium ossifragum*)
HCB

28 Ash (*Fraxinus excelsior*)
HCB

29 Greater Celandine (*Chelidonium majus*)
HCB

28

29

(Papaver dubium) and the rough, or round prickly-headed poppy *(Papaver hybridum)*.

Greater Celandine *Chelidonium majus* (photo 29)

Other common names: Celandine Poppy; Wart Wort

Although implied by the common name, this plant is not related to lesser celandine *(Ranunculus ficaria)* which belongs to a different family (Ranunculaceae).

Greater celandine grows throughout most of Britain except parts of Scotland, in banks and hedgerows, but is often found near old buildings, where it has probably survived from earlier times when it was grown as a medicinal plant. It was applied to corns and warts or taken internally to treat liver, lung and gastrointestinal disorders, and rheumatism.[10]

Greater celandine has erect, branched, smooth or slightly hairy stems and grows up to 60 cm high. The basal leaves have long stalks and the upper ones short stalks. The leaves, which are bluish-green below, are deeply divided into distinct oval segments which have irregularly scalloped edges. The flowers, borne in loose terminal clusters throughout the summer, are 2-2.5 cm across and have bright yellow petals and greenish-yellow stamens. The fruit is an elongated pod-like capsule which contains white-tipped black seeds.

Poisonous principles   Greater celandine is said to contain many potentially toxic alkaloids of which the most frequently named are chelidonine and a-homochelidonine (both chemically related to papaverine, found in *Papaver* species), chelerythrine, sanguinarine and protopine. However, the plant rarely causes poisoning as it is unpalatable, having an acrid taste and a pungent, foetid smell. The sap of the plant (latex) is yellowish-orange in colour, but turns red on exposure to the air.

Poisoning in animals   The plant has a long-standing reputation for being poisonous to animals, but this is apparently based largely on adverse effects of its medicinal use and a single report, early this century, of poisoning of cattle in Britain.[11] The herd had been noticed eating, throughout the summer, greater celandine which grew luxuriantly along a hedge, without adverse effect. In the autumn, when the seed capsules were ripe, many of the animals became poisoned and some died after eating the plant. The clinical signs included excess salivation and urination, thirst, drowsiness, cessation of bowel movement and staggering gait. Violent convulsions occurred when the animals were approached and touched. Calves suckled by the poisoned cows were unaffected. Post-mortem examination revealed gastrointestinal irritation.

Other less well documented cases refer to the drastic purgative action of the plant with consequent dehydration from which animals may die.

The practice (now largely discontinued) of applying externally the juice of the plant (or an infusion of it) to minor skin injuries, as a wash to remove parasites, or for the treatment of certain eye disorders often resulted in irritation and soreness which required further treatment.[9]

Human poisoning

The juice of the plant can cause irritation and blistering of the skin. The death of a four-year-old child, who developed haemorrhagic gastroenteritis and circulatory failure after eating the plant, is recorded.[12]

PHYTOLACCACEAE

Pokeweed *Phytolacca americana*

Other common names: Pokeberry; Pigeonberry; Inkberry; American Nightshade

Pokeweed is not native in Britain but has been introduced from the USA as a garden plant. In a few localised areas it has escaped and become naturalised. It is a perennial shrub which grows up to 3 m high. The leaves are light green, thick and prominently veined. They are generally oval, but are pointed at the tip and taper towards the stalk. The small, white or greenish flowers are borne in a spike up to 20 cm long, and the fruit is a purple berry with red, staining juice.

All parts of the plant, but especially the thick, fleshy taproot and the unripe green or reddish berries, are said to be poisonous. The ripe berries appear to be the least poisonous and have been used in making pies.[1] The young shoots are also considered safe to eat as a cooked vegetable if the cooking water is discarded.[1]

Poisonous principles

The precise nature of these in *Phytolacca americana* (and some other *Phytolacca* species) is not known and several old names persist for the supposed toxins. It is known, however, that the plants contain water-soluble substances (sometimes referred to as alkaloids) with the action of saponins, of which the most frequently named are phytolaccin and phytolaccatoxin.

Poisoning in animals

Pokeweed is poisonous to cattle, sheep, horses and pigs.[2] It has an acrid taste and burns the tongue. The symptoms, which develop 1-2 hours after eating pokeweed, include severe diarrhoea, vomiting (where possible), salivation, muscular cramps, weak breathing, impaired vision and

184

drowsiness; coma and death may result.[3] Most recorded cases of *Phytolacca* poisoning are in pigs. In one outbreak in the USA, the roots of the plant eaten by pigs caused them to run about aimlessly as though blind. Their eyes were inflamed and they staggered as they moved and were unusually docile.[4] In another, more serious, incident involving mature sows, *Phytolacca* poisoning resulted in paralysis of the hindquarters and death.[5] Another pig fed pieces of root of the plant became unsteady, lay down and was unable to rise.[5] Jerking movements of the legs were observed. The animal was killed, and post-mortem examination of this and the sows showed ulceration with haemorrhages of the stomach and intestines. Dark red coloration and extreme swelling of the liver were recorded for the sows.

Chickens are said to eat the berries of the plant without ill effect and wild birds often feed on them, but turkeys have been poisoned by eating pokeberries.[6] Addition of liquidised fresh pokeberries to the diet of young turkeys reduced weight gain. Hock disorders, sometimes causing inability to stand or walk, developed. Post-mortem examination of birds that died revealed fluid accumulation in the abdominal cavity and gall bladder. There is some evidence that ingestion of the berries has an adverse effect on the immune responses of the birds, but this is inconclusive.[7]

In New Zealand, pokeweed continues to be a potential toxic hazard, particularly to cattle. The plant tends to flourish after the removal of sheep from an area and although chemical weedkillers are effective against seedlings, the mature shrubs are difficult to eliminate.[8]

Human poisoning
Most cases involve children who may become seriously ill after eating raw berries. In the USA in 1959-60 there were 97 reported cases of ingestion of pokeberries, mostly by children aged 2-3.[9] Pain, vomiting and diarrhoea were reported. An adult man who ate pokeweed root in mistake for horse radish experienced a sore mouth and throat and extreme lassitude, with yawning. Severe vomiting, exhaustion and dizziness followed and breathing became difficult. The pupils were contracted and the skin cold and clammy. Vomiting persisted for 12 hours and a bitter taste for 48 hours before recovery.[10] In a recent episode in the USA,[11] a group of campers became ill after eating a salad containing pokeweed leaves that had been boiled twice (a process reputed to make them edible). Headache, dizziness and gastrointestinal disturbances with stomach cramps were experienced; symptoms lasted for up to 48 hours. An extract of the plant (pokeweed mitogen) is used experimentally because of its ability to influence cell division; it affects the division of human white blood cells,[12] and induces the proliferation of both B and T lymphocytes.

PINACEAE

Pine *Pinus* spp

The leaves of pine trees native to Britain are unlikely to be eaten by animals because the needles are sharp, but those of other species, notably of a pitch pine, the western yellow pine *(Pinus ponderosa)*, cause pregnancy complications, chiefly in cattle, in the USA.[1][2] If eaten in the last three months of pregnancy, the animals may abort. Uterine contractions are weak, the cervix is incompletely dilated, there is excess bleeding and placental retention. Calves that survive are often weak.

POLYGONACEAE

Buckwheat *Fagopyrum esculentum*

Buckwheat is cultivated on a very small scale in Britain, particularly in the fens. It occurs occasionally on waste ground, but is not a native plant. It is an erect annual with few branches, leaves longer than broad with rounded or slightly pointed lobes at the base, and pink or white flowers borne on a branched inflorescence.

Poisonous principles A pigment, fagopyrin, present in the plant is thought to be the active principle, and clinical signs have been produced in domestic and laboratory animals given the pigment orally. Several attempts have been made to identify it, and various fractions have been separated.[1][2][3] Fagopyrin is probably a naphthodianthrone derivative.

Poisoning in animals When dehusked, the black, triangular seeds are considered harmless and are often incorporated into animal feeds or seed mixtures for cage birds and poultry.[4] Under certain conditions, however, animals that eat the fresh or dried plant in fairly large quantities develop dermatitis on white or unpigmented areas of the skin if exposed to sunlight. Animals which are housed or have heavily pigmented skin are unaffected. Such photosensitivity has been reported in sheep, cattle, pigs, goats and fowls.[5] Although pigs are said to be less susceptible,[6] cases have been reported in the USSR.[7] It is usually considered to be primary photosensitivity, as the main symptoms are the direct result of sunlight on the skin, but there may be concurrent jaundice, indicating secondary involvement of the liver and interference with its function.

186

Affected animals usually develop reddening and blistering of the skin within 24 hours of eating the plant and exposure to strong sunlight, but delayed reactions can also occur.[8] The lesions often became necrotic and are slow to heal. Occasionally nervous symptoms with agitation, possibly due to intense irritation of the skin,[6] convulsions, somnolence and prostration may develop. In one outbreak in France,[9] cattle fed on buckwheat plants were unaffected while housed, but when transferred to pasture in sunny weather, they soon became recumbent, moving only when stimulated. Severe skin lesions, thirst and emaciation were prominent features. In the USSR[8] sheep showed similar symptoms, with initial excitement followed by paralysis. In addition to an intense skin reaction on the bare parts of the head, incoordination was reported in turkeys which gained access to a field of unripe buckwheat.[4] The term 'fagopyrism' is sometimes used for the condition induced by buckwheat poisoning.

Treatment Symptomatic treatment of the skin lesions may be required; a change of diet and removal from sunlight (preferably by housing) are obviously desirable.

Human poisoning The grain of buckwheat (whole or ground into flour) is used extensively for human food in some countries, and is imported into Britain. As only dehusked grain is offered for sale for human consumption in this country, it is unlikely that poisoning will occur here. Allergic reactions to the plant are far more common than the photosensitisation reaction in man.

Sheep's Sorrel *Rumex acetosella* (photo 30)

Other common name: Sour Grass (a misnomer, as the plant is not a true grass)

This common perennial plant is found throughout Britain on rough and cultivated land and heaths on acid soils. It is virtually absent from calcareous soils.

Stalked leaves grow from the basal rhizome and also on the erect reddish stem which may be up to 30 cm tall. A small, ragged, transparent sheath is present at the point of attachment of the leaf, the blade of which is elongated, pointed at the tip and has, at the base, two narrow pointed lobes which are usually directed sideways or slightly forwards. The branched inflorescence may be up to 15 cm long and is usually leafless. The male and female flowers appear in mid summer, closely attached to the stem or on short stalks. They are superficially similar, but are borne on separate plants. The flowers are reddish-brown and less than 0.5 cm across. The thin, outer segments tend to curve inwards around the inner ones which enlarge slightly and harden to form an outer covering for the fruit which is triangular, up to 1.5 mm across and contains tiny dark seeds.

Common Sorrel *Rumex acetosa*

Other common name: Sour Dock

This plant resembles sheep's sorrel but is larger, (the furrowed stem sometimes growing up to 100 cm tall) and is more tolerant of chalky soil. The leaves are up to 10 cm long, have a more irregular edge with broad points, especially near the base, where the two lobes point downwards beside the stalk. The upper leaves have scarcely any stalk and tend to clasp the stem. The inflorescence is up to 40 cm high and resembles that of sheep's sorrel, but the flowers grow on short stalks in early and mid summer, tend to be pendulous, and have outer segments that turn back after flowering to reveal the capsule.

Poisonous principles

Both plants contain oxalates, which have long been regarded as their poisonous principle. However, under certain conditions, sorrel accumulates nitrates in sufficient concentration for them to cause poisoning. An unidentified substance, tentatively called rumicin, has also been incriminated, and more recently it has been suggested that anthraquinone glycosides present in the plants are the toxins. In the few recorded cases of severe poisoning attributable to the plant, the clinical signs in affected animals are consistent with oxalate poisoning.

Poisoning in animals

The likelihood of poisoning, particularly by *Rumex acetosella,* is reduced in areas where liming of the land is common agricultural practice, as this discourages growth of the plant.

The plants have a pleasantly sharp taste and are palatable to animals; the leaves are sometimes gathered for use in salads. Animals which eat sorrel are not often poisoned, and the conditions under which poisoning does occur are not clearly defined. The nutritional status of the animal, calcium deficiency, acclimatisation to the plant by previous feeding of small quantities, the variable concentration of oxalates in the plants and the amount eaten are factors which may influence reactions to eating sorrel.

Soluble oxalates are detoxified during digestion, particularly in ruminants, but if eaten in large enough quantities they may be absorbed into the blood, where they combine with blood calcium, forming calcium oxalate and causing calcium deficiency (hypocalcaemia). Acute hypocalcaemia can lead to rapid death, but this is unusual. Disturbance of calcium metabolism can interfere with bone formation and milk production in pregnant and lactating animals. The most common effect of oxalate poisoning is accumulation of calcium oxalate crystals in the kidneys, where some tubules may become completely blocked, causing renal failure. Oxalate crystals may form in the brain, causing disorders of the central nervous system and sometimes paralysis, or in the rumen where haemorrhages of the walls may occur.

Most reported cases of poisoning have involved sheep. An outbreak in New Zealand[10] (now attributed to *Rumex acetosella* and not, as originally reported, to *Rumex acetosa,* which is rare in that country) resulted, in one flock, in the death of 10% of the ewes whereas their 5-8 week old lambs were unaffected. In other similar outbreaks, 10% of a flock of 240 sheep died, and 25% of another flock of 800 were affected. Clinical signs included staggering and, in severe cases, falling and inability to rise. Some animals developed a nasal discharge and all had muscular spasms and abnormal breathing. Coma usually preceded death. Post-mortem examination revealed oxalate crystals and inflammation of the kidneys. In an outbreak in Britain,[11] five sheep died, and many others in the flock of 90 became ill after being allowed access to a field where a dense crop of sorrel *(Rumex acetosa)* had grown up after seeding with grass had failed. The symptoms included loss of muscular coordination, falling and inability to rise, frothing at the mouth, dilated pupils and coma. The severity of the reaction was attributed to the animals having eaten a large quantity of sorrel in a short period. In cattle, reports on the effects of eating sorrel are inconsistent. Experimental feeding of housed bullocks[12] with up to 100 kg of sorrel over a six-week period had no adverse effects. Other bullocks, which had previously been pastured, ate sorrel reluctantly. In lactating ewes and cattle the initial signs of oxalate poisoning resemble milk fever, and there may be a favourable response to calcium injection (the standard treatment for milk fever), but this response is only transient, as kidney failure develops later.

Early literature[13] records poisoning in horses, as well as sheep, as a result of eating *Rumex acetosella.* The signs were similar to those already described for sheep, but also included a slow, feeble pulse, sunken eyes and periods of quiescence followed by redevelopment of the clinical signs.

Chickens are said to be resistant to oxalate poisoning because of the high calcium content of their intestines.

Rhubarb *Rheum rhaponticum*

Medicinal use of the rhizomes of rhubarb has been recorded for thousands of years; the reddish leaf stalks are eaten after cooking, but the large blades of the leaf are poisonous.

Poisonous principles   All parts of the plant, but particularly the green part of the leaves, contain oxalates (usually of calcium or potassium); these are irritant poisons. There is, however, some doubt that the oxalates are the main toxic constituents of rhubarb. Anthraquinone glycosides present may be at least partly responsible.

Poisoning in animals   Animals rarely have access to the plant, but can be poisoned by it. A goat which ate rhubarb leaves stood with outspread legs, protruding eyes and an open mouth. The animal was foaming at the mouth, and crying and produced sour-smelling green vomit and profuse diarrhoea.[14] A sow which ate rhubarb leaves thereafter refused all other food and died two days later.[15] Post-mortem examination revealed severe inflammation of the stomach and intestines which contained decaying leaves, and smelled strongly of rhubarb. In the USA, nine pigs were poisoned after eating a wheelbarrow full of rhubarb leaves thrown to them as feed.[16] They foamed at the mouth, staggered and died in convulsions 3-4 hours after the first clinical signs. On another farm, the death of a cow under similar circumstances was reported; fowls have been poisoned in Australia.

Human poisoning   Many cases of poisoning and some fatalities have resulted from eating cooked green leaves of rhubarb as a vegetable.[17] [18] This practice was even recommended in Britain during the 1914-18 war, when food was scarce. As with many other poisonous plants, the amount eaten which causes poisoning varies in different individuals. The rhubarb leaves eaten in one fatal case[19] contained only 1.3 g oxalic acid per kg, whereas 5 or 6 times this concentration is considered a fatal dose. Symptoms often begin within an hour of eating the leaves and include cramp-like abdominal pains, nausea, vomiting, weakness and drowsiness; blood clotting is reduced. There may be muscular twitching and convulsions. A woman in early pregnancy aborted before dying from poisoning.[17] More recently, two children who ate raw rhubarb leaves and stalks (20-100 g) developed vomiting and jaundice. There was liver and kidney damage. In these and other cases[20] it has been thought that the toxic reaction was due to anthraquinone glycosides rather than oxalates. Analysis of the urine for the presence of oxalate crystals may help in the diagnosis of poisoning.

There are occasional reports of other members of the Polygonaceae having caused poisoning abroad, but cases have rarely been recorded in Britain, although some of the plants are native to this country. They include wireweed or common knotgrass *(Polygonum aviculare)*, water pepper *(Polygonum hydropiper)* and persicaria or redshank *(Polygonum persicaria)*. The plants contain a sharp, acrid juice which is irritant to the skin and, if eaten, they cause gastrointestinal irritation and inflammation.[21]

Outbreaks of suspected nitrite poisoning by *Polygonum aviculare* occurred in horses in Australia.[22] The animals, which were observed eating the plant when other pasture plants were scarce, were found lying down unable to rise and with abrasions on their sides acquired by struggling. Some of the animals died. In Britain, a goat died after eating *Polygonum cuspidatum*.[23]

PRIMULACEAE

Scarlet Pimpernel *Anagallis arvensis*

Other common names: Shepherd's Weatherglass; Poor Man's Weatherglass

This small annual or perennial plant is widely distributed throughout Britain, although less common than formerly as a weed of cultivation. It usually lies loosely on the surface of the ground, but some branches are erect. The four-angled, much branched stems grow up to 30 cm long and bear small (usually less than 2 cm) paired, stalkless leaves which are oval, but pointed at the tip. The flowers appear on slender stalks from the leaf axils from mid to late summer and are 10-15 mm across. They are bright orange-red (rarely pink or blue) and have usually five minutely toothed lobes, giving a star-like appearance. The fruit is a brown, three-angled capsule about 5 mm across.

Poisonous principles

The nature of these is uncertain, although scarlet pimpernel has a long-standing reputation for being poisonous. Aerial parts of the plant are said to contain a glycosidal saponin, the roots another saponin (cyclamin), and an acrid volatile oil has also been isolated. It appears that the plants are poisonous only for limited periods and under certain unknown conditions, so that it is not surprising that there are conflicting reports on their toxicity. There are, however, sufficient authenticated reports of field cases and feeding experiments to warrant treating the plant as poisonous.

Poisoning in animals

Early literature states that scarlet pimpernel irritates the intestines and stupefies the nervous system.[1] The plant is reported to produce gastrointestinal symptoms in the dog and horse, to be toxic to poultry and rabbits and (the seed) to birds.[2] An outbreak in Pennsylvania of poisoning, in which six calves died, was attributed to scarlet pimpernel which was exposed and heavily grazed when the grass in the pasture had been eaten low.[3] In Iraq, horses and mules suffered severe anaemia, listlessness and debility[4] when, owing to lack of rain, their normal food was in short supply and was supplemented with plant material collected by hand and containing a large quantity of scarlet pimpernel. Respiration was shallow, the pulse weak and faeces varied from normal to loose. Dark coloured froth formed during urination. Recovery was slow, but complete, in animals given vitamins, iron and a change of straw. Most other reports involve sheep. In one case in Australia,[5] sheep, pastured on land where a prolific growth (90%) of pimpernel had followed ploughing, developed diarrhoea. Rumination was suppressed and the animals were weak, staggered when forced to move and some became recumbent and died. Samples of *Anagallis* from this pasture were taken at intervals of 2-3 weeks and fed experimentally to sheep. On the first occasion fatal poisoning developed, but there was evidence of decreasing toxicity in successive samples. The results were similar with fresh or dried plants. More recently in South Africa,[6] poisoning of sheep, all of which died, was attributed to *Anagallis arvensis* after other sheep had been fed experimentally with the plant and developed the same clinical signs. These included difficult breathing, depression, stiffness of gait, leg weakness, recumbency and, in the terminal stages, coma and a rapid drop in body temperature. Typical post-mortem lesions are haemorrhage of the kidneys, heart and intestines and congestion of the lungs and liver.

Human poisoning Contact with the leaves of this plant and many others in the family can cause dermatitis in man.[7]

RANUNCULACEAE

Because of their abundance and widespread distribution in pastures in Britain, the buttercups, crowfoots and spearworts are the members of the Ranunculaceae most likely to cause poisoning in this country. In general, grazing animals reject these plants because of their acrid taste, but when other food is scarce or when young animals (particularly calves) are first turned out to pasture they tend to overeat them. Under such conditions some animals may develop a taste for the plants and continue to eat them, even deliberately choosing them when other food is available.

Poisonous principles Those present in plants of the Ranunculaceae family are of three kinds: a volatile, oily, irritant substance, protoanemonin[1] [2] (which is a product of hydrolysis of the toxic glycoside ranunculin, present in the plant), various alkaloids and glycosides.

PROTOANEMONIN GROUP

Species of *Anemone, Caltha, Clematis* and *Ranunculus* contain protoanemonin or (in the plants whose poisonous constituents have not been studied in detail) a substance which is probably protoanemonin and which has the same toxic effects.

Wood Anemone *Anemone nemorosa* (photo 32)

This plant grows throughout Britain and is often abundant, especially as a ground cover plant in deciduous woodland, except on water-logged soils. Wood anemones are perennials with slender, brown rhizomes from which the basal leaves grow after flowering. The basal leaves have three rounded lobes which are further subdivided. Three other leaves grow in a single ring on the otherwise naked flower stalk. These leaves appear to be more numerous, because of their subdivision into smaller lobes. The flowers, which appear in early spring, have usually 6-7 white or pinkish-white petal-like segments. They are 2-4 cm across and are borne singly at the top of the stalk. The seeds form in a downy, globular cluster of fruits.

Animals may eat wood anemones during early spring when other green food is scarce.

Pasque Flower *Anemone pulsatilla*

This local plant of dry, calcareous soils is, regrettably, becoming rare in Britain, partly as a result of its being dug up and replanted in gardens because of its attractive pendulous dull violet or purple bell-shaped flowers.

Young cattle in Yugoslavia were poisoned by eating *Anemone pulsatilla* and meadow buttercup *(Ranunculus acris)*.[4]

Kingcup *Caltha palustris*

Other common name: Marsh Marigold (this plant is not related to other marigolds which are members of the Compositae family).

This plant is common in wet areas throughout Britain, often forming luxuriant growth in partial shade. The form of the plant is variable, so that precise details and dimensions of its parts cannot be given. Most of the leaves grow on stalks from the base of the plant. They are smooth, bright green and shaped like broad hearts with an elongated point at the tip. The edges are variably toothed. The flowers are borne in early summer on hollow, erect or prostrate stems which may grow up to 30 cm high. The flower consists of 5-8 petal-like segments which are golden-yellow above and often greenish beneath. There may be up to 100 yellow stamens in the centre of the flower. The fruits in the seed head split open as they dry.

Traveller's Joy *Clematis vitalba* (photo 33)

Other common name: Old Man's Beard

This perennial plant is a rampant climber with stems up to 30 m long, often completely obscuring the vegetation over which it climbs. The stems are woody and up to 10 cm in diameter at the base, where they twine strongly round each other or around other trees and shrubs. Longitudinal splitting of the bark, often with peeling, is a characteristic feature. The leaves are compound and have 3-5 stalked leaflets which are oval but pointed at the tip. The fragrant flowers are borne at ends of the stems or in the axils of the leaves in loose, stalked clusters. They are up to 2 cm in diameter and have greenish-white petal-like sepals. The fruits (achenes) form in large heads and have long, whitish, feathery plumes that form the hairy mass from which the plant derives its name of old man's beard.

All parts of the plant are said to be poisonous and the sap can cause blistering of the skin. Animals rarely eat this plant because of its acrid taste and its irritant effect on the mouth. If it is eaten, it causes gastrointestinal irritation and severe abdominal pain; death may result.[5] Numerous fragments of leaves and stems of *Clematis alba* were recovered at post-mortem examination of a cow which died a few hours after first showing symptoms.[6] Before death the animal was breathing noisily and had inflamed, swollen eyes, ulceration of the muzzle, loss of muscle tone, abdominal pain and weakness.

Meadow Buttercup *Ranunculus acris*

Other common names: Common Buttercup; Field Buttercup; Tall Buttercup; Crowfoot

This much branched, hairy perennial plant is widespread in pastures and damp meadows throughout Britain except on acid soils. The stems are erect or may creep along the ground but do not form roots. The basal leaves have long stalks and the upper ones short stalks. The leaf blades are hairy and deeply divided into 2-7 lobes which are themselves deeply indented and toothed. The flower stalks are also hairy, and may be 15-100 cm tall, depending on the nature of the soil. They terminate in loose, irregular clusters of flowers up to 25 mm across. The petals are rounded, glossy and bright yellow (occasionally pale yellow or white); the sepals are close to the petals and not turned back; the seeds develop singly in small (2.5-3 mm) fruits (achenes) which are smooth, have a short hooked beak and are tightly grouped together.

Ranunculus acris is reputed to cause poisoning in cattle and sheep, but when fed at the flowering stage to cattle in increasing amounts up to 25 kg per day for two weeks, the animals gained weight and showed no ill effects, although initially they were reluctant to eat the plant.[7] In other experiments,[8] steers fed an average of 7 kg and sheep 3.5 kg of the green plant daily were unaffected. In Yugoslavia, five cattle on a pasture where *Ranunculus acris* and pasque flower *(Anemone pulsatilla)* were prevalent, developed chocolate-coloured diarrhoea, blood-stained urine and decreased body temperature.[4] Paralysis of a pig after eating the plant is reported.[9] Severe swelling of the eyes, nose, muzzle and lips developed in a dog which ate the plant; leaves, stems and flowers were seen in vomit.[10]

Bulbous Buttercup *Ranunculus bulbosus*

Other common name: St. Anthony's Turnip

This perennial, hairy plant occurs throughout Britain in dry pastures, grassy slopes and garden lawns, but is less common in the north. It grows from a rounded or flattened stem tuber which bears fleshy roots. The stems are usually erect up to 40 cm high (usually shorter) and bear deeply cut, three-lobed leaves of which the central lobe is long-stalked. The flowers are 1.5-3 cm in diameter and develop in loose clusters on hairy, furrowed stems. The petals are bright yellow (rarely pale yellow or white) and the sepals turn back against the stem. The single-seeded fruits (achenes), which are tightly grouped together, are finely pitted, dark brown with a paler border and have a short beak at the tip.

This species was suspected of poisoning a cow in Britain.[11] The animal salivated and coughed and there was a mucous discharge from the nostrils. Swaying of the hindquarters and uneasy movements of the legs were noticed. A period of noisy breathing preceded recovery.

The bulbous base of the plant has caused human poisoning, particularly in children, when eaten in mistake for the edible underground parts of other plants.[5]

Lesser Celandine *Ranunculus ficaria*

Other common name: Pilewort

This ground cover plant is common throughout Britain in moist areas, often in woodland. The heart-shaped leaves are stalked, shiny, dark green and somewhat fleshy; some have a small bulbil in the axil. They grow on the flowering stems and also form a rosette at the base of the plant where there are fibrous roots and a cluster of characteristic elongated whitish root tubers up to 2.5 cm long. The flowers form in early spring and are borne singly on erect stems up to 15 cm high. They are 2-3 cm in diameter, have oval petals with pointed tips and are bright yellow, becoming paler with age. The single-seeded fruits (achenes) often abort, but those which remain are slightly downy, more or less spherical with a single narrow ridge (keel). A fairly common subspecies *(Ranunculus ficaria* ssp. *ficaria),* found especially in sunnier areas, has no axillary bulbils and broader, overlapping petals.

Lesser celandine is known to have poisoned sheep and cattle,[5] though there is no recent report of poisoning.

Lesser Spearwort *Ranunculus flammula*

This plant is common in marshes, wet pastures and beside streams throughout Britain. It is a perennial with hollow, erect or creeping stems which grow up to 80 cm high and may root at nodes near the base. The lower leaves are stalked and generally oval with pointed tips while the upper ones have short stalks and grow up to 15 cm long, being more elongated and pointed. All of the leaves have parallel veins and smooth or slightly toothed edges. The flowers are borne in summer on slightly hairy stalks singly or a few together in a loose cluster. The petals are pale yellow and glossy and the sepals yellowish-green. The fruits (achenes) develop in a globular head, are 1-2 mm long, oval with a blunt beak at the tip and a minutely pitted surface.

This species has caused poisoning in sheep and cattle.[5]

Celery-leaved Crowfoot *Ranunculus sceleratus*

Other common names: Celery-leaved Buttercup; Cursed Crowfoot

This plant is generally an annual although it occasionally survives a winter. It grows throughout Britain, usually in muddy places beside shallow water. The plant has fibrous roots and a stout, erect, hollow stem which grows up to 60 cm high and is hollow and branched. The lower leaves have long stalks with three deeply segmented, toothed lobes near the top, giving them a superficial resemblance to edible celery, although the stalks are thinner. The stem leaves have short stalks and are divided into narrower segments. The flower stalks are smooth, furrowed and branched and bear loose clusters of flowers with pale yellow petals and greenish sepals of almost equal size. The single-seeded fruits (achenes) are numerous, about 1 mm across and crowded together in a tight oval group.

This is reputed to be the most poisonous *Ranunculus* species, but it may be that because of its rich, luxuriant growth it is eaten in larger quantities than other species. All classes of livestock are susceptible, but poisoning is reported most frequently in cattle.[12][13] Severe blistering of the mouth was seen in housed goats fed *Ranunculus acris* and *Ranunculus sceleratus*. One animal died and two others were severely ill.[5] On a pasture consisting mainly of *Ranunculus acris* and *Ranunculus sceleratus* a horse developed paralysis, muscle tremors, colic and convulsions; there was also loss of hearing and sight. Recovery occurred in a few days but general weakness persisted for two weeks.[14]

Creeping buttercup *(Ranunculus repens)* is common in Britain, whereas greater spearwort *(Ranunculus lingua)*, globe flower *(Trollius)*, meadow rue *(Thalictrum* spp.*)* and pheasant's eye *(Adonis annua)* have a limited distribution. None of these have been recorded as having caused poisoning in Britain, but as they contain protoanemonin, or a similar substance, they should be regarded as potentially toxic.

Poisonous principle

Protoanemonin is present in variable amounts,[3] and is at its highest concentration during flowering. It is an unstable compound, readily converted by polymerisation into an inert, non-toxic crystalline substance, anemonin. This occurs during drying of the plant, so that hay containing buttercups (or other plants of the Ranunculaceae family which contain protoanemonin) is safe to use for animal feeding.

Poisoning in animals

The clinical signs of protoanemonin poisoning are similar in all animal species. In the early stages, salivation, inflammation of the mouth and abdominal pain occur. They may be followed by severe ulceration of the mouth and damage to the digestive and urinary systems. Dark coloured diarrhoea and dark or blood-stained urine are produced and at this stage the animals have an unsteady gait, particularly of the hind legs; vision is often impaired or lost. Convulsions usually precede death, although fatal poisoning is rare. The *Ranunculus* species that occur in pastures can be eradicated by the use of hormone weedkillers such as 2,4-dinitrophenylhydrazine (2,4-D). It is recommended that treated areas should not be grazed for at least 14 days after application because, after treatment, the plants are consumed readily by animals even if they were not grazed before.[15] This may be due to loss of a selective instinct on the part of the animal, increased palatability of the plant during growth disturbances caused by the chemicals, or the development of a taste for the weedkiller itself.

Human poisoning

Ingestion of species containing protoanemonin and related compounds by adults and children has caused few problems in Britain, presumably because they have an acrid taste and cause burning in the mouth and throat. Other symptoms may include abdominal pain and diarrhoea. Emesis and stomach lavage are not usually necessary; demulcents should be given to soothe the digestive tract.

ALKALOID GROUP

Monkshood *(Aconitum napellus)*, columbine *(Aquilegia)* and larkspur *(Delphinium)* contain toxic alkaloids.

Monkshood *Aconitum napellus* (photo 31)

Other common names: Aconite; Wolfsbane

According to most authorities *Aconitum napellus* is an aggregate of forms varying in morphological detail in different ecological and geographical areas. The form most often encountered in Britain is *Aconitum anglicum*. Wild aconites are now seldom found in Britain except in a few localised areas of south-west England and Wales, usually beside streams, in the shade. Many forms of aconite are cultivated in gardens throughout the country and in some areas these have become naturalised.

Monkshood is a perennial plant with a dark, tuberous tap root and a usually unbranched stem up to 100 cm high. The leaves are light green, soft and more or less triangular in outline, but deeply and irregularly divided into narrow pointed segments. The flowers form in a terminal spike and are blue or bluish mauve and helmet-shaped. The fruits usually form in a close group of three elongated follicles, up to 2 cm long, and contain seeds with winged edges.

Poisonous principles

The plant contains the alkaloid aconitine; other similar alkaloids including isoaconitine, lycaconitine and napelline are also present. Because of the highly toxic nature of aconitine, monkshood has the reputation of being the most poisonous British plant. Despite this, or perhaps because its poisonous nature is so well known that it has been removed from places where animals could eat it, there are very few reports of poisoning by the plant. It is thought that, in the USA, some cases of

30

30   Sheep's Sorrel (*Rumex acetosella*)
HCB

31   Monkshood (*Aconitum napellus*)
JH

32   Wood Anemone (*Anemone nemorosa*)
JH

31   32

33a

33b

33 Traveller's Joy (*Clematis vitalba*) (a) flowers
(b) fruit
HCB

34 Cherry Laurel (*Prunus laurocerasus*). The ripe
berries are black.
HCB

35 Deadly Nightshade (*Atropa bella-donna*).
HCB

36 Foxglove (*Digitalis purpurea*)
HCB

34   35   36

poisoning attributed to aconites were due to ingestion of the closely related larkspurs *(Delphinium* spp.), which are much more common plants. The alkaloid content varies according to the part of the plant examined, the stage of growth and the growing conditions.

Poisoning in animals

The aconite alkaloids are toxic either by ingestion or, to a lesser extent, by absorption through the skin. The effect is at first stimulatory, with rapid breathing and excitation of heart muscles, but soon becomes depressive, with numbness progressing to paralysis, slow laboured breathing and low, irregular pulse.[16][17] Death, which may occur within an hour of eating the plant, results from asphyxia and circulatory failure and is usually sudden. A fatal dose of dried root of the plant has been estimated as 5 g for the dog and 350 g for the horse.[17] Cattle which had eaten considerable quantities (an estimated 5 kg each) of delphiniums and monkshood discarded from a garden showed little evidence of pain, but were unable to rise, and had cold skin, dilated pupils and very feeble breathing and pulse. Despite attempts to save the two animals they both died within five hours. Post-mortem examination revealed the plants in the stomach, changes in the heart and lungs consistent with suffocation but little damage to the digestive system.[5] Cases of poisoning in horses and in man have been described in early literature.[18]

Human poisoning

Burning of the mouth and throat, abdominal pain, vomiting accompanied by intense thirst, headache, coldness, slow pulse, paralysis, convulsions, delirium and coma have been reported.[18][19] Cases of fatal human poisoning have resulted from aconite roots being eaten in mistake for horse radish.

Treatment

There is no specific antidote for aconite poisoning. Stomach lavage, warmth, oxygen to assist breathing and drugs to stimulate the heart may be beneficial.

Larkspur *Delphinium* spp

Larkspur is not a native plant in Britain, but some species have been introduced and become established locally, and many annual and hybrid perennials (delphiniums) are cultivated throughout the country. Although there is considerable variation in the size and form of *Delphinium* species, they closely resemble monkshood but are generally larger; the elongated spur on the flowers is a distinguishing feature. As in monkshood, the flowers are usually blue, but many shades of the colour are found and some are white or mauvish-red.

Poisonous principles All species of *Delphinium* are poisonous, as they contain alkaloids similar to the aconitines. The most frequently named are delphinine and ajacine or ajaconine. Methyllycaconitine has been isolated from *Delphinium brownii* (not a British species). The concentration of toxic alkaloids is highest in young plants and in the seeds.[16]

Poisoning in animals *Delphinium* poisoning causes severe and often fatal illness, with symptoms similar to those produced by the aconite alkaloids, but it is unlikely that animals will be poisoned by *Delphinium* in Britain unless they have access to gardens or garden rubbish containing the plants. Cattle in particular will consume the plants readily if they are available, and in North America[20] where larkspur (mainly tall larkspur, *Delphinium barbeyi)* is well established, especially in the Western Ranges,[21] it is considered the most dangerous plant in the area and is responsible for many deaths. The injection of calves with methyllycaconitine has caused agitation, difficult breathing and incoordination;[22] an effective treatment was the intravenous injection of physostigmine (0.08 mg/kg body weight). In New Zealand, poisoning of rams occurred after eating *Delphinium hybridum* which had been thrown to them from a garden.[23] Of 16 rams which ate the plants, eight died within a few hours with symptoms including incoordination, violent muscular spasms, particularly of the hind limbs, and inability to rise. An earlier outbreak of poisoning of sheep due to eating *Delphinium consolidum*[24] occurred in New Zealand. The symptoms were similar to those described in the rams. Spraying of the plants with weedkillers appears to increase their toxicity[20] and palatability.[21]

Human poisoning This is an unlikely occurrence, but a man who ingested an unknown number of leaves and seeds of delphinium developed symptoms five hours later.[25] These included nausea, vomiting, abdominal pain, blurred vision and dry skin and mouth. Restlessness, agitation and dilation of pupils persisted for 12 hours, after which full recovery occurred.

Columbine *Aquilegia vulgaris*

Although a native plant, columbine occurs only locally in Britain in shady woods, on calcareous soils or peaty fens. Many other species and hybrids are grown in gardens. As the plants contain alkaloids similar to those of the aconites, they are potentially toxic, but no cases are recorded of their having caused poisoning.

GLYCOSIDE GROUP

Plants in the *Helleborus* genus contain glycosides.

Hellebores *Helleborus* spp

There is confusion over the common names of these plants as some species of *Veratrum* (Liliaceae) are called false, or white hellebore or simply hellebore. *Veratrum* spp. are also poisonous plants but do not occur in Britain.

In Britain the native species are *Helleborus foetidus* and *Helleborus viridis*. Both plants are restricted to calcareous soils and are local in distribution. These two plants, subspecies of them and also Christmas and Easter or Lent roses *(Helleborus niger)* and their numerous hybrids are grown in gardens throughout the country.

Stinking Hellebore *Helleborus foetidus*

Other common name: Bear's Foot

This perennial plant has a robust branched, overwintering stem which grows up to 80 cm high and bears stalked leaves, the bases of which sheath the stem. The leaves are light green and tough, and are divided into long narrow segments with toothed edges. The flowers develop in spring in loose clusters. They are drooping, 1-3 cm across and have insignificant petals but prominent yellowish-green, incurved, petal-like sepals tinged reddish-purple at the tips. The fruits are 2-5 carpels which are slightly joined near the base and bear the persistent styles of the flower above. They contain smooth, black seeds with a white fleshy ridge.

Green Hellebore *Helleborus viridis*

Other common name: Bear's Foot

This perennial plant is similar to the stinking hellebore but is shorter, does not have an overwintering stem, has leaves which are shorter and less prominently toothed, and uniformly yellowish-green flowers which open wide when mature.

Christmas and Easter Rose *Helleborus niger*

This plant is sometimes, incorrectly, named *Veratrum nigrum*. The plants in this groups are variable in form, but in general the leaf segments are wider and more coarsely toothed than those of the wild species, and the petal-like sepals of the flower may be white, pinkish or uniformly dark reddish-purple.

Poisonous principles
These are glycosides, with various names including helleborin(e), helleborein(e) and helleborigenin(e). Their toxicity remains after drying and storage.

Poisoning in animals
Both in animals and man this occurred formerly when decoctions of hellebores were used as purgatives, local anaesthetics or abortives or to clear parasitic infestations on the skin. It is not clear whether poisoning by application to the skin took place by skin absorption or whether the animals may have licked the treated areas. It is now more likely that poisoning will occur after animals have had access to growing or discarded garden plants.

When applied to the neck of cattle to remove lice, a preparation of green hellebore resulted in prostration, loss of appetite, cessation of rumination and swelling of the neck. Loss of condition of the coat, muscular tremors and difficult breathing were also reported.[26] Bullocks which had eaten green hellebore plants discarded from a garden developed abdominal pain, fluid faeces and moved with great reluctance.[27] Some animals died within 2-3 days and others after 10-11 days. A slow, irregular pulse, convulsions and coma sometimes precede death.[28] Dark coloured diarrhoea containing blood and mucus, violent straining alternating with quiet periods, and excessive, frequent urination have also been recorded in cattle and sheep.[5] Post-mortem examination reveals inflammation of the digestive tract, sometimes with ulceration. Haemorrhages occur in the intestines and around the heart.

Human poisoning
This is now rare, since medicinal use of hellebores has been abandoned because of the risks, but disturbance of vision and abortion occurred in a pregnant woman who used a decoction of hellebores to remove lice.[26] Drinking milk from poisoned cows has caused diarrhoea and vomiting.[5]

Treatment
There is no specific antidote, but treatment of hellebore poisoning should include administration of demulcents to retard intestinal irritation. Sedatives may be needed to control convulsions.

Baneberry *(Actaea spicata)*

Other common name: Herb Christopher

This native local plant that bears small, black berries, is limited in its distribution to limestone soils of northern England. *Actaea* is reputed to be poisonous, although little is known of the toxic principle. Symptoms including digestive system disturbances and delirium can result from eating the plant.[5]

RHAMNACEAE

Buckthorn *Rhamnus cathartica*

Other common names: Purging Buckthorn; Common Buckthorn

This thorny, deciduous shrub is usually 4-6 m tall and is a native of Britain where it grows mainly on calcareous soils. The branches are opposite and grow almost at right angles to the main stem. The old bark is fissured and scaly, with an orange blaze. The buds have dark scales and from them develop stalked, dull green leaves which turn yellow or brownish in autumn. They are oval, with prominent veins and small, regular serrations at the edges. The male and female flowers, which appear from early to mid summer, are borne on separate plants. They are small, inconspicuous and yellowish-green. The fruit is a 3-4 seeded berry which changes from green to black as it ripens.

Alder Buckthorn *Frangula alnus*

This shrub (formerly named *Rhamnus frangula)* grows on damp, peaty soils in many parts of Britain, but is absent from Scotland. It is commonly 4-5 m high, has no thorns, and the branches grow upwards at an acute angle to the main stem. Except in very old trees the bark is smooth. The buds have no scales but are covered with brownish hairs. The shiny, green, stalked leaves, which turn yellow or red in autumn, are oval with a pointed tip and not toothed. Small, whitish-green bisexual flowers develop in groups of two or three throughout the summer. The fruits are berries which change from green to red and then purplish-black as they ripen.

Poisonous principles Both of these shrubs contain glycosides which, on hydrolysis, yield purgative anthraquinones. Of these, emodin (a trihydroxymethylanthraquinone) is the active principle of some purgative drugs, such as the common laxative, cascara sagrada, which is derived from the dried bark of *Rhamnus purshiana*.

Poisoning in animals In dogs, overdosing with a laxative prepared from *Rhamnus cathartica* has caused illness and death, with severe gastrointestinal haemorrhages.[1] Poisoning by the growing plants is rare, but a fatal case is reported in a cow[2] which ate a large amount of leaves, twigs and berries of *Frangula alnus*. The animal became ill suddenly and developed diarrhoea, vomiting, cramps, slow pulse and slight fever before death, which occurred within a few hours of eating the plant. Post-mortem examination revealed leaves of the shrub in the stomach, and gastrointestinal inflammation.

Human poisoning In the past, this has sometimes followed the medicinal use by adults of buckthorn as a laxative or abortive, but now most frequently involves only children, who eat the berries or chew the twigs. The symptoms are usually mild and limited to transient abdominal pain with vomiting and diarrhoea, but, depending on the quantity eaten, there may be violent haemorrhagic, gastrointestinal symptoms accompanied by fluid depletion and kidney damage; muscular convulsions, difficult breathing and collapse may occur.[3] [4]

Treatment should include the induction of vomiting (with a suitable emetic such as syrup of ipecacuanha) if this has not already occurred, or stomach lavage (for adults), after which fluids and demulcents should be given.[5]

ROSACEAE

This family includes many common fruit trees (grown commercially or in gardens) such as apple *(Pyrus malus)*, pear *(Pyrus communis)*, cherry *(Prunus cerasus)*, peach *(Prunus persica)* and plum *(Prunus domestica)*, blackthorn or sloe *(Prunus spinosa)* which grows wild in Britain, almond *(Amygdalus communis)*, various ornamental shrubs, and cherry laurel *(Prunus laurocerasus)*. In this country, cherry laurel is the most likely of these to cause poisoning.

Cherry Laurel *Prunus laurocerasus* (photo 34)

The name of this plant sometimes causes confusion with the plant commonly called laurel or bay *(Laurus nobilis),* which is a member of the Lauraceae family, and with spurge laurel *(Daphne laureola),* a member of the Thymeleaceae.

Cherry laurel is not native in Britain, but has become naturalised in many places and grows as an evergreen shrub or small tree, up to 6 m high. It is commonly found in parks or gardens, where it is often used for hedging. The bark is dark and fairly smooth and the leaves elongated (up to 18 cm long), narrowing to a rounded point at the tip. They are leathery, dark green and glossy above and have stalks 5-10 cm long. The white or creamy-white flowers are borne in erect clusters. The fruits are single-seeded, purplish-black ovoid berries up to 1 cm long. There are several cultivated forms with different growth habits, leaf sizes and colours.

Poisonous principles   The kernels in the seeds of fruits of this family and the leaves of some (including cherry laurel) contain cyanogenic glycosides. The most common of these is amygdalin, but others, including prunasin, are also found. The glycosides yield hydrocyanic acid when hydrolysed by the appropriate enzymes in crushed plant material or, in some circumstances, in the digestive system. During hydrolysis, glucose and benzaldehyde are also produced, the latter being responsible for the almond smell of the stomach contents and tissues of poisoned animals. Hydrocyanic acid inactivates cellular respiratory enzymes (cytochrome oxidases), and it is oxygen starvation of the central nervous system that causes death. The toxic reaction depends not only on the cyanogenic glycoside content of the plants, which may vary (concentration higher in young plants and during summer), but also on the amount ingested, the rate of digestion, the degree of maceration of the plant tissue, the size and type of animal, and its ability to detoxify hydrocyanic acid.[1] The cyanogenic properties of cherry laurel have been known for many years and sometimes exploited, e.g. by amateur entomologists, who have killed insects by placing them in a closed vessel containing crushed leaves of the plant.

Poisoning in animals   All animals are susceptible to cyanide poisoning. The minimum lethal dose of hydrocyanic acid in most species is 2 mg/kg body weight.[2] It has been stated that, in cattle, 1 kg of cherry laurel leaves would be sufficient to kill a 500 kg animal.[3] Ruminants are more susceptible than monogastric animal (e.g. horse, pig, dog) to poisoning with cyanogenic plants, as hydrolysis of the glycosides, resulting in hydrocyanic acid production, can also occur in the rumen, where the pH is favourable for the activity of the hydrolysing enzyme. In non-ruminants, the high acidity of the stomach contents inhibits the plant enzymes, although these may be active during further digestion in the duodenum. The situation is somewhat complicated by the fact that, as well as being more susceptible, ruminants like other animals) can also detoxify hydrocyanic acid, converting it to non-toxic thiocyanate by the action of the enzyme rhodanese.[1] The severity of poisoning is therefore determined by many factors.

In acute poisoning, animals may die suddenly, but in less severe cases the clinical signs[3][4] include respiratory difficulties, dilated pupils, muscular tremors, distension of the abdomen with gas (particularly in cattle), falling and sometimes convulsions. Visible mucous membranes are bright red initially, because oxygen from the blood is not being transferred to the tissues.

In one well documented case,[5] two ewes were found dead and a number of others became ill after grazing in a public park in Scotland. The pasture was poor, and the sheep had free access to a hedge of cherry laurel. The clinical signs were characteristic of cyanide poisoning and included breathing difficulties, jerky movements, staggering, and in some cases falling and convulsions. The severity of the reaction varied between animals, but in all cases lasted for no longer than a few minutes at a time, after which the signs abated rapidly. They recurred, however, at irregular intervals throughout the flock for five days, when all the animals were slaughtered. It was suggested that the repeated attacks occurred with successive regurgitation and mastication of rumen contents. Post-mortem examination did not reveal any definite lesions, but portions of cherry laurel leaves, in various stages of maceration, were found in the rumen of some of the ewes. In a follow-up experiment,[6] a sheep given 115 g of minced cherry laurel leaves in water showed increased respiration, followed by collapse, grinding of teeth, salivation and attempts to vomit, twitching of facial muscles and galloping movements of the limbs; death occurred one and a half hours later. This sheep was apparently unaffected when fed previously with 100 g of the leaves.

Stones from the fruit of some members of the Rosaceae have also been known to poison animals. In one outbreak, 18 pigs died after feeding on plum stones left after jam or fruit juice preparation.[7] In Norway when, after a heavy crop, plums were added to feed given to bacon pigs,[8] a very distinct almond taste was noticed in the meat, irrespective of the method of preserving or cooking. Cattle have been poisoned by eating cherry leaves,[9] plum stones[10] or bitter almonds.[11]

Post-mortem examination Little evidence of poisoning will be found, except for plant fragments in the stomach, if death occurred rapidly. In cases where death was delayed, however, the changes (similar in all species) include bright red blood, purplish-blue coloration of organs and tissues (due to lack of oxygen), congestion of the lungs with blood and an almond smell from the stomach contents and, sometimes, from the cut surfaces of other organs.

Human poisoning Cherry laurel poisoning is rare, but can occur if children eat the berries, or if the leaves are used by mistake for those of the 'true' laurel or bay *(Laurus*

206

nobilis) for flavouring food.[3] The kernels of fruits, or almonds are the most likely source of poisoning by members of the Rosaceae in man. The so-called 'sweet' almonds have a lower content of cyanogenic glycosides than 'bitter' almonds. In separate outbreaks in Israel,[12] eight children were poisoned after eating a large number of apricot kernels, and 16 children became seriously ill after eating a dessert prepared from the kernels. Such desserts are common local dishes but prolonged boiling of the kernels is part of the normal preparation, and an acid environment is also maintained, inhibiting the activity of the enzyme that releases hydrocyanic acid. This pre-treatment was omitted in the outbreak reported. In the first incident the symptoms began two hours after the kernels were eaten and included vomiting, distress, faintness, weakness, unsteadiness, rapid breathing, flushed face and headache. One child became comatose and died. In the second incident, symptoms became apparent half an hour after eating the dessert. They were similar but more severe, and three children died. Although apricot kernels are often eaten in some countries, poisoning rarely occurs, possibly because the amygdalin content varies considerably (from 9 to over 200 mg/100 g), the concentration being higher in wild apricots.[12] In a case reported from the USA, a man died of cyanide poisoning after eating a cupful of apple pips.[13] The common practice of adding a few fruit stone kernels to the fruit in jam making should present no hazard, as the prolonged boiling involved and the acidity of the fruit will inhibit the enzymes responsible for releasing hydrocyanic acid.

Treatment This must be initiated quickly as hydrocyanic acid is absorbed readily. Stomach lavage or an emetic (such as syrup of ipecacuanha) should be given. The most effective treatment is intravenous injection of sodium thiosulphate;[3] [4] this combines with hydrocyanic acid forming non-toxic thiocyanate which is excreted readily. Intravenous sodium nitrite[3] [4] helps to induce the formation of methaemoglobin, which combines with hydrocyanic acid to give non-toxic cyanmethaemoglobin. In man the inhalation of amyl nitrate (to dilate blood vessels) is also recommended.[14]

In North America, cyanide poisoning by various cherry trees, particularly the leaves of the wild black cherry *(Prunus serotina)* and the chokecherry *(Prunus virginiana)* cause significant losses of livestock.[15] All parts of these bushes or trees contain prunasin, the concentration being highest in dry years. Higher prunasin levels have been demonstrated in buds and flowers than in fruit;[15] leaves may contain many times the amount considered dangerous. Death, preceded by signs typical of cyanide poisoning, has been reported in three horses and a cow,[16] and a young dog[17] that ate chokecherry leaves. These species of *Prunus,* with high cyanogenic glycoside content, do not occur in Britain except as ornamentals. A two-year-old boy who had eaten five or six berries from an ornamental cherry in this country developed blisters on the tip of his tongue and had flushed cheeks and a rapid pulse.[18]

Hawthorn *(Crataegus monogyna)* was thought to be the cause of urine discoloration[19] in cows that had eaten berries in a year when the crop was very heavy. The urine was normal in colour initially, but changed to orange, then brown on the floor of the milking parlour, and stained the feet of the animals; a temporary drop in milk yield was recorded. The bark of hawthorn contains the toxic lactone glycoside aesculin, but no reports of poisoning from this source have been found.

Other members of the Rosaceae suspected of causing poisoning include *Pyracantha*. An eighteen-month-old boy vomited after eating berries of this plant.[18] It is often assumed that the berries of this and other similar shrubs such as *Cotoneaster* are poisonous, and children who have eaten them are often referred to hospital. These berries are, however, of only doubtful or low toxicity.

SALICACEAE

Willow *Salix* spp

Human poisoning, with severe abdominal pain, has been reported after eating leaves of a willow tree.[1]

SCROPHULARIACEAE

Foxglove *Digitalis purpurea* (photo 36)

The foxglove is widely distributed throughout Britain, particularly in open places in woods and on heaths and hillsides. It is often the dominant plant species at the stage of regeneration of clearings or burnt areas, before shrubs and trees become re-established.

The plant is an erect biennial (occasionally perennial) with a flowering stem up to 150 cm in height. Basal leaves develop in the first year and grow up to 30 cm long. They are coarsely veined, generally oval in shape but tapering to a point at the tip and narrowing towards the short stalk, which is often winged. The underside of the leaves and, to a lesser extent, the upper side and the stem are covered with short, soft hairs, giving the plant a greyish-green appearance. The bracts on the flowering stem are similar to, but smaller than the leaves, the upper ones being the smallest and usually lying close to the stem. The inflorescence matures from mid to late summer as a terminal spike which may bear more than 50 flowers. These are purplish-pink (occasionally white), pendulous, tubular structures, 4-5 cm long. At the opening of the tube there is a projecting lip which is often paler on the inside and usually spotted with purple or brown, the spots sometimes being ringed with white. The fruit is an oval capsule, pointed at the tip, which opens when dry and light brown to reveal the very numerous, tiny, dark brown seeds.

Poisonous principles

Foxglove contains cardiac glycosides variously named as digitoxin, digitalin, digitonin, digitalosmin, gitoxin and gitalonin. During digestion they are split by hydrolysis into a sugar and a non-sugar component (aglycone). The aglycones have a direct influence on the muscles of the heart, this action being potentiated by the glycoside sugar.[1][2] The toxicity of the plant is unaffected by drying, storage or boiling, and hay containing the plant can poison animals.

Poisoning in animals

Foxglove is not usually eaten and there are few reports of poisoning. When food is scarce, animals may eat the plant, and even develop a craving for it after they have been poisoned. A female goat which had become ill after eating foxglove recovered after several days' housing, but when returned to the field, went straight back to the plants and began eating them.[3] Most animals appear to be susceptible to *Digitalis* poisoning, which has been reported in sheep,[4] horses,[3] pigs,[5] goat,[3] deer[3] and turkeys.[6]

Clinical signs of *Digitalis* poisoning, which are basically the same in all species, include diarrhoea, abdominal pain, irregular pulse, tremors and convulsions.[1][2][7]

In Scotland, foxgloves were suspected of poisoning four sheep[4] that died after signs that included dullness, abdominal pain, frequent urination and diarrhoea. The sheep had been sheltering from a storm, behind a bank upon which young foxgloves were growing. Some of the plants appeared to have been eaten. In another case, also in Scotland, two colts on very bare pasture with numerous foxglove plants died after showing clinical signs resembling tetanus, but with very loud heartbeats. Post-mortem examination revealed foxgloves in the stomach.[3] Five of a group of ten pigs died within 24 hours after they had been given feed containing 50-100 g of foxglove leaves.[5] The most prominent post-mortem findings were gastrointestinal inflammation, punctiform necrosis of the border of the spleen and fatty degeneration of some nerve fibres in the heart.

A more detailed account[3] has been given of foxglove poisoning in a herd of farmed deer in Scotland in the winter of 1975-76. One of three hinds and seven of 64 calves died in an enclosure in which foxglove was growing.

Most were found dead, but before death one calf showed a sharp drop in body weight from 36.5 to 30.5 kg over two weeks, and dullness, weakness, a haemorrhagic watery diarrhoea and a slow but strong heartbeat. Sixteen other calves which had lost weight recovered after removal to another pasture. Post-mortem examination of the deer revealed foxglove leaves in the rumen, distension of the heart with clotted blood, and engorged blood vessels in the gastrointestinal tract, liver, kidneys, brain and lymph nodes. Analysis of body tissues by thin layer chromatography showed the presence of digitoxin. There were similar clinical and post-mortem findings in a 13-month-old deer given 60 g of powdered foxglove leaves containing 0.35 mg/g of a digitoxin-like substance.

Human poisoning

The symptoms reported are similar to those in animals and include nausea and gastrointestinal disturbances. Headache often occurs and the heartbeat is irregular; there may be convulsions. Poisoning has occurred in children who have eaten the flowers or drunk water from vases which contained foxgloves.[8] A man who drank tea made from the leaves of foxglove became weak, with increasing nausea and noticed yellow halos around objects. He also had an abnormally fast heartbeat.[9]

Digitalis poisoning (from medicinal preparations) has been suggested as a possible explanation of the halos and predominance of yellow in Vincent van Gogh's late paintings.[10] On two occasions he painted his physician holding a foxglove plant.

Treatment

In general, treatment is symptomatic; stomach lavage or a suitable emetic (such as syrup of ipecacuanha) may be used in man and non-ruminant animals. Poisoned pigs were treated successfully with 1% atropine and 0.3 ml of 1% apomorphine.[5]

Water Betony *Scrophularia aquatica*

Other common name: Water Figwort

This is an erect perennial which grows up to 100 cm high in wet ditches and meadows or beside streams or ponds throughout England and Ireland but is rarely found in Scotland.

The four-angled, winged stems, bear leaves, with winged stalks, in opposite pairs. The leaves have serrated edges, are pointed at the tip and generally oval in shape, although there may be one or two small lobes at the base. The inflorescence is made up of branching stalks which bear, throughout the summer, loose clusters of brownish-purple flowers, with greenish undersides. The flowers are up to 1 cm across, and have a basal rounded tubular portion which opens into five small lobes, the upper two being joined together at the base. The fruit is a more or less spherical, but angled, capsule which contains small, rough, oval seeds.

Poisonous principles The plant contains glycosides which are thought to be responsible for its toxicity.

Poisoning The plant has an unpleasant odour and taste and is not usually eaten by animals. There has, however, been one report of poisoning of young cows. The symptoms were excitement, accelerated respiration, dilated pupils, congested mucous membranes of the mouth with slight ulceration, infrequent and painful urination, profuse dark foetid diarrhoea, thirst, loss of appetite and decreased milk production. Older cows were unaffected. Treatment with purgatives and stimulants resulted in complete recovery within two days.[11]

Other members of the Scrophulariaceae family include toadflax *(Linaria* spp.*),* other figworts *(Scrophularia* spp.*),* lousewort *(Pedicularis* spp.*),* yellow rattles *(Rhinanthus* spp.*)* and cow wheat *(Melampyrum* spp.*).* These also contain poisonous glycosides which could cause illness or death in the unlikely event of animals eating a sufficient quantity of them.

SOLANACEAE

The poisonous species of this family in Britain can be classified according to their poisonous principles: tropane alkaloids in *Atropa bella-donna, Datura stramonium* and *Hyoscyamus niger;* the alkaloids nicotine and anabasine in *Nicotiana tabacum;* the alkaloidal glycoside solanine in *Solanum* species.

Deadly Nightshade *Atropa bella-donna* (photo 35)

Deadly nightshade is native in Britain, in localised areas of woodland and scrub or at the edges of fields, chiefly on calcareous soils in south-east England, but is now rather uncommon. Other members of the Solanaceae family are often wrongly called deadly nightshade or belladonna.

The plant is smooth or slightly hairy with erect, branching stems which grow annually up to 1.5 m high from the perennial, fleshy rootstock. The leaves are borne on short stalks on the stems, sometimes arranged alternately, but more often in pairs of unequal size. They are up to 20 cm long, generally oval in shape but narrowing near the stalk and terminating in a point. The drooping flowers are borne singly on short stalks in the axils of leaves or the fork of branches. They are up to 3 cm long with a basal tubular portion widening into five obtuse lobes. The most common colour for the flowers is a dull brownish purple but they may be a pale bluish purple, violet or have tinges of green. The fruit is a shining black berry with its base partially enclosed by the five pointed lobes of the persistent calyx.

Poisonous principles

Atropa bella-donna contains various tropane alkaloids: hyoscine (also known as scopolamine), atropine and hyoscyamine. The last two are the *dl-*and *l-*tropic acid esters of tropine,[1] [2] respectively. It is difficult to determine accurately the relative amounts of these two stereoisomers present in the living plant, as they are readily converted from one form to another (e.g. by hydrolysis, alkalis or heat), and may be changed during the extraction process. It has been stated that hyoscyamine occurs in the flowers, fruits and seeds, scopolamine in the root and atropine in the whole plant.[3] Other toxic components isolated have been named apoatropine, noratropine, belladonine, tropacocaine and meteloidine.[4] The toxic effects of these alkaloids differ only in their severity and the relative proportions of each present.

Poisoning in animals

The plant is seldom eaten but it did cause the death of three calves which strayed into a derelict garden.[5] Parts of the leaves and stems were found in the rumen at post-mortem examination. Poisoning has also been reported in pigs[6] which ate the plant during a drought; they were found lying down and kicking and were unable to stand. They had dilated pupils and inflamed mucous membranes. The animals exhibited nervous excitation and died the next day. In a goat, strongly dilated pupils, dry mouth, feeble rapid pulse, difficult respiration, continuous weak crying and cessation of gastric movement occurred.[7] Post-mortem examination revealed detachment and inflammation of the gastric and intestinal mucous membranes; leaves and stems of *Atropa bella-donna* and elder *(Sambucus nigra)* were found in the stomach. The symptoms were typical of deadly nightshade poisoning, but may have been exaggerated by the simultaneous presence of elder. Rabbits are not poisoned if they eat deadly nightshade, as they possess an enzyme, atropinesterase, which inactivates the alkaloids.[8] Their flesh, however, can cause poisoning if eaten by other animals or man.

Human poisoning

Most cases involve children, who eat the berries, but deliberate or accidental consumption of berries or concoctions of leaves by adults has been also reported. Between 1967 and 1979, 34 incidents of poisoning by the plant were recorded by a Poisons Information Unit.[9] In each case more

212

than five berries had been eaten, and all developed symptoms of varying severity. The most serious poisoning usually results from large numbers of berries being eaten raw or cooked, when mistaken for the fruit of other plants, e.g. bilberries *(Vaccinium myrtillus)*. A family ate approximately 150 g each of the stewed berries, and developed gastrointestinal symptoms, convulsions and, in one case, coma.[9] All recovered within six days. Another adult ate 10-15 raw berries and, after six hours, developed abdominal pain, vomiting, dry mouth, visual disturbances, disorientation, dilated pupils and rapid pulse.[10]

A useful, although not necesarily diagnostic, test for poisoning by *Atropa bella-donna* involves placing a few drops of urine from the patient into the eye of another animal, the pupil of which will dilate fully within 30 minutes in bright light, while the other eye reacts normally.[5]

Treatment Where possible, and soon after consumption of the plant, vomiting should be induced, stomach lavage performed and activated charcoal given to adsorb any residual poisonous material.[3] Sedation may be required. A specific antidote, physostigmine salicylate (3 mg in 1 mg doses, injected intramuscularly at intervals of several hours) has proved effective in neutralising the most dangerous effects of the alkaloid in man;[10] this measure, however, should be considered only in very serious cases. Preparations containing morphine or opiates should be avoided as they have a synergic action with atropine.

Thorn Apple *Datura stramonium* (photo 37)

Other common name: Jimsonweed

Thorn apple is not native in Britain, but it now has very localised distribution in southern England, growing mainly on cultivated ground, rubbish tips and embankments. It is sometimes grown in gardens. The plant is a smooth, wide-branching annual which grows up to 1 m high in Britain. The leaves are stalked and up to 20 cm long with irregular lobes terminating in pointed teeth. The flowers are borne singly on stalks in forks of the stem in early summer. They are funnel-shaped, up to 10 cm long and either white or purple. They, and the rest of the plant, have an unpleasant odour. The fruit, which appears in autumn, is a prickly, ovoid or globular capsule containing numerous wrinkled black seeds.

Poisonous principles These are the alkaloids hyoscyaminc (an isomer of atropine which blocks the parasympathetic nervous system) and hyoscine (sometimes called scopolamine) which is hallucinogenic. Traces of atropine may also be

213

present.[11] All parts of the plant are poisonous, although the concentration of alkaloids may differ in plants grown in different climatic regions. In India, *Datura stramonium* grown at an altitude of 2000 m had no adverse effects when fed to bulls, goats and sheep (two of each). When grown at a lower altitude the same quantity of the plant caused poisoning when fed to the same animals;[12] factors other than altitude may, of course, have been involved.

In the past, *Datura* was used in various medicinal preparations, and for the relief of asthma by inhaling smoke from burning leaves. It has also been used as an anaesthetic and a hallucinogen.[13] Medicinal and culinary use of the plant, however, has often resulted in poisoning. A famous case of human poisoning occurred in 1679 in Jamestown, USA. Soldiers who ate the plant in a salad experienced what was described as a very pleasant comedy, and it was from this incident that *Datura* acquired the common name Jimsonweed (Jamestown weed).

Poisoning in animals

This is very rare in Britain. Because of its strong odour and unpleasant taste, animals do not eat the growing plant, provided that other vegetation is available. Poisoning can occur, however, if *Datura* is incorporated into hay, or its seeds into grain which is fed to livestock. Poisoning or suspected poisoning has been reported in horses,[14] cattle,[12 15] buffaloes,[16] sheep,[12 17 18] goats[12 18] and pigs.[19 20] The clinical signs usually include restlessness, incoordination, dilation of pupils, paralysis and increased respiration rate; death may result. In the USA, *Datura* was thought to be the cause of poisoning in 15 ponies[14] which developed impaired vision and intermittent muscular spasms; 11 died after 7-17 days. The ponies had been given feed which contained a large amount of *Datura stramonium* seeds. Also in the USA, *Datura* was suspected of causing congenital arthrogryposis (persistent joint contraction) in 25 piglets in eight litters over a period of five years. The litters farrowed in an area surrounded by dense growth of *Datura*. The sows had shown signs of poisoning, such as incoordination, during pregnancy.[20] Experimentally, leaves and fruits of *Datura stramonium* given by stomach tube resulted in reduced water intake, tremors, rapid breathing, incoordination and recumbency in both sheep and goats; some animals died.[18] Post-mortem findings included haemorrhages of liver, kidney and heart and congested blood vessels in the lungs. In Scotland, eight ewes died after eating kale from a crop contaminated with *Datura stramonium*. This case is unusual, as it occurred outside the normal range of the plant.[17]

Datura seeds are sometimes harvested with crops such as soya beans, and poisoning of livestock could result from feeding with contaminated soya bean products.[21] From experimental feeding with *Datura* seeds, it was found that laying hens could tolerate up to 2,000 seeds a day, but 100 seeds caused 3-week-old chicks to lose weight.[22] Cattle tolerated up to 7 g, and pigs 5 g of *Datura* seeds daily. Both of these amounts are greater than the

37

37   Thorn Apple (*Datura stramonium*)
     JH

38   Henbane (*Hyoscyamus niger*)
     HCB

39   Woody Nightshade (*Solanum dulcamara*) (a)
     flowers (b) fruit. Often confused with Deadly
     Nightshade (35)
     HCB

38

39a

39b

40a

40b

40 Black Nightshade (*Solanum nigrum*) (a) flowers (b) fruit. The ripe berries are black. The form of this plant is very variable.
HCB

41 Spurge Laurel (*Daphne laureola*)
JH

42 Hemlock (*Conium maculatum*). The similarity in appearance of many umbelliferous plants can lead to mistaken identification.
JH

41

42

highest recorded natural contamination of soya (0.023%).[23] Pigs were poisoned by being fed *Datura* seeds equivalent to 2.7 mg hyoscyamine per kg of body weight;[19] in a similar experiment pigs tolerated up to 2.2 mg hyoscyamine per kg of body weight in barley and soya meal contaminated with ground *Datura* seeds.[24] When fed meal contaminated with whole seeds the pigs reduced their food consumption (presumably because of the unpalatable taste) and consequently lost weight. They showed no signs of poisoning with a dose of up to 2 mg hyoscyamine per kg body weight, although this may not be an accurate estimate of hyoscyamine absorption, as undigested seeds were found in faeces.

Human poisoning Symptoms usually include dryness of the mouth and throat, dilation of pupils incoordination, retention of urine, hallucinations, muscle twitching, drowsiness, nausea, delerium, coma and, sometimes death. [16 25 26] A man was poisoned after he drank a herbal tea brewed from leaves of *Datura*.[27] The first effects were flushing, incoordination, restlessness, blurred vision and thirst, followed by hallucinations and deranged behaviour. It was estimated that the patient ingested about 10-15 mg of total alkaloids. The alkaloids hyoscine and/or atropine have been incriminated as the agents responsible for the toxicity of honey from *Datura* and other solanaceous plants.[28] Such honey is unlikely to be produced in Britain as these plants are not sufficiently common.

Treatment This is usually symptomatic. A purgative such as magnesium sulphate may eliminate any toxic material remaining in the digestive tract. Sedatives (such as diazepam) may be indicated. Antidotes to atropine (parasympathomimetics) are not recommended.[29]

Henbane *Hyoscyamus niger* (photo 38)

Although native in Britain, this rather spectacular plant is now seen only occasionally in sandy, coastal areas, waste places or adjacent to old buildings, where the plants sometimes survive from their former cultivation for medicinal purposes.

Henbane is a sturdy annual or biennial plant, up to 80 cm high. The whole plant has a strong, unpleasant smell and is hairy and somewhat sticky. The stem is woody at the base, where there are stalked leaves, up to 20 cm long, usually with a few irregular, large teeth. The stem leaves are arranged alternately; they have no stalks, are unevenly lobed and the upper ones clasp the stem. The inflorescences are borne in the forks of lower branches or laterally from upper shoots. The bracts are leaf-like and the flowers funnel-shaped, 2-3 cm across and yellowish or white (occasionally mauve). They are conspicuously marked with a network of dark red or purple veins; the anthers of the stamens and the interior, basal part of the flowers are also purple. After flowering, the calyx continues to grow, around the fruit, its five points hardening to form spines. The exposed cap of the fruit is shed, when ripe, revealing numerous seeds.

Poisonous principles
All parts of the plant, but particularly the roots, are poisonous. Henbane contains alkaloids of the same group (tropane) as those in *Datura*. The main alkaloid is hyoscyamine, but hyoscine (scopolamine), a hallucinogen, and atropine are also present. Preparations of the plant have been used medicinally for eye disorders, rheumatism and sedation.[30] In the Middle Ages, it was used in sorcery.[30]

Poisoning in animals
Hyoscyamus has a long-standing reputation for being poisonous,[31] but there are few actual reports. It is probable that the disagreeable odour and sticky texture of the plant make it unattractive to animals. In one outbreak in Poland,[32] when *Hyoscyamus niger* was present in cut forage, cows developed nervous signs including restlessness, excitation and convulsions; four of eight animals were slaughtered. Post-mortem examination revealed 0.7% of henbane shoots in the rumen contents, degeneration of heart muscle and bluish coloration (cyanosis) of mucous membranes. Similar nervous signs were reported in other cattle after eating henbane but, in addition, dilation of pupils, difficult breathing, increased heart rate and bloat were seen in adult cattle; incoordination occurred in calves.[33] No outbreaks appear to have been reported in animals in Britain since early this century.[34] Henbane retains its toxicity after drying (dried leaves are said to contain 0.04% alkaloids)[35] and storage. It is said to impart an unpleasant taint to the milk of cows that eat it.[36]

Human poisoning
As with many other plants used medicinally, there have been incidents of accidental poisoning by henbane reported, mainly in the older literature,[31] [37] but there have also been some recent cases reported in Britain.[38] The symptoms are similar to those in animals. The roots of the plant have caused poisoning when eaten in mistake for those of other plants. When boiled roots were eaten, typical symptoms, including blurring of vision, dry mouth, confusion, dilated pupils and rapid heartbeat, persisted for 12 hours.[38] Dizziness, nausea, headache, euphoria and hallucinations can occur.[39] An inconsistent finding reported is excess salivation, while other reports mention dryness of the mouth. It has even been suggested that this salivation is a feature distinguishing henbane poisoning from that caused by *Atropa* and *Datura*. It appears, however, that the allusions to salivation are repeated from one old reference.[31] Poisoning has resulted from eating honey made from solanaceous plants, including henbane, atropine and/or hyoscine being the toxic principles.[29] This is most unlikely to occur in Britain as the plant is not sufficiently common.

216

Treatment   Stomach lavage or the induction of emesis, and physostigmine injections are recommended.

Tobacco *Nicotiana* spp

Tobacco for smoking is not grown commercially in Britain, but this, and several ornamental varieties, are cultivated in gardens. The poisonous principles are alkaloids, of which the best known is nicotine. Both animals and man have been poisoned after contact with agricultural pesticides containing nicotine, and adverse effects have followed its internal and external use in veterinary medicine.[40] Death occurred within four hours in two pigs that ate growing tobacco plants after breaking loose and entering a garden. At post-mortem examination, the plants were found in the stomachs, but there was no other indication of the cause of death.[40] Congenital defects have been recorded in the USA in many newborn pigs[41] after feeding burley tobacco forage *(Nicotiana tabacum)* to pregnant sows, and in calves[42] after experimental feeding of *Nicotiana glauca* to cows during pregnancy (particularly in the early stages). It is thought that the alkaloid anabasine, rather than nicotine, is responsible for these abnormalities which are mainly skeletal deformities, resulting in locomotory and postural disorders.

Woody Nightshade *Solanum dulcamara* (photo 39)

Woody nightshade is common throughout Britain except for some northern areas and Scotland. It is sometimes found growing along the ground on waste land or on shingle near the sea, but occurs most frequently as a climbing plant in woods and hedges where it scrambles and trails over bushes and trees. The roots are perennial and the stems woody at the base, to which they usually die back in winter. They grow up to 2 m long and bear dark green, pointed leaves up to 8 cm long. These have smooth edges, but one to four (usually two) deeply indented lobes near the base. The upper leaves may be oval or heart-shaped, without basal lobes. The flowers appear in summer in loose clusters. They are purple in colour (rarely white), about 1 cm across, and usually have five pointed lobes. The stamens are a prominent feature as they cohere and project from the centre of the flower as a bright yellow cone. The fruits are oval, green berries which become shiny red when ripe.

Poisonous principles

All parts of the plant contain solanine, an alkaloidal glycoside which varies chemically according to the composition of the glycone; composition of the aglycone component (solanidine) is constant.[43] The glycoalkaloids of the Solanaceae are degraded during maturation of the fleshy fruit. It is suggested that this loss of chemical defence occurs to make the fruits attractive to animals, who will eat them and thus act as dispersal agents.[44] The berries should not, however, be considered safe, as poisoning has occurred from eating them. It is impossible to determine visually whether degradation of the toxin is complete.

Poisoning in animals

This is uncommon, and no recent cases have been recorded. Early literature quotes conflicting reports, one stating that the fruits have no harmful properties and another that poultry died as a result of pecking the berries.[45] Straying sheep, which ate the plant developed rapid respiration, feeble intermittent pulse, elevated temperature, dilated pupils, green diarrhoea, staggering and falling before death.[46] Post-mortem examination revealed dark, tarry blood, contracted ventricles of the heart, and parts of the stem and seeds of the plant in the stomach. *Solanum dulcamara* poisoning in cattle[47][48] caused nervous excitement, rapid pulse, incoordination, muscle tremors and subnormal temperature. One animal salivated profusely and another developed oedema of the front part of the body. Fruits and seeds of woody nightshade were found in material regurgitated by the cattle, and the flesh of a slaughtered animal smelled strongly of the plant.

Human poisoning

This is usually caused by eating the berries, whose bright colour is attractive to children. A Poisons Information Unit[49] recorded 25 cases of ingestion of the plant in Britain between 1963 and 1979. Of these, 19 were asymptomatic, but varying degrees of abdominal pain, flushing of the skin and tiredness were seen in the others. A fatal case of woody nightshade poisoning of a 9-year-old girl has been reported.[50] She experienced abdominal pain, vomiting, thirst, distressed breathing, restlessness and exhaustion. Some improvement was achieved after stomach lavage, administration of an enema and fluid therapy, but this was followed by further deterioration, with shallow respiration, cyanosis and extreme weakness preceding death. Post-mortem examination revealed acute inflammation and small haemorrhages of the mucous membranes of the stomach and intestines. Small fragments of the skin of woody nightshade berries were seen on microscopic examination of stomach contents. The lungs were congested and oedematous, and the liver was fatty and necrotic. A product, consistent with solanine, was extracted from the liver. Woody nightshade berries were growing (entangled with blackberries) where the child had been playing. Treatment is symptomatic; stomach lavage and rehydration are recommended.

Black Nightshade *Solanum nigrum* (photo 40)

Other common name: Garden Nightshade

Black nightshade, which has almost world-wide distribution, occurs throughout England but is found only very locally in Scotland. It is a highly successful and very troublesome weed of cultivated land. Both morphological and physiological variations occur in different locations and between different populations, some of which are developing resistance to herbicides.[51]

Solanum nigrum is an erect, much branched annual (occasionally biennial) plant varying in height, according to its habitat, from below 10 cm up to 60 cm. The stems are smooth or very slightly hairy and bear stalked oval or diamond-shaped, dull green leaves which may or may not have coarsely toothed margins. White, or occasionally pale mauve flowers about 0.5 cm across, with pointed petals and yellow stamens appear in clusters on the stem from mid to late summer. The fruit is a shiny globular berry, green at first, usually ripening to black, although some forms are red or persistently green. Each berry contains numerous seeds which have a high germination rate and may retain their viability for many years.[52]

Black nightshade can cause serious problems at harvesting, as the berries may be collected with such crops as peas, beans or maize from which they are difficult to separate; alternatively, they may contaminate crops with the thick juice released from them when squashed. Dissemination of the plant can occur if its seeds are collected with crop seeds such as sugar beet, for subsequent sowing.

Poisonous principles All parts of the plant, but particularly the green unripe berries, contain the glycoalkaloid solanine, the concentration of which increases in the leaves as the plant matures. Other toxic alkaloids also present are chaconine and solasodine, the latter having been found experimentally to cause foetal malformations in hamsters.[53] Nitrates and nitrites also occur in variable amounts in black nightshade,[54] and may contribute to its toxic effects. The amounts of the poisonous principles present vary greatly with climate, season and soil type. The concentration of solanine is reduced in silage,[52] as acid hydrolysis in the fermentation process converts solanine to solanidine, which is less toxic. The alkaloid content of the plant is also reduced when it is boiled and the water discarded. The toxic potential of the plant has been utilised experimentally in the production of an anthelmintic, a 0.1% extract of crushed dry leaves having killed the miracidia of *Fasciola gigantica* in five minutes.[55] Variability in the toxic alkaloid and nitrate concentrations of the plants in different situations accounts for the conflicting reports of their being harmless in some cases (for example, when a horse consumed 3 kg of the green plant without ill effects,[56] or in Mauritius and Reunion where people eat the cooked plant like spinach),[57] and harmful in other cases (when deaths occurred in pigs on land where the plant was growing[58] and among children after eating the berries[59]).

Poisoning in animals Black nightshade should be considered as potentially toxic to all animals. Cattle, sheep, goats, pigs, dogs and poultry can be severely poisoned.[60] In an outbreak of black nightshade poisoning in pigs,[58] rapid pulse and respiration, pale mucous membranes, widely dilated pupils, low body temperature, incoordination and tremors were reported. In a valuable herd of British Saanen goats, severe abdominal pain, vomiting, depression and staggering movements occurred.[61] In the latter outbreak, leaves of the plant were seen in ingested material. In India, calcium deposits in blood vessels of Corriedale sheep[62] were thought to have been caused by ingestion of *Solanum nigrum* which grew in the area where the animals were kept. The effects were similar to those of enteque seco, a form of calcinosis, among sheep in Argentina, associated with ingestion of *Solanum malacoxylon* (a species which does not occur in Britain). In addition to symptoms similar to those described for pigs and goats, cattle may develop areas of oedema[63] around the lower jaw, neck and front of the body, including the top of the forelegs. Laboured respiration, dark coloured diarrhoea following constipation, lack of rumination, dry muzzle and cold extremities have also been reported in cattle.[52]

Human poisoning Symptoms associated with *Solanum nigrum* poisoning in man are headache, vomiting, diarrhoea, elevated temperature, dizziness, speech impairment and unconsciousness.[60] Death may occur due to cardiac or respiratory failure. Although, when ripe, the berries are the least toxic part of the plant and are sometimes eaten without ill effects,[64] consumption of berries may produce mild abdominal pain, vomiting and diarrhoea, or even cause acute illness and death. The toxicity of berries appears to be variable; unripe (green) fruits should always be considered poisonous. Treatment consists of symptomatic and supportive measures after stomach lavage, or induction of vomiting.

Potato *Solanum tuberosum*

Although potatoes (the underground stem tubers of the potato plant) are a major food, they can, under certain conditions, cause poisoning in animals and man.[65]

Poisonous principles These are alkaloids, the most frequently named of which is solanine, first isolated in the 1820s. This substance is, however, a mixture of glycosides having the aglycone solanidine in common. Degradation products of the glycosides have also been isolated and named. The chief toxic glycosides are α-solanine and α-chaconine, although phenolic compounds (chlorogenic and caffeic acids) and coumarins (scopolin, umbelliferone, coumarin) are also present.[66]

The stems, leaves, flowers and fruits (haulm) of the potato plant contain solanine and other toxic substances, but most cases of poisoning involve ingestion of potato tubers which have sprouted or been exposed to light and become green. In such tubers the solanine content may be as high as 0.05%, compared with the average value of 0.008% in properly stored tubers; there is, however, some evidence that gravimetric determinations of alkaloid content can give erroneously high figures as compared with more sophisticated chromatographic methods. The toxic substances are present at their highest concentration in the skin, eyes and sprouts of the tubers. Infection of tubers with the potato blight fungus, *Phytophthora infestans*, increases the concentration of toxins in the tubers. Boiling in water reduces, but does not eliminate the alkaloids or render safe potatoes which have become green. These may be used, however, after storage in the dark for 2-3 weeks or until all traces of green have disappeared. A possible source of poisoning is from berries of potato plants that grow, from a previous crop, among peas or beans and are harvested with the latter.[67] The concentration of alkaloids in these berries may be 10-20 times that in tubers. Many of the newer varieties of potatoes used in Britain produce fruits more freely than older varieties.

Poisoning in animals
Potato tubers can provide a useful addition to animal feed, and the vines, harvested before senescence and used for silage, can be a nutritious feed for ruminants. In Canada, silage made with 75% potato haulms was readily acceptable to sheep.[68] There are, however, many reported incidents of poisoning in animals as a result of being fed with parts of the plant. Whole potatoes, their sprouts or peelings have poisoned pigs in several countries including Britain.[69] In Poland, 28 outbreaks of solanine poisoning involving 180 pigs were diagnosed between 1949 and 1961, and there was a 64% mortality.[70] Some animals die suddenly, while in others there are nervous signs including restlessness, incoordination and convulsions, the animals often appearing dazed or semi-comatose. Loss of appetite, excess salivation, vomiting and diarrhoea or constipation are also seen, and dilation of pupils and circulatory failure may occur. In addition, a generalised, dry eczema appeared in pigs whose feed had been mixed with water in which potato peelings had been cooked.[71] Necrosis of the feet, necessitating amputation, developed in some cases.

Outbreaks of poisoning in cattle have followed feeding with green, decayed or sprouting potatoes[72] or with excessive quantities of potato pulp[73] (up to 60 litres per animal daily). The symptoms were similar to those described for pigs. Feeding large quantities of stored potatoes to young cattle over long periods is a well recognised cause of severe chronic anaemia in many European countries.[74]

Sheep may also be affected, although they are less likely to be fed potatoes than pigs or cattle. In the USA, 14 of 39 sheep became weak and uncoordinated and died shortly after eating green cull potatoes which had been spread on their pasture.[75]

A horse developed gastrointestinal symptoms and a weak pulse and died after being fed greened potato sprouts.[76]

A dog became unusually quiet, then comatose, with dilated pupils, irregular weak pulse and slow breathing. Unconsciousness persisted for a period of four days, after which the animal was killed. Post-mortem examination revealed ten small, green potatoes in the stomach, which was acutely inflamed. There was blood-stained urine in the bladder.[77]

Poultry, however, seem more resistant to solanine as, in feeding trials, laying pullets tolerated green haulm, cooked and raw green potato sprouts and ground tubers as 10% of their diet.[78]

Although not recorded in domestic animals, deaths and rib abnormalities have occurred in the foetuses of rats given potato sprouts or solanine,[66] [79] and the young of many litters died before weaning. It has been suggested that solanine may interfere with milk production.

Post-mortem findings, which are similar in all animals, are those of non-specific gastroenteritis with occasional haemorrhages of the intestinal mucous membranes and degeneration of heart muscle and liver.

Human poisoning This can result from eating potato haulm as a vegetable[80] but is unlikely to occur except under conditions of food shortage. Children have been poisoned by eating potato fruits, and abdominal pain and vomiting have been reported.[49] Most cases of poisoning in man involve badly stored or very old tubers. The family of a hotel proprietor were poisoned by eating potatoes baked in their skins, while guests in the hotel, who ate potatoes from the same source, but without skins, were unaffected.[81] The potatoes were of excellent flavour and appearance but analysis revealed a solanine content of 0.05%. More recently, 78 schoolboys were poisoned after eating potatoes from a sack which had been stored for several weeks.[82] Symptoms began 8-10 hours after eating the potatoes, when there was generalised abdominal pain, followed by vomiting and diarrhoea. The severity of the reaction varied between individuals, three boys becoming dangerously ill and 17 requiring admission to hospital. Varying degrees of restlessness, delirium, visual disturbances, drowsiness or coma were experienced, but the boys made a complete recovery, most within a few days and all within 4-5 weeks. Analysis revealed the presence of α-solanine and α-chaconine at concentrations of up to 0.012%, as determined by chromatographic methods. It has been suggested that alkaloids in potatoes (particularly tubers infected with the potato blight fungus) eaten during pregnancy, may be a cause of human birth defects.[82] Although experimental work has demonstrated the presence of some potentially teratogenic substances in potatoes,[84] there is no evidence for a connection between the consumption of potatoes and birth defects.

Treatment is symptomatic, but should include fluid replacement. Tranquillisers or anticonvulsants may be required.

Tomato *Lycopersicon lycopersicum*

The haulm of the tomato plant contains solanine but rarely causes poisoning, as the only part of the plant eaten regularly is the fruit, in which the concentration is too low to cause any harm. Feeding pigs with green sideshoots picked from tomato plants by growers has caused acute illness and death.[74]

TAXACEAE

Yew *Taxus baccata*

Other common names: English Yew; Common Yew

Yew is native in Britain, where it grows wild in southern England as an evergreen tree or bush, usually on chalk. It has, however, been planted throughout the country for hundreds of years and is suitable for hedges and topiary. In the past, yew was sometimes associated with religious rituals and the trees were planted in churchyards, which were enclosed, and therefore inaccessible to livestock. The Irish yew *(Taxus baccata* var. *fastigiata),* occasionally called the churchyard yew, is often grown in Britain, and the Japanese yew *(Taxus cuspidata)* is sometimes planted in parks and gardens.

Yew trees grow up to 20 m high and may attain a great age. The trunks of old trees are massive and gnarled. The bark of yew is reddish-brown, scaly and somewhat fibrous. The branches of the common yew spread more or less horizontally from the trunk and a typical specimen tree has a roughly triangular outline. The branches of the Irish yew are more erect and the trees are consequently more rounded and compact in habit. The leaves are inserted close together all around the stems, but, in the English yew, they spread in one plane in two opposite ranks, giving a flat appearance to the twigs. The leaves are dark green, uniformly narrow, 1-3 cm long, shiny and slightly convex on the upper side. The male and female flowers are almost always borne on separate trees. They are small, pale greenish-yellow, and inconspicuous; they are found in the leaf axils in spring. The seeds develop singly from the flowers and are partially surrounded by the fruit (aril) which is a bright pinkish red, fleshy, translucent cup.

Poisonous principles All parts of the tree, except the fleshy fruit, contain significant concentrations of taxin(e), a complex mixture of alkaloids that is absorbed rapidly from the digestive tract and interferes with the action of the heart. The alkaloid ephedrine, as well as a volatile oil and traces of a cyanogenic glycoside, taxiphyllin, are also present. The volatile oil may be the cause of the intense irritation sometimes seen in the stomach. The toxicity of yew is not decreased by wilting or drying, so that clippings and fallen leaves are as toxic as the fresh plant.

Poisoning in animals In the past, there have been conflicting reports on the toxicity of yew for animals,[1] it being considered by some that if eaten often, but in small quantities, there are no toxic effects; yew has even been fed intentionally. Poisoning was said to occur only when considerable amounts of yew were eaten, often in the absence of adequate supplies of other feed. Such information is misleading, and yew should never be fed to animals as the risk of rapidly fatal taxine poisoning is too great; yew is even considered by some to be the most toxic plant in Britain. Similar toxic reactions occur with all species of yew. Because of its long-standing and well-known reputation for being poisonous, farmers do not allow animals near yew. Most recent cases of poisoning have resulted from accidents (when fallen branches of yew have been browsed by animals, or when fences have been broken, giving animals access to the trees), or through ignorance of the toxicity of the trees (such as when garden refuse, including yew hedge clippings, is thrown onto grazing land). An unusual outbreak in Ohio, USA, resulting in the death of several fairground bulls,[2] occurred when their attendants, not realising the dangers, enlarged the enclosure of the animals, using a hedge of Japanese yew as a boundary.

Yew is most toxic in winter,[3] a time when animals are more likely to eat it, as other food is scarce. In experimental work, yew twigs offered to adequately fed cattle, horses, sheep and goats were not eaten,[2] but, irrespective of their nutritional status, animals have been poisoned by yew throughout the year. Most outbreaks involve cattle or horses, but yew poisoning has also been recorded in sheep,[4] deer,[5] poultry,[4] kangaroos[5] and game birds.[6] The lethal dose has been estimated as 1-10 g/kg body weight for ruminants and 0.5-2 g/kg for horses;[7] other estimates are lower than this. The clinical signs reported in cattle[8][9] and horses[10][11] are similar. They include muscular trembling, uncoordinated movements, coldness, rapid then weak pulse, and sometimes excitability preceding stupor and collapse, during which breathing may be accompanied by groaning; in others sudden collapse is the only sign. In many cases, signs are never seen, as the animals may die only a few hours after eating yew; death usually follows collapse, with or without convulsions, but a recent outbreak in Britain is of interest as it emphasises that yew poisoning is not necessarily fatal. Of 24 cattle which broke into a copse which contained an Irish yew tree, two died and yew leaves were found in their rumens. The others appeared unaffected, but some hours later two other animals started staggering and developed pronounced stiffness of the hind legs. Almost immediately they collapsed and lay apparently dying, but within five minutes they had risen and made a spontaneous recovery.[12] In some cases there may, in addition, be dilation of pupils and abdominal pain.[13] Yew poisoning, with typical signs after one hour and death 15 minutes later, occurred in a pony given, by stomach tube, a strained aqueous, extract of ground yew twigs and berries.[11]

Post-mortem findings
It is not unusual for there to be no evidence of poisoning, other than the presence of yew in the stomach. There may, however, be inflammation of the stomach and intestines, particularly if death did not occur for two or three days. One report states that the right side of the heart is usually flaccid, dark and filled with blood having a tarry appearance, while the left side is contracted and empty.[13]

Human poisoning
As with other plants where toxicity has been known from antiquity, yew has been used medicinally to 'steady the heart' and was said to be an antidote for adder bites and rabies.[1] There are reports of adults who have died after taking a medicinal decoction prepared from yew leaves.[13]

The toxicity of yew fruits has been the subject of controversy for many years. It is now generally accepted that the red, fleshy aril is not poisonous or is of very low toxicity, but that the seeds are poisonous. The berries are attractive to children and are most often eaten by them.

Vomiting, lethargy, abdominal pain and elevated body temperature were reported in a two-year-old child who ate berries; an adult who ate 30 berries became drowsy and experienced generalised stiffness and abdominal pain. In other cases, involving the ingestion of 40 or more berries, there were no symptoms, possibly because only the fruit was eaten, the seeds being swallowed without chewing and passed out with the faeces.[14]

The possibility of fatal human poisoning by yew has been known at least since Roman times,[1] but is a rare occurrence. A case was reported in Germany in 1975, however, of a woman who ate 4-5 handfuls of yew leaves.[15] Within an hour dizziness was experienced, followed by nausea, abdominal pain, rapid heart beat and dilated pupils. Later the pulse became slow and breathing weak; death resulted from respiratory and heart failure.

Treatment
In animals and man there should be rapid removal of stomach contents, by the induction of vomiting, lavage or surgery (in ruminants). In man, syrup

of ipecacuanha is the emetic of choice. Otherwise, basic symptomatic and supportive treatment is all that can be given.

THYMELAEACEAE

Mezereon *Daphne mezereum*

Other common names: Spurge Olive; Spurge Flax; Dwarf Bay; Wild Pepper (often confused with those of *Daphne laureola*).

Mezereon grows as a compact, erect, deciduous shrub up to 100 cm tall in woodlands on calcareous soils. It is local in distribution and now very rare in Britain, many specimens having been removed to gardens where both wild and cultivated varieties are grown. The smooth, light green leaves are usually 3-10 cm long, rarely more than 1 cm wide and taper to a point at both ends. The fragrant pink (occasionally white or purple) flowers appear in small clusters in early spring, before the leaves. The basal tubular portion of the flower expands into four lobes 8-12 mm across, on which there are often dark pink lines. The fruit is an oval, scarlet berry, up to 12 mm across, which often persists into the winter.

Spurge Laurel *Daphne laureola* (photo 41)

Other common names: Wood Laurel; Copse Laurel (often confused with those of *Daphne mezereum)*

The name of this plant can cause confusion with other shrubs whose common name is also laurel. They are, however, unrelated botanically, the other laurels being species of *Prunus* and belonging to a different family (Rosaceae).

Spurge laurel has a widespread distribution throughout England and Wales, mainly on calcareous soils, but is seldom abundant. It is an erect, sparingly branched shrub, growing up to 100 cm in height. It is evergreen, the leaves which remain at maturity being clustered together near the top of the plant. The leaves are tough, smooth, glossy green and up to 12 cm long. They are narrow where attached to the stem then widen gradually up to 2-4 cm before terminating in a blunt point. The midrib is a prominent feature, lying along the slightly grooved longitudinal axis of the leaf. The flowers develop in short 5-10 flowered clusters in the axils of the leaves throughout the spring. They are green with yellow stamens appearing where the tubular base of the flower opens into four lobes, 8-10 mm across. The fruit is an oval berry up to 12 mm across. It is green at first, then bluish and finally black when fully ripe.

Poisonous principles Those of mezereon, spurge laurel and other *Daphne* species not found in Britain are the same, and are contained in the acrid irritant sap of all parts of the plant, particularly the bark and berries. Information on the nature of these poisonous principles is confusing. *Daphne* species contain the dihydroxycoumarin glycoside daphnin(e) and its hydrolysis product daphnetin (daphnitin); the hydroxycoumarin, umbelliferone; a resin, mezerein (or its anhydride, mezereinic acid), and daphnetoxin. One or more of these components are sometimes referred to less specifically as glycosides, and daphnin in particular as a lactone glycoside. It is generally agreed that the coumarins are responsible for the acrid taste while mezerein is the toxic component.

Poisoning in animals *Daphne* is usually avoided because of its unpalatability, but can cause poisoning if eaten. The practice (now largely discontinued) of giving crushed dried leaves of *Daphne* to horses as a treatment for intestinal worms resulted in some cases of abdominal pain and poisoning. A cart-horse which ate *Daphne laureola*, while waiting to be unloaded, refused further food and developed severe abdominal pain, a staggering gait and laboured breathing. The following day the animal died after excessive purgation and an elevated body temperature. Post-mortem examination revealed inflammation, swelling and blood-stained contents of the gastrointestinal tract.[1] Experimental feeding of *Daphne* to another horse produced similar symptoms, but was not fatal.[2] In three days the animal ate only 100-150 g of the plant. *Daphne* berries thrown to a litter of 10-week-old pigs resulted in the sudden death of all but the smallest one which had not gained access to the trough.[3] All the pigs vomited before death, and post-mortem examination revealed white, burned patches in the mouth and stomach, which was intensely inflamed.

Human poisoning This usually involves children who mistake the ripe berries for currants, and has been reported from the time of Dioscorides (first century A.D.) to the present.[4][5][6] Because of their acrid taste, usually only a very few berries are eaten, and the symptoms, which include a burning sensation in the mouth, nausea, abdominal pain, vomiting and diarrhoea are relatively mild and transient. However, if a sufficient quantity of the plant or its berries is eaten, there may be extreme prostration, shivering, pallor, dilated pupils, violent vomiting and diarrhoea with blistering and shedding of the lining of the oral and intestinal mucous membranes. Convulsions may occur and muscular twitching and somnolence may persist for several days. Treatment by stomach lavage, or with an emetic (syrup of ipecacuanha) if appropriate, demulcents and fluids is recommended.

TRILLIACEAE

Herb Paris *Paris quadrifolia*

Herb paris grows in damp woods, chiefly on calcareous soils. It is a native British plant, local in distribution, being absent from most western areas of the country and from Ireland.

The plant is perennial and has a creeping rhizome and a stem up to 40 cm high, with four (occasionally more) leaves 6-12 cm long arranged in a whorl around it. The leaves are oval in shape, pointed at the tip and narrowing where they join the stem. A single yellowish-green flower appears in spring, and in mid-summer the fruit, a single blue-black berry, develops.

Poisonous principles Published information on the nature of these is confusing. They have been referred to as saponins or glycosides, and the names most often quoted are paristyphin and paridin. All parts of the plant are said to be poisonous, but the plant appears to be very unpalatable, and few authenticated cases of poisoning in livestock have been reported.

Poisoning in animals Ingestion of berries by dogs and gallinaceous birds, resulting in unsteadiness, vomiting and abdominal pain has been recorded.[1] Horses fed experimentally with the plant[2] (1.3 kg) at the ripe berry stage showed, on the first evening, increased excitability, elevation of the head, muscular twitching, constant licking of the lips and increased pulse rate. The following day the pulse was still rapid (54 per minute); yellowing of the mucous membranes was apparent and persisted for three days. When 2 kg were fed, there was general weakness and yellowing of mucous membranes. The horses refused to eat the plant unless it was sweetened.

Human poisoning Reported cases refer to children, who sometimes eat the berries, thinking them to be bilberries *(Vaccinium myrtillus)*. Symptoms including vomiting, diarrhoea, colic, painful micturition and painful bowel movements develop initially. Headache, dizziness, difficulty in breathing and narrowing of the pupils occur later.[3]

Treatment In both animals and man this is symptomatic, but is rarely necessary because, due to its unpleasant taste, the plant is not normally eaten in sufficient quantity to cause severe poisoning.

UMBELLIFERAE

In this large family, which has species of over 40 genera native in Britain, most plants are harmless; parts of some are edible, e.g. the roots of carrot and parsnip, the stem of angelica, the leaf stalk of celery, the leaves of parsley and fennel, and the seeds of caraway; a few are suspected of being poisonous, e.g. water parsnip *(Sium latifolium)* and cow parsley *(Anthriscus sylvestris);* some are of relatively low toxicity, e.g. fool's parsley *(Aethusa cynapium).* Three which can cause severe poisoning are hemlock *(Conium maculatum)*, hemlock water dropwort *(Oenanthe crocata)* and cowbane *(Cicuta virosa).*

The Veterinary Investigation Diagnosis Analysis (VIDA) records for 1975-77 show that nearly 10% of all cases of plant poisoning in animals reported to Veterinary Investigation Centres in Britain during that period involved these three plants.[1]

Accurate identification of plants in this family presents difficulties due to the superficial similarity of many of them, and mistaken identity has resulted in many human cases of poisoning. Fool's parsley and hemlock have been mistaken for true parsley *(Petroselinum crispum)*, and curly leaved varieties of the culinary herb are now grown commercially, partly to avoid such mistakes. The roots of fool's parsley have been mistaken for young turnips or radishes, those of cowbane for parsnip, and those of hemlock water dropwort for carrot or parsnip.

The many alternative common names used for British members of the family are an additional source of confusion as a name applied to one plant, e.g. hemlock, may be part of the name of other different plants such as hemlock water dropwort or water hemlock. Without positive identification, none of the wild Umbelliferae should be eaten, and they should be considered as potentially toxic to animals.

Hemlock *Conium maculatum* (photo 42 and fig. 1)

Hemlock grows in damp places and open woods throughout Britain, although it is less common in the north. The plant is an erect, branched biennial (sometimes annual or perennial) which may exceed 2 m in height. The leaves are up to 30 cm long, with finely divided leaflets having deeply serrated edges giving the plant a rather delicate appearance. The inflorescence (umbel) produced in early summer is 2-5 cm across and bears numerous white flowers 2 mm in diameter. The root is a white, fleshy, usually unbranched, tap root. Characteristic features of the plant are the irregular purple blotches on the smooth, slightly ridged, hollow stem, the laterally compressed fruits which have five prominent wavy longitudinal ridges and are about 3 mm long when ripe, and the odour of mice emitted by all parts of the plant when bruised or crushed.

The poisonous nature of hemlock has been recognised from very early times, and an extract of the plant was used by the Greeks for the execution of Socrates in 399 B.C. In 1578, in a translation of a herbal from French, Henry Lyte called it a 'naughtie and dangerous herbe'. It was used in medicine, but this ceased in the 19th century owing to the uncertain actions of the preparations.

Poisonous principles

The toxicity of hemlock is due to the presence of a group of poisonous alkaloids: coniine, N-methylconiine, gamma-coniceine, conhydrine and pseudoconhydrine. All these highly poisonous alkaloids act in a similar way, inducing paralysis, convulsions, and death from respiratory paralysis. All parts of the plant contain the alkaloids, the roots at all times containing the least. Before flowering the leaves contain the most alkaloids, but the greatest concentrations are found in the flowers and fruits. The alkaloid content, however, does vary with the climatic conditions; in sunny summers the average weight of the fruits and thus the quantity of alkaloids can be twice those under wet, cloudy conditions. When dried in hay, the plant is said to lose its toxicity.

Poisoning in animals

The unpleasant mousy odour of hemlock is not attractive to animals. Poisoning of livestock occurs mostly in spring, when pastures are short and the young leaves are growing among the more luxuriant grasses of sheltered hedge banks and the sides of ditches, although at this period of the year they are at their least poisonous stage.

The hemlock alkaloids produce paralysis of the motor nerve endings and stimulation followed by depression of the central nervous system. They cause nausea and vomiting at an early stage of their action. Large doses can slow the heart rate. Respiration is generally accelerated and deepened at first, but eventually becomes slow and laboured and finally ceases, while the heart is still strong and consciousness has just disappeared.

Animal species differ in susceptibility: cows developed severe signs of toxicity when given as little as 3.3 mg coniine per kg body weight, mares when given 15.5 mg per kg, whereas ewes were quite resistant, showing only moderate signs when given 44 mg per kg.[2] Clinical signs appear within a few hours of ingestion of the plant, and in cattle,[3] sheep[4] and goats[5] include apathy, rapid respiration, difficulty in movement, salivation, frequent regurgitation, muscular tremors, ruminal atony, groaning, grinding of teeth, diarrhoea, and a drop in milk yield. Convulsive attacks have occasionally been described. Poisoning has also been reported in horses,[6] pigs,[7] chickens and rabbits.[8] In 1971 in the USA, *Conium maculatum* poisoning was observed in pregnant sows, which gave

230

Fig. 1. Hemlock
(Conium maculatum)

231

birth two months later to malformed piglets and also piglets with the central nervous signs of hemlock poisoning.[9] In Britain, limb deformities have been reported in piglets born to sows with access to hemlock, although signs of hemlock poisoning were not observed in the sows.[10] Limb deformities have been produced experimentally in the calves of cows given coniine[11] or the fresh green plant.[12] It is reported that animals which survived for eight hours after the onset of symptoms have recovered comparatively quickly. There are no specific post-mortem findings.

Human poisoning Fatal poisoning has occurred as a result of mistaking the plant for wild carrot or parsley. The symptoms are similar to those in animals, with vomiting, dilation of the pupils, incoordination, coldness of the extremities, coma, convulsions and eventually death from respiratory paralysis.

Treatment This is symptomatic; charcoal may be given to adsorb the alkaloids, respiration assisted and convulsions controlled, e.g. with diazepam. In man, an emetic (10-15 ml of syrup of ipecacuanha) and stomach lavage are recommended.

Hemlock Water Dropwort *Oenanthe crocata* (fig. 2)

Other Common name: Dead Men's Fingers

This plant has a scattered distribution throughout Britain in damp places, particularly on calcareous soils. Hemlock water dropwort is an erect perennial, 50-150 cm high, with branched stems which are grooved and hollow. The compound leaves are triangular in outline, 30 or more cm long, and have leaflets with bluntly toothed edges. The inflorescence (umbel) is 5-10 cm across and is formed in early spring, from dome-shaped clusters of white flowers; cylindrical fruits, 4-6 mm long when ripe, develop in autumn. Characteristic features of the plant are the leaf stalks, which entirely sheath the stem, the flower styles which are erect and protrude above the petals, and the rootstock which is composed of five or more fleshy, pale yellow or white finger-like tubers (hence the alternative common name, dead men's fingers). When damaged, these exude juice which becomes yellowish on exposure to the air.

Poisonous principle The active principle, oenanthetoxin, is a poly-unsaturated higher alcohol, chemically very similar to cicutoxin found in cowbane *(Cicuta virosa).* It is a convulsant poison which is not affected by drying and storage. Man and all the domestic animals are susceptible to its effects. The roots are the most

Fig. 2. Hemlock
Water Dropwort
*(Oenanthe
crocata)*

toxic part of the plant and very small amounts are sufficient to cause the death of animals. There appears to be some seasonal variation in the amount of toxin in the roots, with the greatest concentration in winter.

Poisoning in animals Poisoning of farm stock usually occurs from eating roots which have been brought to the surface during ditching or drainage operations. Death is rapid and few symptoms may be seen before it occurs. Horses[13] and cattle[14] show salivation, dilated pupils and spasmodic convulsions; they usually die in a convulsion. Sheep are less susceptible to its effects than other animals; at least half of a poisoned flock may recover from acute poisoning; after subsidence of the acute symptoms they may develop diarrhoea for about two days, and then slowly return to normal. Pigs which have eaten the roots of hemlock water dropwort may vomit for a short time, but death is usually sudden, without the appearance of any symptoms. There are no specific diagnostic lesions at post-mortem examination.

Human poisoning Fatal cases have occurred when the leaves of hemlock water dropwort have been mistaken for those of celery, and the tuberous roots for parsnips.[15] [16] [17]

Treatment Medical and veterinary treatments follow similar lines. First-aid treatment consists of keeping the patient warm and avoiding any excitement. Stomach lavage should be performed and attempts made to control the convulsions by intravenous injection of barbiturates or other anti-convulsants.

Six other *Oenanthe* species occur in Britain, all of which are considered poisonous but to a lesser degree than hemlock water dropwort. *Oenanthe pimpinelloides* is suspected of poisoning cattle,[18] while *Oenanthe aquatica* poisoning has been reported in cattle in Poland[19] and *Oenanthe silaifolia* poisoning in man in Greece.[20] The symptoms that these other species produce are not so acute, and are of the depressive type, generally not progressing to convulsions.

Cowbane *Cicuta virosa* (fig. 3)

This plant is very localised in its distribution in Britain, being confined to shallow water, ditches and marshes in East Anglia, small parts of the Midlands, areas on the east and west coasts of mainly the southern parts of Scotland, and Northern Ireland.

Cowbane is a stout, erect perennial, 30-130 cm high with a somewhat ridged, hollow stem. The compound leaves are up to 30 cm long, have

Fig 3. Cowbane
(Cicuta virosa)

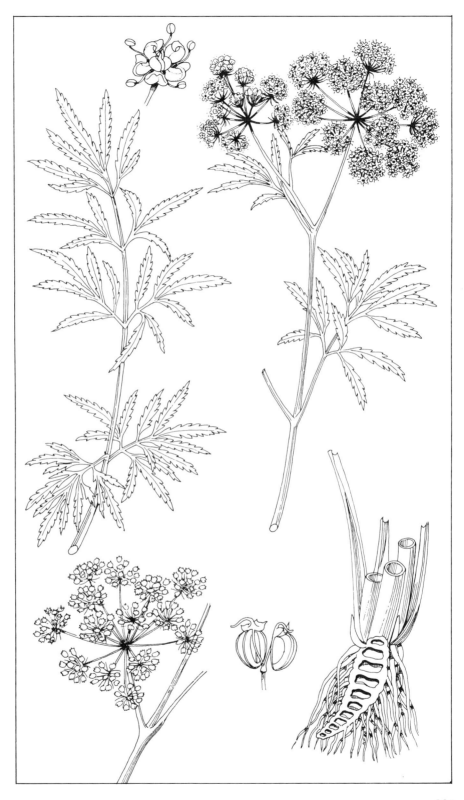

hollow stalks and narrow, elongated, unequally toothed segments up to 10 cm long. The inflorescence (umbel) develops in mid-summer and is 7-13 cm in diameter and bears numerous white flowers. The ripe fruits are up to 2 mm across, rounded at the base and tapering slightly towards the apex. Characteristic features of the plant are the elongated leaflets and the underground parts, the roots growing from a thick, white, fleshy portion which is divided internally by cross partitions into a series of hollow compartments.

Poisonous principle The active principle is a highly unsaturated higher alcohol, cicutoxin, which is found in the yellow juice of the roots and in smaller quantities in the stems. It is present in greatest concentration between late autumn and early winter. Its action on the body is that of a convulsant poison, and part of a root has been enough to kill horses, cattle and children. Cowbane roots may be dug up and left lying on the surface after cleaning out ditches. As the poison persists in the dried plant, it may cause the death of an animal long after it has been unearthed. The leaves and stem are poisonous, but to a lesser extent; they are sometimes eaten when the grass is short.

Poisoning Signs of cowbane poisoning in animals and man are similar, with nausea, salivation, widely dilated pupils (constricted pupils have occasionally been noted), vomiting, abdominal pain, muscular spasms, violent convulsions, and death from asphyxia. There is no diarrhoea. Clinical signs appear within an hour of ingestion, and death can occur in a few hours; animals that survive 5-6 hours generally recover completely in 4-5 days. Recently, cases have been described in horses,[21] [22] [23] cattle[22] [24] [25] and man;[26] [27] pigs appear to be less susceptible.[22] In one recent outbreak in East Germany,[28] nine of 62 beef cattle were found dead during a drought when there was little green growth except for cowbane near a lake; roots of the cowbane had been exposed by a drop in the water-level and showed signs of having been eaten. Clinical signs in another eight affected animals were hyperactivity, dilation of pupils, salivation, slight bloat, colic, staggering, muscular spasms, and convulsions. One of the eight died with signs of respiratory paralysis, the other seven had recovered in three days after removal from the area.

Post-mortem examination may reveal no diagnostic lesions, although congestion of blood vessels and haemorrhages have been reported in the gastrointestinal tract.

Treatment is the same as that for hemlock water dropwort.

Fool's Parsley *Aethusa cynapium*

This annual plant is common on pastures, cultivated ground and waste land throughout Britain, but is found infrequently in the north. Fool's parsley grows up to 120 cm high and has hollow, finely lined, somewhat bluish-green stems. The compound leaves are finely divided into narrow segments and the flat-topped inflorescence (umbel) is 2-6 cm across. The fruits are oval, ridged longitudinally and 3-4 mm in diameter. The 3-4 narrow, pointed bracteoles, up to 1 cm long, which are present on the outer side of the stalks of individual rays, are characteristic of the plant.

Poisonous principles
The plant is unpalatable in the fresh state and emits a repulsive odour which becomes greater when crushed or bruised. The poisonous principle has not been determined precisely, although it is said to contain the alkaloid cynapine and also a coniine-like alkaloid.[29] It seems that a large quantity of the plant has to be eaten to produce poisoning, and there may be variations in its toxic properties with stage of development and climate. Hay containing the plant is harmless to livestock.

Poisoning
Ataxia, particularly affecting the hindquarters, and death have been reported in a sow and her piglets, which consumed a large quantity of fool's parsley after being deprived of green feed.[30] Indigestion, panting and ataxia have been seen in goats,[31] and poisoning has been reported in cattle and horses.[32] Poisoning in man has occurred from mistaking the leaves for parsley and the roots for radishes; symptoms have included nausea, vomiting, diarrhoea, salivation, headache, muscular tremors and stiffness of the limbs.[33] Treatment should include stomach lavage or the induction of emesis; fluid replacement and other symptomatic measures may be required.

Giant Hogweed *Heracleum mantegazzianum*

This plant is not native in Britain but was introduced from the Caucasus and found a place among the more exotic garden plants. Early in this century it escaped and since then has become naturalised in various localities, not only near water but also on waste ground. When fully grown, giant hogweed can be distinguished from other members of the Umbelliferae by its size, the hollow, ridged stem being up to 3.5 m high and the compound leaves 1 m long. The inflorescence (umbel), which develops in early summer, can be 50 cm in diameter and has numerous rays up to 20 cm long. The fruit may measure 13 mm across and is oval or elliptical in shape. Apart from its huge size, characteristic features of the plant are the red spots on the stem and the strong, resinous, aromatic smell which is readily noticeable when the plant is cut or crushed.

Giant hogweed contains furocoumarins (psoralens) which produce a dermatitis in man by making the skin hypersensitive to sunlight. After contact of the bare skin with the plant and exposure to the sun, affected areas of the skin become red within 24 hours and blisters develop within another 24 hours. The associated lymph nodes may be tender. The blisters can be large and very irritating, but they subside in a few days, often leaving a brown pigmentation on the affected parts.[34] [35] Although this plant has not been incriminated as a cause of skin lesions (by contact) or poisoning (by ingestion) in animals, it is possible that these could occur.

Furocoumarins (psoralens) are found in several other Umbelliferae, including wild and cultivated parsnips *(Pastinaca sativa)*. Like giant hogweed, these plants can also sensitise the skin to sunlight and lead to dermatitis. This may develop in individuals handling the cultivated plants in the course of their work[36] or those coming into contact with the wild plant. Recently a case has been reported of a child who had extensive skin lesions on the exposed parts of her body after playing on waste ground where wild parsnip plants were flowering.[37] The skin is affected only if exposed to plant sap and ultraviolet irradiation (as in bright sunlight). The skin changes can vary from a reddening to oedema and severe blistering. The dermatitis that develops on the hands of celery growers is a well recognised condition known as 'celery rash'; this is now thought to result from infection of the celery plants with the fungus *Sclerotinia*.

PLANTS AFFECTING MILK

It has been recognised for many years that the consumption of certain plants can cause a drop in yield, or even a temporary cessation of milk production. This is, however, difficult to assess accurately as loss of condition in a lactating animal, from whatever cause, including plant poisoning, may lead to a drop in milk yield. Whether or not yield is decreased, some plants also impart an unpleasant taste or odour to milk, and change its physical composition, rendering it unsuitable for making butter or cheese, e.g. *Oxalis* spp. The plants incriminated belong to several different families, and the constituents responsible for the taint are not necessarily of the same type. Many of the plants causing milk taint are poisonous, while others are not, or only doubtfully so, e.g. the cresses *(Coronopus* spp.) and the pepperworts *(Lepidium* spp.). Taint can often be detected even when only small quantities of affected milk are added to bulk collections. Tasting is one of the routine tests performed on milk samples from individual farms and also from bulk tanks in this country.

It has been established that, although they may not cause a taint, some plant and fungal toxins (e.g. from bracken, and aflatoxin) are present in the milk of animals that have eaten them. The possibility of human poisoning resulting from drinking such milk, however, has not been proved conclusively and remains an open question.

From time to time lists and tables have been compiled of the plants that can have adverse effects on milk (see below). These are useful for reference, but the information contained in some of them is derived from old reports, and no recent, authoritative publication on this subject, applicable to Britain, is available. The following lists include only those plants mentioned, because of their toxicity, in the main text of this book; they do not necessarily cover all of the plants in Britain that could affect milk.

PLANTS THAT CAN REDUCE MILK YIELD

Aconitum napellus	Monkshood
Allium spp.	Onion and Garlic
Beta vulgaris	Beet
Bryonia dioica	White Bryony
Chenopodium album	Fat Hen
Cicuta virosa	Cowbane
Claviceps purpurea	Ergot
Colchicum autumnale	Meadow Saffron
Conium maculatum	Hemlock
Crataegus monogyna	Hawthorn
Cupressus spp.	Cypress
Cynoglossum officinale	Hound's Tongue
Endymion non scriptus	Bluebell
Equisetum spp.	Horsetail

Frangula alnus	Alder Buckthorn
Fraxinus excelsior	Ash
Hedera helix	Ivy
Hyoscyamus niger	Henbane
Hypericum perforatum	St. John's Wort
Laburnum anagyroides	Laburnum
Mercurialis spp.	Mercury
Papaver spp.	Poppy
Pteridium aquilinum	Bracken
Quercus spp.	Oak
Ranunculus spp.	Buttercup
Raphanus raphanistrum	Radish
Rhododendron ponticum	Rhododendron
Rhamnus spp.	Buckthorn
Ricinus communis	Castor Oil Plant
Rumex spp.	Sorrel
Scrophularia aquatica	Water Betony
Solanum tuberosum	Potato, green
Taxus baccata	Yew
Trifolium spp.	Clover

PLANTS THAT CAN TAINT MILK

Aethusa cynapium	Fool's Parsley
Allium spp.	Onion and Garlic
Beta vulgaris	Beet
Brassica campestris	Turnip
Capsella bursa-pastoris	Shepherd's Purse
Compositae family	several plants
Conium maculatum	Hemlock
Coronopus spp.	Cress
Equisetum spp.	Horsetail
Hedera helix	Ivy
Hyoscyamus niger	Henbane
Laburnum anagyroides	Laburnum
Lotus corniculatus	Birdsfoot Trefoil
Melilotus spp.	Sweet Clover
Mentha spp.	Mint
Oxalis spp.	Wood Sorrel
Pisum spp.	Pea
Pteridium aquilinum	Bracken
Quercus spp.	Oak
Ranunculus spp.	Buttercup
Raphanus raphanistrum	Radish
Solanum tuberosum	Potato, green
Taxus baccata	Yew

References (Plants affecting milk)

FENTON, E.W. Poisonous and Milk-tainting Plants. Edinburgh and East of Scotland College of Agriculture, 1931, New Series-No. 4, 56 pp. (combined with Symptoms and First Aid to Stock, by E.D.S. Robertson).

FORSYTH, A.A. British Poisonous Plants. HMSO, London, UK. Ministry of Agriculture, Fisheries and Food Bulletin 161, 1968, 118-120 (amended 1979, 119-121).

McBARRON, E.J. Medicinal and Veterinary Aspects of Plant Poisons in New South Wales. Department of Agriculture, New South Wales, Australia. 1976, 150-153.

RICHTER, H.E. [The influence on milk quality of indigenous plants (Austria). I Excretion of toxins of animal origin in milk]. *Wiener Tierärztliche Monatsschrift* 1963, 50, 692-699.

RICHTER, H.E. [The influence on milk quality of indigenous plants (Austria). II. Changes in taste and smell]. *Wiener Tierärztliche Monatsschrift* 1964, 51, 266-280.

RICHTER, H.E. [The influence on milk quality of indigenous plants (Austria). II. Changes in taste, smell and colour]. *Wiener Tierärztliche Monatsschrift* 1965, 52, 635-644. (Continuation of previous paper by this author, above).

GLOSSARY

These definitions apply to the terms as used in this book, and are not necessarily complete.

abomasum   Fourth stomach of ruminant.

abortion   Premature birth of non-viable foetus.

achene   Single-seeded fruit that does not split open on ripening.

acidosis   Increased acidity in the stomach contents and body fluids of ruminants.

acute   Sudden and severe, referring to a disease.

addiction   Habitual, compulsive intake, with adverse effects.

agglutinate   Aggregate into clumps.

alimentary   Relating to the digestive tract.

alkalosis   Increased alkalinity in the stomach contents and body fluids of ruminants.

allergen   Substance that induces an allergic reaction.

allergic   Relating to the response to an allergen.

allergy   Hypersensitivity (especially to food component or skin contact).

anaemia   Condition in which the number of red blood cells and the haemoglobin content of blood is decreased.

analgesic   Pain-relieving drug.

anthelmintic   Substance that destroys or expels parasitic (especially intestinal) worms.

anther   Pollen-bearing part of flower.

anticoagulant   Substance that impedes or prevents coagulation (especially of blood).

antidote   Substance that counteracts the adverse effects of another substance.

anus   Terminal orifice of digestive tract.

asphyxia   Cessation of breathing associated with inadequate blood levels of oxygen.

astringent   Causing contraction of tissues, with reduction or cessation of their secretions.

ataxia   Impaired control over body (especially locomotory) functions; incoordination.

awn   Bristle-like appendage of fruit of grasses.

axil   Upper angle between leaf and stem of plant.

axillary   Arising from the axil of a plant.

biennial   Plant that produces flowers and usually dies in its second year.

bifid   Deeply cleft into two parts.

bilirubin   A red bile pigment.

bloat   Distension of the rumen of cattle and sheep with gases.

bract   Leaf-like structure at the base of an inflorescence.

bracteole   Leaf-like structure at the base of a flower stalk.

brisket   Fore and under part of the chest wall of cattle and sheep; sternal region.

bulbil   Small axillary bulb of plant.

caecum	Part of large intestine; the 'blind gut'.
calcareous	Containing calcium carbonate, such as chalk or limestone.
calcinosis	Deposition of calcium salts in body tissues where it does not normally occur.
calyx	Outer portions (sepals) of some flowers, often enclosing the flower bud.
carcinogen	Substance that can induce tumour formation.
cardiac	Relating to the heart.
carpel	Unit of the female part of a flower.
cerebrum	Largest part of the brain.
cervix	Neck (of the uterus).
chromatography	Process for separating chemical substances by differential deposition in absorptive material.
chronic	Of slow progress and long duration, referring to a disease.
cirrhosis	Progressive fibrosis of the liver.
colic	Severe, often spasmodic, abdominal pain.
colon	Part of large intestine.
coma	Prolonged unconsciousness.
congenital	Existing from birth (defect etc.).
congestion	Presence of an abnormally large amount of blood in the blood vessels of a part of the body.
conjunctiva	Lining of the eyelids and outer membrane of the eye.
conjunctivitis	Inflammation of the conjunctiva; 'pink eye'.
cultivar	Variety of plant produced by selective breeding.
cyanosis	Bluish tinge of mucous membranes and skin, resulting from lack of oxygen in the blood, as occurs in cyanide poisoning.
deciduous	(Of trees) shedding leaves annually.
defaecation	Passing of faeces.
delirium	Confused state of mind, often accompanied by agitation and incoherent speech.
demulcent	Soothing medicament to relieve inflammation, particularly of the digestive tract.
dermatitis	Inflammation of the skin.
diuresis	Increased urination.
diuretic	Substance that increases the volume of urine.
duodenum	Part of small intestine, leading from the stomach.
dyspnoea	Difficulty in breathing.
ecology	Study of living things in relation to their environment.
eczema	Form of dermatitis, often with fissuring and itching.
electrolyte	Compound which, in aqueous solution, readily dissociates into electrically charged particles (ions) and makes possible the conduction of an electric current through the solution.
embryo	Organism in the early stages of prenatal development; an early foetus.
emesis	Vomiting.

243

emetic	Substance that induces vomiting.
endemic	(Of a disease) regularly or consistently present in a region or among a group of individuals.
ensilage	Preservation of green feed in a silo.
enteric	Relating to the intestines.
enzootic	Denoting an animal disease indigenous in an area.
enzyme	Substance produced by living cells that catalyses a biochemical reaction.
epithelium	Layers of cells covering or lining interior and exterior body surfaces.
euphoria	Feeling of well-being, often exaggerated and without justification.
excretion	Process of elimination from the body of undigested material or waste products of metabolism.
extremities	Parts of the body most remote from their points of attachment to the trunk.
faeces	Waste matter eliminated from the digestive tract.
family	Taxonomic group to which organisms of related genera belong.
foetus	Unborn young after it has taken form in the uterus.
fibrosis	Formation of fibrous tissue at abnormal sites.
floret	Individual flower of a composite flower head.
friable	Easily crumbled.
frond	Leaf and stem of plant, especially of ferns.
follicle	(Of a plant) dry fruit that splits open on one side when ripe.
gallinaceous	Bird belonging to the order Galliformes, including the domestic fowl.
gangrene	Necrosis of part of the body, usually as a result of obstruction of blood supply.
gastritis	Inflammation of the stomach.
gastroenteritis	Inflammation of the stomach and intestines.
gastrointestinal	Relating to the stomach and intestines.
generic	Relating to a genus.
genus	Taxonomic group to which organisms of related species belong.
gills	Thin, radiating structures on the underside of the cap of a fungus.
glume	Bract of grass flower.
goitre	Abnormally enlarged thyroid gland.
goitrogen	Substance that induces goitre.
habitat	Natural environment of plant or animal.
haemagglutin-ation	Aggregation of blood cells into clumps.
haematuria	Presence of blood or red blood cells in urine.
haemodialysis	Separation of (especially toxic) substances from the blood by passage across a semipermeable membrane.
haemoglobin	Red pigment in red blood cells.
haemoglobinuria	Presence of haemoglobin in urine.
haemolysis	Destruction of red blood cells with release of haemoglobin.
haemolytic	Relating to haemolysis.

244

haemoperfusion	Separation of (especially toxic) substances from the blood by passage through adsorbent material.
haemorrhage	Bleeding.
hallucination	Strongly perceived sense of illusory objects or events.
hallucinogen	Substance that can induce hallucinations.
hepatotoxic	Relating to substances that damage the liver.
herbaceous	Relating to non-woody plants.
herbicide	Substance whose application can kill vegetation.
histology	Study of microscopic structure of cells, organs and tissues.
hock	Tarsal joint of the hind leg.
hybrid	Plant resulting from the fertilisation of one species (or subspecies) with another.
hydrolysis	Chemical splitting of compounds to simpler compounds with the uptake of water.
hypocalcaemia	Subnormal concentration of calcium in the blood.
hypothermia	Subnormal body temperature.
inflammation	A pathological process, affecting blood vessels and surrounding tissues and characterised by redness, warmth, swelling and pain.
inflorescence	Part of plant bearing the flowers.
ingestion	Intake of food or drink.
intraperitoneal	Within the peritoneal (abdominal) cavity.
intravenous	Within a vein.
jaundice	Pathological condition involving the passage of bile pigments into the blood, with consequent yellowish coloration of the skin and other tissues.
ketosis	Metabolic disorder in which the ketone content of blood increases and that of glucose decreases.
lacrimation	Secretion or flow of tears, especially when excessive.
lactic acidosis	Increased acidity of the rumen contents due to accumulation of lactic acid after feeding excess carbohydrate.
lactation	Milk secretion.
laminitis	Inflammatory condition of the hoof.
larynx	Part of the throat; 'voice box'.
lassitude	Weariness. Lack of desire to be active.
latent	(Of a disease) present, but not currently apparent; potential.
lavage	Washing-out of an organ (usually stomach).
lesion	Pathological change in tissues.
leukocytosis	Abnormally large number of white blood cells.
lymph	Fluid that flows in lymphatic vessels.
lymph node	Gland of the lymphatic system.
lymphocyte	Type of blood cell.

macrophage	Large cell with single nucleus. Ingests damaged or dead cells.
malignant	Severe, progressive and often not responsive to treatment (especially of a tumour).
metabolism	Chemical changes occurring in the functioning of the body.
micturition	Passing of urine.
monogastric	Having a single stomach (e.g. man, pig).
mucous membrane	Lining membrane, particularly of digestive and upper respiratory tracts.
mucus	Clear, semi-fluid, viscid secretion from a mucous membrane.
mutagen	Agent inducing a genetic change in cells.
myocardium	Muscular wall of heart.
narcotic	Inducing drowsiness, sleep or state of unconsciousness.
nausea	Inclination to vomit.
necrosis	Death of cells or portion of tissue or organ.
necrotic	Relating to necrosis.
nectar	Sweet-tasting secretion of flowers.
nephritis	Inflammation of the kidneys.
neuro-	Relating to nerves or the nervous system.
oedema	Swelling of tissue as a result of fluid accumulation.
oesophagus	Portion of digestive tract leading from the throat to the stomach; gullet.
oestrogen	Substance inducing female characteristics; female sex hormone.
oestrus	(Of animals) stage in female sexual circle when mating can occur; 'heat'.
offal	Internal organs and parts removed from the carcass of animals at slaughter.
omasum	Third compartment of the forestomach of ruminants.
ophthalmic	Relating to the eye.
oral	Relating to the mouth.
papule	Small, raised pimple on the skin.
paranoia	Mental disorder, characterised by delusions (often of persecution).
parturition	Giving birth.
perennial	A plant that lives for several years even if the above-ground parts die down annually.
peripheral	Relating to the outer part or surface.
peritoneum	Thin layer of tissue that lines the abdominal cavity and covers most of the body parts within it.
photosensitisation	Light-induced reaction of skin to light, in the presence of a photosensitive agent.
photosensitivity	Presence of a photosensitive agent in the skin.
placenta	Organ, attached to the inner wall of the uterus, by which the foetus is nourished.
polymer	Substance of high molecular weight made up of a chain of identical units.
polymorphic	Existing in several different forms.

246

post-mortem examination	Examination of a body after death.
prolapse	Displacement of an internal organ, such that part of it may be visible externally (especially digestive or female genital tracts).
psychic	Relating to the mind.
psychedelic	Expanding or heightening consciousness and awareness.
pulmonary	Relating to the lungs.
purgative	Substance promoting evacuation of the bowel. Laxative.
rectum	Terminal portion of intestine.
recumbent	Lying down.
rehydration	Replacement of lost fluids.
renal	Relating to the kidney.
respiration	Breathing.
retina	Light-sensitive layer on the inner surface of the eye.
rhizome	Underground stem.
rickets	Skeletal deformity, especially of limb bones, resulting from deficiencies of calcium and vitamin D.
rodenticide	Substance used to kill rodents.
rumen	Large forestomach of ruminants; paunch.
rumenotomy	Incision of the rumen.
ruminal atony	Cessation of ruminal movement.
rumination	Chewing the cud.
salivation	Production of (excessive amounts of) saliva.
scouring	Severe (usually watery) diarrhoea.
sedative	Agent inducing state of calmness.
sepal	One of the outer (usually green) parts of a flower, often enclosing the flower bud.
septicaemia	Presence of disease-producing microorganisms in the blood.
serum	Clear, watery fluid portion of the blood.
silage	Green feed preserved in a silo.
stamen	Part of flower consisting of the pollen-bearing anther and its filament.
stigma	Pollen receptor of the female part of the flower.
spore	Small, usually single celled, reproductive portion of simple, non-seed-bearing plants.
stimulant	Agent inducing increased activity.
stipule	Scale-like or leaf-like portion present at the base of the leaf stalk of some plants.
stomatitis	Inflammation of the mucous membranes of the mouth.
style	Portion of female part of plant between the stigma and the ovary.
subcutaneous	Beneath the skin.
supportive	(Of treatment) for the maintenance of essential body functions.
symptomatic	(Of treatment) aimed at alleviating specific clinical signs.

syndrome Group of clinical signs that, collectively, are present in and indicative of a certain condition or disease.

spasm Involuntary, temporary contraction of muscle.

species Taxonomic status of organism subordinate to genus and superior to variety.

tap root Simple, tapering, main root of a plant.

taxonomy Systematic classification, especially of living organisms.

teratogen Substance that can induce abnormal development (often malformation) of a foetus.

therapy Treatment.

thorax Chest.

topical application Local, external use of therapeutic substance.

tranquilliser Substance given to relieve a state of agitation.

tremorgenic Producing muscular tremors.

tumour Abnormal mass of tissue that grows continuously and excessively.

tympany Distension of the rumen with gases; bloat.

uraemia Accumulation of nitrogenous waste (mainly urea) in the blood.

urethra Canal through which urine is discharged from the bladder.

vacuolation Formation of minute spaces in cells or tissues.

variety Taxonomic unit of lower status than species.

vasodilator Substance that dilates blood vessels.

vertigo Sensation of dizziness.

whorl Three or more plant parts of the same kind, that arise at the same level (e.g. a ring of leaves on a stem).

BIBLIOGRAPHY (BOOKS)

FUNGI

LANGE, M.; HORA, F.B. *Collins Guide to Mushrooms and Toadstools.* Collins, London, UK. 1963. 257pp.

LINCOFF, G.; MITCHEL, D.H. *Toxic and Hallucinogenic Mushroom Poisoning. A Handbook for Physicians and Mushroom Hunters.* Van Nostrand Reinhold Co., New York, USA. 1977. 267pp.

PEGLER, D.N. *The Mitchell Beazley Pocket Guide to Mushrooms and Toadstools.* Mitchel Beazley, London, UK. 1981. 168pp.

REID, D. *Mushrooms and Toadstools.* Kingfisher Books, Ward Lock Ltd., London, UK. 1980. 124pp.

RUMACK, B.H.; SALZMAN, E. (Editors) *Mushroom Poisoning: Diagnosis and Treatment.* CRC Press Inc., Florida, USA. 1978. 263pp.

WAKEFIELD, E.M.; DENNIS, R.W.G. *Common British Fungi.* Saiga Publishing Co. Ltd., Hindhead, Surrey, UK. 2nd Edition. 1981. 216pp.

GENERAL

ALTMANN, H. *Poisonous Plants and Animals* (Chatto Nature Guides). Chatto & Windus, London, UK. 1980. 143pp.

ARNOLD, R.E. *Poisonous Plants.* Terra Publishing Inc., Jefferstown, Kentucky, USA. 1978. 152pp.

BARTÍK, M.; PISKAČ, A. (Editors) *Veterinary Toxicology.* Elsevier Scientific Publishing Co., Amsterdam, Netherlands. 1981. 346pp.

BENTZ, H. (Editor) *Nutztiervergiftungen. Erkennung und Verhütung.* (in German) Gustav Fischer Verlag, Jena, Germany. 1969, 432pp.

BOHOSIEWICZ, M. *Toksykologia Weterynaryjna.* (in Polish) Panstwowe Wydawnictwo Rolnicze i Leśne, Warsaw, Poland. 1970. 376pp.

CLAPHAM, A.R.; TUTIN, T.G.; WARBURG, E.F. *Flora of the British Isles.* University Press, Cambridge, UK. 2nd Edition. 1962. 1269pp.

CLARKE, M.L.; HARVEY, D.G.; HUMPHREYS, D.J. *Veterinary Toxicology.* Baillière Tindall, London, UK. 2nd Edition. 1981. 328pp.

CONNOR, H.E. *The Poisonous Plants in New Zealand.* E.C. Keating, Government Printer, Wellington, New Zealand. 1977. 247pp.

COOPER, P. *Poisoning by Drugs and Chemicals, Plants and Animals.* Alchemist Publications, London, UK. 3rd Edition. 1974. 252pp.

CORNEVIN, C. *Des Plantes Vénéneuses et des Empoissements qu'elles Déterminent.* (in French) Librairie de Firmin-Didot, 56 rue Jacob, Paris, France. 1887. 524pp.

DE BRUYN, J.W.; SCHNEIDER, F. *Giftige Planten in en am Huis.* (in Dutch) A.A. Balkema, Rotterdam, Netherlands. 1976. 191pp.

DERIVAUX, J.; LIÉGEOIS, F. *Toxicologie Vétérinaire.* (in French) Vigot Frères, Paris, France. Desoer, Liège, Belgium. 1962. 332pp.

DOULL, J.; KLAASSEN, C.D.; AMDUR, M.O. (Editors) *Casarett and Doull's Toxicology. The Basic Science of Poisons.* Macmillan, New York and Baillière Tindall, London. 2nd Edition. 1980. 778pp.

GUSYNIN, I.A. [*The Toxicology of Poisonous Plants.*] (in Russian) Gosudarstvennoe Izdatel'stvo Sel'skokhozyaistvennoi Literatury, Moscow, USSR. 3rd Edition. 1955. 330pp.

HAILS, M.R.; CRANE, T.D. *Plant Poisoning in Animals. A Bibliography from the World Literature, 1960-1979.* Commonwealth Bureau of Animal Health, Weybridge, Surrey, UK. 1983. 158pp.

HARDIN, J.W.; ARENA, J.M. *Human Poisoning from Native and Cultivated Plants.* Duke University Press, Durham, North Carolina, USA. 2nd Edition. 1974.

HENSLOW, G. *Poisonous Plants in Field and Garden.* Society for Promoting Christian Knowledge, London, UK. 1901. 189pp.

JEAN-BLAIN, C. *Les Plantes Vénéneuses.* (in French) La Maison Rustique, Librairie de l'Académie d'Agriculture, 26, rue Jacob, 75006, Paris, France. 1973. 140pp.

JOHNSON, C.; JOHNSON, C.P.; SOWERBY, J.E. *British Poisonous Plants.* John Van Voorst, London. 2nd Edition. 1861. 76 + 32pp.

KEBLE MARTIN, W. *The New Concise British Flora.* Michael Joseph, London, UK. 1982. 247pp.

KEELER, R.F.; VAN KAMPEN, K.R.; JAMES, L.F. *Effects of Poisonous Plants on Livestock.* Academic Press, New York and London. 1978. 600pp.

KINGHORN, A.D. (Editor) *Toxic Plants.* Columbia University Press, New York, USA. 1979. 195pp.

KINGSBURY, J.M. *Poisonous Plants of the United States and Canada.* Prentice-Hall, Inc., New Jersey, USA. 1964. 626pp.

KINGSBURY, J.M. *Deadly Harvest. A Guide to Common Poisonous Plants.* George Allen and Unwin Ltd., London, UK. 1967. 128pp.

LAMPE, K.F.; FAGERSTRÖM, R. *Plant Toxicity and Dermatitis.* Williams and Wilkins Co., Baltimore, USA. 1968. 231pp.

LIENER, I.E. (Editor) *Toxic Constituents of Plant Foodstuffs.* Academic Press, New York and London. 2nd Edition. 1980. 502pp.

LONG, H.C. *Plants Poisonous to Live Stock.* University Press, Cambridge, UK. 1917. 119pp.

McBARRON, E.J. *Medical and Veterinary Aspects of Plant Poisons in New South Wales.* Department of Agriculture, New South Wales, Australia. 1976. 243pp.

MORTON, A.G. *History of Botanical Science.* Academic Press, London and New York. 1981. 474pp.

MUENSCHER, W.C. *Poisonous Plants of the United States.* Macmillan Co., New York, USA. 1939. 266pp.

NICHOLSON, J.A. *Lander's Veterinary Toxicology.* Baillière, Tindall and Cox, London, UK. 3rd Edition. 1945. 329pp.

NORTH, P.M. *Poisonous Plants and Fungi.* Blandford Press, London, UK. 1967. 161pp.

PAMMEL, L.H. *Manual of Poisonous Plants.* Cedar Rapids, Iowa, USA. 1911. 977pp.

RIEMANN, H. (Editor) *Food-borne Infections and Intoxications.* Academic Press, New York and London. 1969. 698pp.

ROSENTHAL, G.A.; JANZEN, D.H. (Editors) *Herbivores. Their Interaction with Secondary Plant Metabolites.* Academic Press, New York and London. 1979. 718pp.

SCHAUENBERG, P.; PARIS, F. *Guide to Medicinal Plants.* Lutterworth Press, Guildford and London, UK. 1977. 349pp + 39 colour plates.

SIMMONDS, N.W. *Evolution of Crop Plants.* Longman, London and New York. 1976. 339pp.

STEYN, D.G. *The Toxicology of Plants in South Africa.* Central News Agency, South Africa. 1934. 631pp.

TAMPION, J. *Dangerous Plants.* David and Charles, Newton Abbot, UK. 1977. 176pp.

TUTIN, T.G. *Umbellifers of the British Isles.* (BSBI Handbook No. 2). Botanical Society of the British Isles, London, UK. 1980. 197pp.

VAHRMEIJER, J. *Poisonous Plants of South Africa that Cause Stock Losses.* Tafelberg Publishers Ltd., 28 Wale Street, Cape Town, South Africa. 1981. 168pp.

VICKERY, M.L.; VICKERY, B. *Secondary Plant Metabolism.* Macmillan Press Ltd., London, UK. 1981. 335pp.

VÖLKER, R. *Lehrbuch der Toxikologie für Tierärzte.* (Fröhner). (in German) Ferdinand Enke Verlag, Stuttgart, Germany. 6th Edition. 1950. 404pp.

VON OETTINGEN, W.F. *Poisoning. A Guide to Clinical Diagnosis and Treatment.* W.B. Saunders Company, Philadelphia and London. 1958. 627pp.

WATT, J.M.; BREYER-BRANDWIJK, M.G. *The Medicinal and Poisonous Plants of Southern and Eastern Africa.* E. & S. Livingstone Ltd., Edinburgh and London, UK. 1962. 1457pp.

WILLIS, J.C. *A Dictionary of the Flowering Plants and Ferns.* University Press, Cambridge, UK. 8th Edition, revised by H.K. Airy Shaw. 1973. 1245pp.

REFERENCES

The references for each of the plant families (arranged alphabetically) are in separate groups, numbered in the order in which they appear in the appropriate section of the text. The sections on fungi and pteridophytes precede those on the other plants.

Square brackets enclosing a title indicate that the original is not in English; most of such papers have English abstracts.

LARGER FUNGI

1 LINCOFF, G.; MITCHEL, D.H. Cyclopeptide poisoning. In: *Toxic and Hallucinogenic Mushroom Poisoning.* Van Nostrand Reinhold Co., New York, USA. 1977, 25-48.

2 RUMACK, B.H. Amanita poisoning: an examination of clinical symptoms. In: *Amanita Toxins and Poisoning. (International Amanita Symposium, Heidelberg, 1978).* Edited by H. Faulstich, B. Kommerell, and T. Wieland. Verlag Gerhard Witzstrock, Baden-Baden, Germany. 1980, 124-130.

3 WIELAND, T.; FAULSTICH, H. Amatoxins, phallotoxins, phallolysin and antamanide: the biologically active components of poisonous Amanita mushrooms. *CRC Critical Reviews in Biochemistry* 1978, 5, 185-260.

4 LAMPE, K.F. Pharmacology and therapy of mushroom intoxications. In: *Mushroom Poisoning: Diagnosis and Treatment.* Edited by B.H. Rumack and E. Salzman. CRC Press Inc., Florida, USA. 1978, 125-169.

5 FAULSTICH, H. Mushroom poisoning *Lancet* 1980, II, 794-795.

6 Poisons Unit. New Cross (Guy's) Hospital, London, UK. Personal communication.

7 VESCONI, S.; LANGER, M.; COSTAN-TINO, D. Mushroom poisoning and forced diuresis. *Lancet* 1980, II, 854-855.

8 WAUTERS, J.P.; ROSSEL, C.; FARQUET, J.J. Amanita phalloides poisoning treated by early charcoal haemoperfusion. *British Medical Journal* 1978, 2, 1465.

9 FLOERSHEIM, G.L. Treatment of experimental poisoning produced by extracts of Amanita phalloides. *Toxicology and Applied Pharmacology* 1975, 34, 499-508.

10 DUDOVÁ, V.; KUBIČKA, J.; VESELSKÝ, J. Thioctic acid in the treatment of Amanita phalloides intoxication. In: *Amanita Toxins and Poisoning. (International Amanita Symposium, Heidelberg, 1978).* Edited by H. Faulstich, B. Kommerell, and T. Wieland. Verlag Gerhard Witzstrock, Baden-Baden, Germany. 1980, 190-191.

11 ZULIK, R.; KASSAY, S.F. The role of thioctic acid in the treatment of Amanita phalloides intoxication. In: *Amanita Toxins and Poisoning. (International Amanita Symposium, Heidelberg, 1978).* Edited by H. Faulstich, B. Kommerell, and T. Wieland. Verlag Gerhard Witzstrock, Baden-Baden, Germany. 1980. 192-196.

12 BARTTER, F.C.; BERKSON, B.; GALLELLI, J.; HIRANKA, P. Thioctic acid in the treatment of poisoning with alpha-amanitin. In: *Amanita Toxins and Poisoning. (International Amanita Symposium, Heidelberg, 1978).* Edited by H. Faulstich, B. Kommerell, and T. Wieland. Verlag Gerhard Witzstrock, Baden-Baden, Germany. 1980, 196-202.

13 ANONYMOUS. Death-cap poisoning. [Editorial]. *Lancet* 1972, I, 1320-1321.

14 FLOERSHEIM, G.L. [Experimental basis for the treatment of death cap (Amanita phalloides) poisoning.] *Schweizerische Medizinische Wochenschrift* 1978, 108, 185-197.

15 VOGEL, G. The anti-amanita effect of silymarin. In: *Amanita Toxins and Poisoning. (International Amanita Symposium, Heidelberg, 1978).* Edited by H. Faulstich, B. Kommerell and T. Wieland. Verlag Gerhard Witzstrock, Baden-Baden, Germany. 1980, 180-189.

16 SCOTT, H.G. Poisonous plants and animals. In: *Food-borne Infections and Intoxications.* Edited by H. Riemann. Academic Press, New York and London. 1969, 543-604.

17 BASTIEN, P. A general practitioner's experience of Amanita phalloides poisoning. In: *Amanita Toxins and Poisoning. (International Amanita Symposium, Heidelberg, 1978).* Edited by H. Faulstich, B. Kommerell and T. Wieland. Verlag Gerhard Witzstrock, Baden-Baden, Germany. 1980, 211-215.

18 GUEST, I. Doctor survives poison. *The Guardian*, September 17, 1981, 7.

19 DUMONT, A.-M.; CHENNEBAULT, J.-M.; ALQUIER, P.; JARDEL, H. Management of Amanita phalloides poisoning by Bastien's regimen. *Lancet* 1981, I, 722.

20 FAULSTICH, H.; FAUSER, U. Amanitin poisoning in the dog. In: *Pathogenesis and Mechanisms of Liver Cell Necrosis. (A workshop on experimental liver injury, Freiburg, West Germany, 1974)*. University Park Press, Baltimore, USA. 1975, 69-74.

21 PIERCY, P.L.; HARGIS, G.; BROWN, C.A. Mushroom poisoning in cattle. *Journal of the American Veterinary Medical Association* 1944, 105, 206-208.

22 CRISTEA, I. [Poisoning of goats by mushrooms.] *Recueil de Médecine Vétérinaire* 1970, 146, 507-512.

23 BRADY, L.R.; BENEDICT, R.G.; TYLER, V.E.; STUNTZ, D.E.; MALONE, M.H. Identification of Conocybe filaris as a toxic basidiomycete. *Lloydia* 1975, 38, 172-173.

24 TYLER, V.E.; BRADY, L.R.; BENEDICT, R.G.; KHANNA, J.M.; MALONE, M.H. Chromatographic and pharmacologic evaluation of some toxic Galerina species. *Lloydia* 1963, 26, 154-157.

25 TRAD, J.; PARAF, A.; OPOLON, P.; ROLLEN, A. [A para-phalloidin syndrome with severe icterus, due to Lepiota helveola (sensu lato).] *Semaine des Hôpitaux de Paris* 1970, 46, 31-34, 2163-2169.

26 EILERS, F.I.; BARNARD, B.L. A rapid method for the diagnosis of poisoning caused by the mushroom Lepiota morgani. *American Journal of Clinical Pathology* 1973, 60, 823-825.

27 WATLING, R. Cortinarius speciosissimus: the cause of renal failure in two young men. *Mycopathologia* 1982, 79, 71-78.

28 KÜRNSTEINER, H.; MOSER, M. Isolation of a lethal toxin from Cortinarius orellanus Fr. *Mycopathologia* 1981, 74, 65-72.

29 GRZYMALA, S. [Experiences with Dermocybe orellana (Fr.) in Poland. B. Mass poisoning.] *Zeitschrift für Pilzkunde* 1957, 23, 138-142.

30 FAVRE, H.; LESKI, M.; CHRISTELLER, P.; VOLLENWEIDER, E.; CHATE-LANAT, F. [Cortinarius orellanus: a toxic fungus inducing severe delayed renal failure.] *Schweizerische Medizinische Wochenschrift* 1976, 106, 1097-1102.

31 SORESINA, P.; LEONI, G. [Cortinarius orellanus and its toxic effects.] *Micologia Italiana* 1978, 3, 9-15.

32 HULMI, S.; SIPPONEN, P.; FORSSTRÖM, J.; VILSKA, J. [Mushroom poisoning caused by Cortinarius speciosissimus. A report on four cases.] *Duodecim* 1974, 90, 1044-1050.

33 SHORT, A.I.K.; WATLING, R.; MacDONALD, M.K.; ROBSON, J.S. Poisoning by Cortinarius speciosissimus. *Lancet* 1980, II, 942-944.

34 GRZYMALA, S. [Clinical study of poisonings by Cortinarius orellanus Fr. mushrooms.] *Bulletin de Médecine Légale et de Toxicologie Médicale* 1965, 8, 60-70.

35 ÖVERÅS, J.; ULVUND, M.J.; BAKKEVIG, S.; EIKEN, R. Poisoning in sheep induced by the mushroom Cortinarius speciosissimus. *Acta Veterinaria Scandinavica* 1979, 20, 148-150.

36 CHILTON, W.S. Chemistry and mode of action of mushroom toxins. In: *Mushroom Poisoning: Diagnosis and Treatment*. Edited by B.H. Rumack and E. Salzman. CRC Press Inc., Florida, USA. 1978, 87-124.

37 LINCOFF, G.; MITCHEL, D.H. Monomethylhydrazine poisoning. In: *Toxic and Hallucinogenic Mushroom Poisoning*. Van Nostrand Reinhold Co., New York, USA. 1977, 49-61.

38 NISKANEN, A.; PYYSALO, H.; RIMAILA-PÄRNÄNEN, E.; HARTIKKA, P. Short-term peroral toxicity of ethylidene gyromitrin in rabbits and chickens. *Food and Cosmetics Toxicology* 1976, 14, 409-415.

39 BRAUN, R.; GREEFF, U.; NETTER, K.J. Liver injury by the false morel poison gyromitrin. *Toxicology* 1979, 12, 155-163.

40 BRAUN, R.; KREMER, J.; RAU, H. Renal functional response to the mushroom poison gyromitrin. *Toxicology* 1979, 13, 187-196.

41 TOTH, B. Synthetic and naturally occurring hydrazones as possible cancer causative agents. *Cancer Research* 1975, 35, 3693.

42 FRANKE, S.; FREIMUTH, U.; LIST, P.H. [Toxicity of the spring morel Gyromitra (Helvella) esculenta Fr.] *Archiv für Toxikologie* 1967, 22, 293-332.

43 PEGLER, D.N. The Mitchell Beazley Pocket Guide to Mushrooms and Toadstools. Mitchell Beazley, London, UK. 1981. 164.

44 HATFIELD, G.M.; BRADY, L.R. Toxins of higher fungi. *Lloydia* 1975, 38, 36-55.

45 GREATOREX, J.C. Some unusual cases of plant poisoning in animals. *Veterinary Record* 1966, 78, 725-727.

46 HUNT, R.S.; FUNK. A. Mushrooms fatal to dogs. *Mycologia* 1977, 69, 432-433.

47 RIDGWAY, R.L. Mushroom (Amanita pantherina) poisoning. *Journal of the American Veterinary Medical Association* 1978, 172, 681-682.

48 LINCOFF, G.; MITCHEL, D.H. Toxic and Hallucinogenic Mushroom Poisoning. A Handbook for Physicians and Mushroom Hunters. Van Nostrand Reinhold Co., New York, USA. 1977, 77-99.

49 Poisons Unit. New Cross (Guy's) Hospital, London, UK. Personal communication.

50 RUMACK, B.H.; SALZMAN, E. Mushroom Poisoning: Diagnosis and Treatment. CRC Press Inc., Florida, USA. 1978, 177.

51 BENEDICT, R.G.; TYLER, V.E.; WATLING, R. Blueing in Conocybe, Psilocybe and a Stropharia species and the detection of psilocybin. *Lloydia* 1967, 30, 150-157.

52 YOUNG, R.E.; MILROY, R.; HUTCHISON, S.; KESSON, C.M. The rising price of mushrooms. *Lancet* 1982, I, 213-215.

53 SOWERBY, J. Coloured Figures of English Fungi or Mushrooms. 1803. Quoted in: *Naturaliste Canadienne* 1971, 98, 415-424. [On the hallucinogenic properties of Psilocybe semilanceata.] by R. Heim.

54 MURRAY, V.S.G.; FRANCIS, J. Review of enquiries made to the NPIS concerning Psilocybe mushroom ingestion, 1978-81. *Abstract, 10th International Congress of the European Association of Poison Control Centres, 3-6 August, 1982*, p.78.

55 MILLS, P.R.; LESINSKAS, D.; WATKINSON, G. The danger of hallucinogenic mushrooms. *Scottish Medical Journal* 1979, 24, 316-317.

56 HATFIELD, G.M.; VALDES, L.J. The occurrence of psilocybin in Gymnopilus species. *Lloydia* 1978, 41, 140-144.

57 PEDEN, N.R.; BISSETT, A.F.; MacAULEY, K.E.C.; CROOKS, J.; PELOSI, A.J. Clinical toxicology of 'magic mushroom' ingestion. *Postgraduate Medical Journal* 1981, 57, 543-545.

58 COOLES, P. Abuse of the mushroom Panaeolus foenisecii. *British Medical Journal* 1980, 280, 446-447.

59 WATLING, R. A Panaeolus poisoning in Scotland. *Mycopathologia* 1977, 61, 187-190.

60 MITCHEL, D.H.; RUMACK, B.H. Symptomatic diagnosis and treatment of mushroom poisoning. In: *Mushroom Poisoning: Diagnosis and Treatment*. Edited by B.H. Rumack and E. Salzman. CRC Press Inc., Florida, USA. 1978, 171-180.

61 Poisons Unit. New Cross (Guy's) Hospital, London, UK. Personal communication.

62 HATFIELD, G.M. Toxins in higher fungi. *Lloydia* 1975, 38, 36-55.

63 MARETIĆ, Z.; RUSSELL, F.E.; GOLOBIĆ, V. Twenty-five cases of poisoning by the mushroom Pleurotus olearius. *Toxicon* 1975, 13, 379-381.

64 HATFIELD, G.M.; SCHAUMBERG, J.P. Isolation and structural studies of coprine, the disulfiram-like constituent of Coprinus atramentarius. *Lloydia* 1975, 38, 489-496.

65 CHILD, G.P. The inability of coprini to sensitise man to ethyl alcohol. *Mycologia* 1952, 44, 200-202.

66 JOSSERAND, M. The ability of coprini to sensitise man to ethyl alcohol. *Mycologia* 1952, 44, 829-831.

67 KÜNG, W. [The ink cap, Coprinus atramentarius (Bull. ex Fr.).] *Schweizerische Zeitschrift für Pilzkunde* 1972, 50, 82-85.

68 LINCOFF, G.; MITCHEL, D.H. Toxic and Hallucinogenic Mushrooms. A Handbook for Physicians and Mushroom Hunters. Van Nostrand Reinhold Co., New York, USA. 1977, 67.

69 COCHRAN, K.W.; COCHRAN, M.W. Clitocybe clavipes: Antabuse-like reaction to alcohol. *Mycologia* 1978, 70, 1124-1126.

70 HAMILTON, A.G. Clouded agarics. *British Medical Journal* 1981, 282, 825.

71 HARLEY, R.M. Royal Botanic Gardens, Kew, Surrey, UK. Personal communication.

72 LINCOFF, G.; MITCHEL, D.H. Toxic and Hallucinogenic Mushroom Poisoning. A Handbook for Physicians and Mushroom Hunters. Van Nostrand Reinhold Co., New York, USA. 1977, 138.

73 COOPER, P. Poisoning by Drugs and Chemicals, Plants and Animals. Alchemist Publications, London, UK. 3rd Edition, 1974, 94-95.

74 HERMS, H. [Morel (Helvella esculenta) poisoning in dogs.] *Berliner und Münchener Tierärztliche Wochenschrift* 1950, 63, 161.

75 STEVENSON, J.A.; BENJAMIN, C.R. Scleroderma poisoning. *Mycologia* 1961, 53, 438-439.

76 VESELSKÝ, J.; DVOŘÁK, J. [The course of a case of poisoning by Tricholoma sulphureum (Bull. ex Fr.) Kumm.] *Česká Mykologie* 1981, 35, 114-115.

ERGOT

1 ANONYMOUS. St. Anthony's Fire. *Lancet* 1951, II, 436.

2 MATOSSIAN, M.K. Mold poisoning: an unrecognised English health problem, 1550-1800. *Medical History* 1981, 25, 73-84.

3 LORENZ, K. Ergot on cereal grains. *Critical Reviews in Food Science and Nutrition* 1979, 11, 311-354.

4 WATSON, R.D. The handling of risks of mycotoxicoses from an ergot epidemic in northern Scotland (a cautionary tale). *Proceedings of the Fourth Meeting on Mycotoxins in Animal Disease. 1981.* 5pp.

5 LONG, E. Ergot — the growing menace to cereal profits. *Farmers Weekly* 1981, October 23, 87.

6 ANONYMOUS. (Ergot) Disease is building up in the East. *Farmers Weekly* 1981, October 23, 87, 89.

7 UKASTA (United Kingdom Agricultural Supply Trade Association Limited) Press Information 1981, 25.

8 BURFENING, P.J. Ergotism. *Journal of the American Veterinary Medical Association* 1973, 163, 1288-1290.

9 GRÖGER, D. Ergot. In: *Microbial Toxins. Vol. 8. Fungal toxins.* Edited by S. Kadis, A. Ciegler and S.J. Ajl. Academic Press, New York and London. 1972, 321-373.

10 DINNUSSON, W.E.; HAUGSE, C.N.; KNUTSON, R.D. Ergot in rations for fattening cattle. *North Dakota Farm Research Bulletin* 1971, 29 (2), 20-22.

11 WHITTEMORE, C.T.; MACER, R.C.F.; MILLER, J.K.; MANTLE, P.G. Some consequences of the ingestion by young and growing pigs of feed contaminated with ergot. *Research in Veterinary Science* 1976, 20, 61-69.

12 FORSYTH, A.A. British Poisonous Plants. HMSO, London, UK. Ministry of Agriculture, Fisheries and Food Bulletin 161, 1968, 20-21 (amended 1979, 17-19).

13 QUINLAN, J. A note on the occurrence of acute ergot (Claviceps purpurea) poisoning in steers. *Journal of the South African Veterinary Medical Association* 1956, 27, 113-114.

14 EDWARDS, C.M. Ergot poisoning in young cattle. *Veterinary Record* 1953, 65, 158-159.

15 WOODS, A.J.; BRADLEY JONES, J.; MANTLE, P.G. An outbreak of gangrenous ergotism in cattle. *Veterinary Record* 1966, 78, 742-749.

16 MANTLE, P.G. Ergotism in sheep. In: *Mycotoxic Fungi, Mycotoxins, Mycotoxicoses. An encyclopedic handbook.* Edited by T.D. Wyllie and L.G. Morehouse. Marcel Dekker Inc., New York, USA. Vol. 2, 1978, 207-213.

17 CLEGG, F.G. A convulsive syndrome in sheep. *Veterinary Record* 1959, 71, 824-827.

18 KALLELA, K. [Unusually high alkaloid content in ergot from pasture grass.] *Proceedings of the 12th Nordic Veterinary Congress, Reykjavik.* A/S Karl Fr. Mortenson, Copenhagen, Denmark. 1974, 284.

19 GREATOREX, J.C.; MANTLE, P.G. Experimental ergotism in sheep. *Research in Veterinry Science* 1973, 15, 337-346.

20 FRIEND, D.W.; MacINTYRE, T.M. Effect of rye ergot on growth and N-retention in growing pigs. *Canadian Journal of Comparative Medicine* 1970, 34, 198-202.

21 WHITTEMORE, C.T.; MILLER, J.K.; MANTLE, P.G. Further studies concerning the toxicity of ingested ergot sclerotia (Claviceps purpurea) to young and growing pigs. *Research in Veterinary Science* 1977, 22, 146-150.

22 WRATHALL, A.E. Reproductive Disorders in Pigs. Commonwealth Agricultural Bureaux, Farnham Royal, UK. 1975, 89-92.

23 BARNIKOL, H.; GRUBER, S.; THALMANN, A.; SCHMIDT, H.L. [Ergot poisoning in pigs.] *Tierärztliche Umschau* 1982, 37, 324-332.

24 ANDERSON, J.F.; WERDIN, R.E. Ergotism manifested as agalactia and gangrene in sows. *Journal of the American Veterinary Medical Association* 1977, 170, 1089-1091.

25 O'NEIL, J.B.; RAE, W.J. Ergot tolerance in chicks and hens. *Poultry Science* 1965, 44, 1404.

26 SPESIVTSEVA, N.A. Mikozy i mikotoksikozy. Izdatel'stvo "Kolos", Moscow, USSR. 2nd Edition 1964, 329.

27 ANONYMOUS. The doom of St. Anthony's Fire. *Farmers Weekly* 1981, October 23, 89.

MYCOTOXINS

1 PATTERSON, D.S.P. Mycotoxins. *Environmental Chemistry* 1982, 2, 205-233.

2 WYLLIE, T.D.; MOREHOUSE, L.G. (Editors). Mycotoxic Fungi, Mycotoxins and Mycotoxicoses. An Encyclopedic Handbook. Marcel Dekker Inc., New York, USA. Vol. 2, 1978. 570pp.

3 CIEGLER, A. Mycotoxins: occurrence, chemistry, biological activity. *Lloydia* 1975, 38, 21-35.

4 The Fertilisers and Feeding Stuffs (Amendment) Regulations. HMSO, London UK. Statutory Instrument 1976, No. 840.

5 The Fertilisers and Feeding Stuffs (Amendment) Regulations. HMSO, London, UK. Statutory Instruments 1982, No. 386.

6 ROBB, J.; KIRKPATRICK, K.S.; NORVAL, M. Association of toxin-producing fungi with disease in broilers. *Veterinary Record* 1982, 111, 389-390.

EQUISETACEAE

1 EVANS, E.T.R.; EVANS, W.C.; ROBERTS, H.E. Studies on bracken poisoning in the horse. *British Veterinary Journal* 1951, 107, 364-371, 399-411.

2 FORSYTH, A.A. British Poisonous Plants. HMSO, London, UK. Ministry of Agriculture, Fisheries and Food Bulletin 161, 1968, 25-26 (amended 1979, 26-27).

3 KINGSBURY, J.M. Poisonous Plants of the United States and Canada. Prentice-Hall, New Jersey, USA. 1964, 114-118.

4 McLEAN, A.; NICHOLSON, H.H. Stock poisoning plants of the British Columbia Ranges. Canada Department of Agriculture 1958, Publication 1037, 23-24.

5 FORENBACHER, S. [Horsetail poisoning of horses — a B_1 avitaminosis.] *Schweizer Archiv für Tierheilkunde* 1952, 94, 153-171.

6 BOCOS, E.I. [Obversations on Equisetum poisoning in animals.] *Revista Zootehnie și Medicină Veterinară* 1971, 21 (8), 57-59.

7 HUDSON, R. Poisoning by horsetail (Equisetum arvense). *Veterinary Journal* 1924, 80, 40.

8 GUSYNIN, I.A. [The Toxicology of Poisonous Plants.] Gosudarstvennoe Izdatel'stvo Sel'skokhozyaistvennoi Literatury, Moscow, USSR. 1955, 109-112.

9 LINDT, S. [Horsetail poisoning in calves.] *Schweizer Archiv für Tierheilkunde* 1959, 101, 461-464.

10 DERIVAUX, J.; LIÉGOIS, F. Toxicologie Vétérinaire. Vigot Frères, Paris, France. 1962, 231-232.

11 LOTT, D.G. The use of thiamin in mare's tail poisoning of horses. *Canadian Journal of Comparative Medicine* 1951, 15, 274-276.

ASPIDIACEAE

1 MURRAY, V. Suspected poisoning by common buckle fern (Dryopteris family). *Irish Veterinary Journal* 1966, 20, 122-124.

2 EDGAR, J.T.; THIN, I.M. Plant poisoning involving male fern. *Veterinary Record* 1968, 82, 33-34.

3 MacLEOD, N.S.M.; GREIG, A.; BONN, J.M.; ANGUS, K.W. Poisoning in cattle associated with Dryopteris filix-mas and D. borreri. *Veterinary Record* 1978, 102, 239-240.

4 ROSEN, E.S.; EDGAR, J.T.; SMITH, J.L.S. Male fern retro-bulbar neuropathy in cattle. *Journal of Small Animal Practice* 1970, 10, 619-625.

DENNSTAEDTIACEAE

1 TAYLOR, J.A. Bracken: an increasing problem and a threat to health. *Outlook on Agriculture* 1980, 10, 298-304.

2 MINISTRY OF AGRICULTURE, FISHERIES AND FOOD. Bracken and its control. Advisory Leaflet No. 190, amended 1978, 8pp.

3 EVANS, I.A. Relationship between bracken and cancer. *Botanical Journal of the Linnean Society* 1976, 73, 105-112.

4 COOPER-DRIVER, G.A.; SWAIN, T. Cyanogenic polymorphism in bracken in relation to herbivore predation. *Nature, London,* 1976, 260, 604.

5 PARKER, W.H.; McCREA, C.T. Bracken (Pteris aquilina) poisoning of sheep in the North York Moors. *Veterinary Record* 1965, 77, 861-866.

6 WATSON, W.A.; TERLECKI, S.; PATTERSON, D.S.P.; SWEASEY, D.; HEBERT, C.N.; DONE, J.T. Experimentally produced retinal degeneration (bright blindness) in sheep. *British Veterinary Journal* 1972, 128, 457-469.

7 ALLSUP, T.N.; GRIFFITHS, W.R. Progressive retinal degeneration in sheep in South Wales. *Veterinary Record* 1978, 103, 268.

8 KELLEWAY, R.A.; GEOVJIAN, L. Acute bracken fern poisoning in a 14-month-old horse. *Veterinary Medicine and Small Animal Clinician* 1978, 73, 295-296.

9 THOMAS, A.J. Bracken poisoning in animals. *Biochemical Journal* 1963, 88, 56P-57P.

10 EVANS, W.C. Bracken thiaminase-mediated neurotoxic syndromes. *Botanical Journal of the Linnean Society* 1976, 73, 113-131.

11 PAMUKCU, A.M.; YALCINER, S.; HATCHER, J.F.; BRYAN, G.T. Quercetin, a rat intestinal and bladder carcinogen present in bracken fern (Pteridium aquilinum). *Cancer Research* 1980, 40, 3468-3472.

12 WOGAN, G.N.; BUSBY, W.F. Naturally occurring carcinogens. In: *Toxic Constituents of Plant Foodstuffs.* Edited by I.E. Liener. Academic Press, New York and London. 2nd Edition, 1980, 329-369.

13 LEACH, H.; BARBER, G.D.; EVANS, I.A.; EVANS, W.C. Isolation of an active principle from the bracken fern that is mutagenic, carcinogenic and lethal to mice on intraperitoneal injection. *Biochemical Journal* 1971, 124, 13P-14P.

14 EVANS, I.A.; JONES, R.S.; MAINWARING-BURTON, R. Passage of bracken fern toxicity into milk. *Nature, London* 1972, 237, 107-108.

15 HARDING, J.D.J. Bracken poisoning in pigs. *Agriculture* 1972, 79, 313-314.

16 EVANS, W.C.; WIDDOP, B.; HARDING, J.D.J. Experimental poisoning by bracken rhizomes in pigs. *Veterinary Record* 1972, 90, 471-475.

17 PENBERTHY, J. Vegetable poisoning(?) simulating anthrax in cattle. *Journal of Comparative Pathology and Therapeutics* 1893, 6, 266-275.

18 ALMOND, N. In: Fern poisoning (editorial). *Joournal of Comparative Pathology and Therapeutics* 1894, 7, 165-167.

19 EVANS, W.C.; EVANS, E.T.R. Studies on the biochemistry of pasture plants — No. 3. The effects of bracken (Pteris aquilina) in the diet of rats, and the problem of bracken poisoning in farm animals. *British Veterinary Journal* 1949, 105, 175-186.

20 STATE VETERINARY SERVICE. Effect of the drought of 1976 on the health of cattle, sheep and other farm livestock in England and Wales. *Veterinary Record* 1982, 111, 407-411.

21 ANONYMOUS. Veterinary Investigation Diagnosis Analysis II 1981 and 1975-81. Published 1982. Epidemiology Unit, Central Veterinary Laboratory, Weybridge, Surrey, UK.

22 TUSTIN, R.C.; ADELAAR, T.F.; MELDAL-JOHNSON, C.M. Bracken poisoning in cattle in the Natal midlands. *Journal of the South African Veterinary Medical Association* 1968, 39, No. 3, 91-99.

23 EVANS, W.C.; EVANS, I.A.; AXFORD, R.F.E.; THRELFALL, G.; HUMPHREYS, D.A.; THOMAS, A.J. Studies on bracken poisoning in cattle. VII. The toxicity of bracken rhizomes. *Veterinary Record* 1961, 73, 852-853.

24 AUSTIN, F.H. Bracken poisoning: a review. *Irish Veterinary Journal* 1964, 18, 22-28.

25 FORSYTH, A.A. British Poisonous Plants. HMSO, London, UK. Ministry of Agriculture, Fisheries and Food Bulletin 161, 1979, 28-30.

26 EVANS, W.C. Bracken poisoning of farm animals. *Veterinary Record* 1964, 76, 365-372.

27 YAMANE, O.; HAYASHI, T.; SAKO, S.; TATEMATSU, S.; TAKEDA, K.; FUKUSHIMA, H. Studies on the haemorrhagic diathesis of experimental bovine bracken poisoning. II. Heparin-like substance level in blood. *Japanese Journal of Veterinary Science* 1975, 37, 341-347.

28 IVINS, L. Central Veterinary Laboratory, Weybridge, Surrey, UK. Personal communication.

29 ROSENBERGER, G. VON. Nature, manifestations, cause and control of chronic enzootic haematuria in cattle. *Veterinary Medical Review* 1971, No. 2/3, 189-206.

30 WATSON, W.A.; BARLOW, R.M.; BARNETT, K.C. Bright blindness — a condition prevalent in Yorkshire hill sheep. *Veterinary Record* 1965, 77, 1060-1069.

31 ROSENBERGER, G. VON; HEESCHEN, W. [Bracken, the cause of bovine enzootic haematuria.] *Deutsche Tierärztliche Wochenschrift* 1960, 67, 201-207.

32 McCREA, C.T.; HEAD, K.W. Sheep tumours in North East Yorkshire. II. Experimental induction of tumours. *British Veterinary Journal* 1981, 31, 21-30.

33 WATSON, W.A.; BARNETT, K.C.; TERLECKI, S. Progressive retinal degeneration (bright blindness) in sheep: a review. *Veterinary Record* 1972, 91, 665-670.

34 JARRETT, W.F.H.; McNEIL, P.E.; GRIMSHAW, W.T.R.; SELMAN, I.E.; McINTYRE, W.I.M. High incidence area of cattle cancer with a possible interaction between an environmental carcinogen and a papilloma virus. *Nature, London* 1978, 274, 215-217.

35 CLARKE, M.L.; HARVEY, D.G.; HUMPHREYS, D.J. Veterinary Toxicology. Baillière Tindall, London, UK. 2nd Edition, 1981, 214-217.

36 PAMUKCU, A.M.; CHING YUNG WANG; HATCHER, J.; BRYAN, G.T. Carcinogenicity of tannin and tannin-free extracts of bracken fern (Pteridium aquilinum) in rats. *Journal of the National Cancer Institute* 1980, 65, 131-136.

37 EVANS, I.A. Bracken carcinogenicity. *Research in Veterinary Science* 1979, 26, 339-348.

ALLIACEAE

1 WILLIAMS, H.H.; ERICKSON, B.N.; BEACH, E.F.; MACY, I.G. Biochemical studies of the blood of dogs with n-propyl disulphide anemia. *Journal of Laboratory and Clinical Medicine* 1941, 29, 996-1008.

2 DIN, Z.Z.; AHMAD, Y.; ELSON, C.E.; QURESHI, A.A. Inhibition of lipid metabolism by garlic and its fractions in chicken liver. *Federation Proceedings* 1982, 41, 544.

3 PIERCE, K.R.; JOYCE, J.R.; ENGLAND, R.B.; JONES, L.P. Acute hemolytic anemia caused by wild onion poisoning in horses. *Journal of the American Veterinary Medical Association* 1972, 160, 323-327.

4 VAN KAMPEN, K.R.; JAMES, L.F.; JOHNSON, A.E. Hemolytic anemia in sheep fed wild onion (Allium validum). *Journal of the American Veterinary Medical Association* 1970, 156, 328-332.

5 LEWIS, G. Ministry of Agriculture, Fisheries and Food, Central Veterinary Laboratory, Weybridge, Surrey, UK. Personal communication.

6 GILL, P.A.; SERGEANT, E.S.G. Onion poisoning in a bull. *Australian Veterinary Journal* 1981, 57, 484.

7 HOTHI, D.S.; ARNEJA, J.S.; CHAWLA, J.S. Onion (Allium cepa) poisoning in bullocks. *Indian Veterinary Journal* 1980, 57, 690-692.

8 HUTCHISON, T.W.S. Onions as a source of Heinz body anaemia and death in cattle. *Canadan Veterinary Journal* 1977, 18, 358-360.

9 LAZARUS, A.E.; RAJAMANI, S. Poisoning due to onion spoilage in cattle. *Indian Veterinary Journal* 1968, 45, 877-880.

10 KIRK, J.H.; BULGIN, M.S. Effect of feeding cull domestic onions (Allium cepa) to sheep. *American Journal of Veterinary Research* 1979, 40, 397-399.

11 JAMES, L.F.; BINNS, W. Effect of feeding wild onions (Allium validum) to bred ewes. *Journal of the American Veterinary Medical Association* 1966, 149, 512-514.

12 FRANKEN, P.; VAN BEUKELEN, P.; BLOK, G. [Onions: not a horse feed.] *Tijdschrift voor Diergeneeskunde* 1980, 105, 529-534.

13 FORSYTH, A.A. British Poisonous Plants, HMSO, London, UK. Ministry of Agriculture, Fisheries and Food Bulletin 161, 1968, 105 (amended 1979, 106).

14 IMADA, O. [Experimental work on onion poisoning in dogs — relationship between the quantity of onion supplied and the onset of disease.] *Bulletin of Azabu University of Veterinary Medicine* 1980, 1, 271-287.

15 SPICE, R.N. Hemolytic anemia associated with ingestion of onions in a dog. *Canadian Veterinary Journal* 1976, 17, 181-183.

16 STALLBAUMER, M. Onion poisoning in a dog. *Veterinary Record* 1981, 108, 523-524.

17 KOBAYASHI, K. Onion poisoning in the cat. *Feline Practice* 1981, 11, 22-27.

18 SPISNI, D.; FRATESCHI, T.L.; MARIANI, A.P.; MARTELLI, F. [Effect of methionine treatment on rabbits made anaemic by feeding on onions.] *Annali della Facoltà di Medicina Veterinaria di Pisa* 1971, 24, 35-46.

19 COWAN, J.W.; SAGHIR, A.R.; SALJI, J.P. Antithyroid activity of onion volatiles. *Australian Journal of Biological Sciences* 1967, 20, 683-685.

20 WATT, J.M.; BREYER-BRANDWIJK, M.G. The Medicinal and Poisonous Plants of Southern and Eastern Africa. E. & S. Livingstone Ltd., Edinburgh and London, UK. 2nd Edition, 1962, 670-679.

AMARYLLIDACEAE

1 HONNEGER, R.E.; FURRER, J. [Some noteworthy causes of death in reptiles.] *Salamandra* 1975, 11, 179-181.

2 NIEUWLAND, I.C.H. [The use of bulbs as cattle feed.] *Tijdschrift voor Diergeneeskunde* 1941, 68, 359-368.

3 LITOVITZ, T.L.; FAHEY, B.A. Please don't eat the daffodils. *New England Journal of Medicine* 1982, 306, 547.

4 Poisons Unit. New Cross (Guy's) Hospital, London, UK. Personal Communication.

5 HARDIN, J.W.; ARENA, J.M. Human Poisoning from Native and Cultivated Plants. Duke University Press, Durham, North Carolina, USA. 1969, 39-40.

AQUIFOLIACEAE

1 STANDRING, G.; GOULDING, R. Poisonous plants. *Nursing Times* 1969, August 7, 1009-1011.

2 SCHILLING, R.; SPEAKER. J. Incidence of plant poisoning in Philadelphia noted as poison information calls. *Veterinary and Human Toxicology* 1980, 22, 148-150.

3 O'LEARY, S.B. Poisoning in man from eating poisonous plants. *Archives of Environmental Health* 1964, 9, 216-242.

ARACEAE

1 OEHME, F.W. The hazard of plant toxicities in the human population. In: *Effects of Poisonous Plants on Livestock*. Edited by R.F. Keeler, K.R. Van Kampen and L.F. James. Academic Press, New York and London. 1978, 67-81.

2 O'MOORE, L.B. Arum maculatum poisoning in cattle. *Irish Veterinary Journal* 1955, 9, 146-147.

3 GLYN, M. An unknown equine condition. *Veterinary Record* 1968, 82, 554.

4 DABIJA, G.; DOMILESCU, C.; NEMŢEANU, S. [Toxicity of Arum maculatum for animals.] *Archiva Veterinaria* 1968, 4, 157-168.

5 STANDRING, G.; GOULDING, R. Poisonous plants. *Nursing Times* 1969, August 7, 1009-1011.

6 Poisons Unit. New Cross (Guy's) Hospital, London, UK. Personal communication.

7 ALTMANN, H. Poisonous Plants and Animals. Chatto and Windus, London, UK. 1980, 112.

8 SCHURZ, J. [Wild arum] *Kosmos* 1976, 72, 74-75.

ARALIACEAE

1 BOHOSIEWICZ, M. Toksykologia Weterynaryjna. Panstwowe Wydawnictwo Rolnicze i Leśne, Warsaw, Poland. 1970, 270.

2 FORSYTH, A.A. British Poisonous Plants. HMSO, London, UK. Ministry of Agriculture, Fisheries and Food Bulletin 161, 1968, 67-68 (amended 1979, 68-69).

3 MAHE-QUINIO, M.; ROSSINYOL, G.; FOUCAUD, A. [Fatal poisoning of chickens by ivy seeds.] *Plantes Médicinales et Phytothérapie* 1975, 9, 182-186.

4 CORNEVIN, C. Des Plantes Vénéneuses. Librairie de Firmin-Didot, Paris, France. 1887, 402-403.

5 GOLDMAN, L.; PRESTON, R.H.; MUEGEL, H.R. Dermatitis venenata from English ivy (Hedera helix). *Archives of Dermatology* 1956, 74, 311-312.

BERBERIDACEAE

1 SCOTT, H.G. Poisonous Plants and Animals. In: *Food-borne Infections and Intoxications*. Edited by H. Riemann. Academic Press, New York and London. 1969, 543-604.

2 Poisons Unit. New Cross (Guy's) Hospital, London, UK. Personal communication.

3 MITCHELL, J.; ROOK, A. Botanical Dermatology. Plants and Plant Products Injurious to the Skin. Greengrass Ltd., Vancouver, Canada. 1979, 131.

BORAGINACEAE

1 MATTOCKS, A.R. Toxic pyrrolizidine alkaloids in comfrey. *Lancet* 1980, II, 1136-1137.

2 KEINDORF, A.; KEINDORF, H.-J. [Nitrate-nitrite poisoning in pigs caused by the intake of comfrey (Symphytum asperum).] *Monatshefte für Veterinärmedizin* 1978, 33, 425-427.

3 ROHRBACH, J.A. Tongue ulcers in cats. *Veterinary Record* 1977, 101, 292.

4 GONNERMANN, H. [Kytta preparations used by veterinary practitioners.] *Tierärztliche Umschau* 1976, 31, 402 and 404.

5 SHIPOCHLIEV, T.A. Pharmacological investigations of some extracts of Symphytum officinale. *20th World Veterinary Congress, Thessaloniki, Greece, 1975,* Summaries vol. 1, 166.

6 SCHAUENBERG, P.; PARIS, F. Guide to Medicinal Plants. Lutterworth Press, Guildford and London, UK. 1977, 54.

7 JORDAN, M. A Guide to Wild Plants. Millington Books Ltd., London, UK. 1976, 106-107.

8 HILLS, L.D. Comfrey Report. The story of the world's fastest protein builder. Henry Doubleday Research Association, Bocking, Braintree, Esses, UK. 1975, 98pp.

9 HIRONO, I.; HIDEKI, M.; HAGA, M. Carcinogenic activity of Symphytum officinale. *Journal of the National Cancer Institute* 1978, 61, 865-869.

10 ANONYMOUS. Recently the herb comfrey has received attention in the press and on television as a possible cause of cancer. Is this correct? *British Medical Journal* 1979, 1, 598.

11 MITCHELL, J.; ROOK, A. Botanical Dermatology. Plants and Plant Products Injurious to the Skin. Greengrass Ltd., Vancouver, Canada. 1979, 140.

12 GREATOREX, J.C. Some unusual cases of plant poisoning in animals. *Veterinary Record* 1966, 78, 725-727.

13 MANDRYKA, I.I. [Cynoglossum officinale (hound's tongue) as a poisonous plant.] *Veterinariya, Moscow* 1979, No. 9, 69-70.

14 SEAMAN, J.T. Pyrrolizidine alkaloid poisoning of horses. *Australian Veterinary Journal* 1978, 54, 150.

15 ST. GEORGE-GRAMBAUER, T.D. Hepatogenous chronic copper poisoning in sheep in South Australia due to the consumption of Echium plantagineum L. (Salvation Jane). *Australian Veterinary Journal* 1962, 38, 288-293.

16 SHARROCK, A.C. Pyrrolizidine alkaloid poisoning in a horse in New South Wales. *Australian Veterinary Journal* 1969, 45, 388.

17 BULL, L.B.; DICK, A.T.; KEAST, J.C.; EDGAR, G. An experimental investigation of the hepatotoxic and other effects on sheep of consumption of Heliotropium europaeum L.: heliotrope poisoning of sheep. *Australian Journal of Agricultural Research* 1956, 7, 281-332.

18 BULL, L.B.; ROGERS, E.S.; KEAST, J.C.; DICK, A.T. Heliotropium poisoning in cattle. *Australian Veterinary Journal* 1961, 37, 37-43.

BUXACEAE

1 FORSYTH, A.A. British Poisonous Plants. HMSO, London, UK. Ministry of Agriculture, Fisheries and Food Bulletin 161, 1968, 57-58 (amended 1979, 59-60).

2 SOEST, H. VAN; GOTINK, W.M.; VOOREN, L.J. VAN DEN. [Box poisoning in swine and cattle.] *Tijdschrift voor Diergeneeskunde* 1965, 90, 387-389.

3 BASTIEN, A.; GRISVARD, M.; JEAN-BLAIN, C.; ROUX, M. [Poisoning of young cattle by box.] *Bulletin de la Société des Sciences Vétérinaires et de Médecine Comparée de Lyon* 1973, 75, 289-290.

4 KRÜGER, A.; MATSCHULLAT, G. [Box poisoning in swine.] *Praktische Tierarzt* 1970, 51, 235-236.

5 VÖLKER, R. Lehrbuch der Toxikologie für Tierärzte. (Fröhner). Ferdinand Enke Verlag, Stuttgart, Germany. 6th Edition, 1950, 322-323.

CANNABACEAE

1 CARDASSIS, J. [Poisoning of horses by Cannabis indica.] *Recueil de Médecine Vétérinaire* 1951, 127, 971-973.

2 FRYE, F.L. Acute cannabis intoxication in a pup. *Journal of the American Veterinary Medical Association* 1968, 152, 472.

3 MERIWETHER, W.F. Acute marijuana toxicity in a dog. (A case report). *Veterinary Medicine* 1969, 64, 577-578.

4 SILVERMAN, J. Possible hashish intoxication in a dog. *Journal of the American Animal Hospital Association* 1974, 10, 517-519.

5 JONES, D.L. A case of canine cannabis ingestion. *New Zealand Veterinary Journal* 1978, 26, 135-136.

6 GODBOLD, J.C.; HAWKINS, B.J.; WOODWARD, M.G. Acute oral marijuana poisoning in the dog. *Journal of the American Veterinary Medical Association* 1979, 175, 1101-1102.

7 CROW, S.E.; SOKOLOWSKI, V. Marijuana intoxication. *Journal of the American Veterinary Medical Association* 1980, 176, 388.

8 THOMPSON, G.R.; ROSENKRANTZ, H.; SCHAEPPI, U.H.; BRAUDE, M.C. Comparison of acute oral toxicity of cannabinoids in rats, dogs and monkeys. *Toxicology and Applied Pharmacology* 1973, 25, 363-372.

CAPRIFOLIACEAE

1 RÎPEANU, M. [Observations on some important cases of poisoning in animals.] *Revista de Zootehnie si Medicină Veterinară* 1963, 13, No. 12, 67-68.

2 CORNEVIN, C. Des Plantes Vénéneuses. Librairie de Firmin-Didot, Paris, France. 1887, 406.

3 KINGSBURY, J.M. Poisonous Plants of the United States and Canada. Prentice-Hall, Inc., New Jersey, USA. 1964, 389-390.

4 Poisons Unit. New Cross (Guy's) Hospital, London, UK. Personal communication.

5 POGORZELSKI, E. Formation of cyanide as a product of decomposition of cyanogenic glycosides in the treatment of elderberry fruit (Sambucus nigra). *Journal of the Science of Food and Agriculture* 1982, 33, 496-498.

6 SZAUFER, M.; KOWALEWSKI, Z.; PHILLIPSON, J.D. Chelidonine from Symphoricarpos albus. *Phytochemistry* 1978, 17, 1446-1447.

SIEGERS, C.-P. [Poisonous plants in our environment. I. Poisonings by plants.] *Zietschrift für Allgemeinmedizin* 1978, 54, 1151-1158.

8 AMYOT, T.E. Poisoning by snowberries. *British Medical Journal* 1885, 1, 986.

9 LEWIS, W.H. Snowberry (Symphoricarpos) poisoning in children. *Journal of the American Medical Association* 1979, 242, 2663.

10 MITCHELL, J.; ROOK, A. Botanical Dermatology. Plants and Plant Products Injurious to the Skin. Greengrass Ltd., Vancouver, Canada. 1979, 158.

CARYOPHYLLACEAE

1 CORNEVIN, C. Des Plantes Vénéneuses. Librairie de Firmin-Didot, Paris, France. 1887, 248-261.

2 FORSYTH, A.A. British Poisonous Plants. HMSO, London, UK. Ministry of Agriculture, Fisheries and Food Bulletin 161, 1968, 47 (amended 1979, 48-49).

3 BUBIEŃ, Z.; KOTZ, J. [Corn cockle poisoning in domestic animals.] *Medycyna Weterynaryjna* 1965, 21, 458-460.

4 KOTZ, J. [Morphology and pathogenesis of corn cockle poisoning in poultry. I. History.] *Medycyna Weterynaryjna* 1964, 20, 200-204.

5 KOTZ, J. [Morphology and pathogenesis of corn cockle poisoning in poultry. II. III. IV.] *Medycyna Weterynaryjna*, 1965, 21, 143-150, 520-524, 730-734.

6 BIRK, Y.; PERI, I. Saponins. In: *Toxic Constituents of Plant Foodstuffs*. Edited by I.E. Liener. Academic Press, New York and London. 2nd Edition. 1980, 161-182.

CELASTRACEAE

1 CORNEVIN, C. Des Plantes Vénéneuses. Librairie de Firmin-Didot, Paris, France. 1887, 271-272.

2 ANHARS'KA, M.A.; BEZRUK, P.H. [Some data on the general pharmacology of glycoside SK.] *Farmatsevtychnyi Zhurnal* 1968, 23, 68-72.

3 FORSYTH, A.A. British Poisonous Plants. HMSO, London, UK. Ministry of Agriculture, Fisheries and Food Bulletin 161, 1968, 56-57 (amended 1979, 58-59).

4 GESSNER, O. [Fatal poisoning of horses by Euonymus europea L.] *Berliner und Münchener Tierärztliche Wochenschrift* 1943, 7/8, 47-48.

5 OETTINGEN, W.F. VON. Poisoning. A Guide to Clinical Diagnosis and Treatment. W.B. Saunders Company, Philadelphia and London. 2nd Edition, 1958, 361.

CHENOPODIACEAE *Beta* spp

1 SIMESEN, M.G.; KONGGARD, S.P. [Experimental investigations on fodder beet poisoning in cattle.] *Nordisk Veterinaer Medizin* 1970, 22, 174-185.

2 WILLIAMS, V.J.; COUP, M.R. Preliminary studies on the toxicity of fodder beet to sheep. *New Zealand Veterinary Journal* 1959, 7, 8-14.

3 PINKIEWICZ, E.; MADEJ, E.; SAMOREK, M. [Fresh fodder beet as a cause of bovine ketosis.] *Proceedings of the 17th World Veterinary Congress, Hannover 1963*, 2, 1377-1378.

4 POP, M. [Mass poisoning of cattle with sugar beet tops.] *Lucrarile Stiintifice Institutul Agronomic Cluj, Serie Medicine Veterinaria Zootehnia* 1965, 21, 105-110.

5 ALEKSEEV, N.P. [The parathyroids in mineral metabolism of bulls fattened on beet pulp.] *Sel'skokhozyaistvennaya Biologiya* 1976, 11, 96-102.

6 O'MOORE, L.B. The nitrate hazard in freshly lifted mangolds. *Irish Veterinary Journal* 1955, 9, 292-293.

7 MINISTRY OF AGRICULTURE, FISHERIES AND FOOD. Bulky feeds for dairy cows. Advisory Leaflet No. 524, 1977, 15pp.

8 KINGSBURY, J.M. Poisonous Plants of the United States and Canada. Prentice-Hall Inc., New Jersey, USA. 1964, 233.

9 SAVAGE, A. Nitrate poisoning from sugar beet tops. *Canadian Journal of Comparative Medicine* 1949, 13, 9-10.

10 FORSYTH, A.A. British Poisonous Plants. HMSO, London, UK. Ministry of Agriculture, Fisheries and Food Bulletin 161, 1968, 52 (amended 1979, 54).

11 JAMES, L.F. Oxalate poisoning in livestock. In: *Effects of poisonous plants on livestock.* Academic Press, New York and London. 1978, 139-145.

12 CONNOR, H.E. The Poisonous Plants in New Zealand. Bulletin 99, New Zealand Department of Scientific and Industrial Research. 2nd Edition. 1977, 25-26.

13 GORIŠEK, J. [Metabolic disorders in dairy cows due to the feeding of sugar beet leaves.] *Proceedings of the 17th World Veterinary Congress, Hannover 1963,* 2, 1343-1344.

14 GORIŠEK, J. [Blood coagulation and calcium content of blood and urine in cows fed sugar-beet leaves.] *Veterinarski Arhiv* 1960, 30, 300-306.

15 ZDELAR, F.; MITIN, V.; BIŠĆAN, J.; TRANGER, M. [Goitre of cattle in Croatia. IV. Effect of fresh sugar beet leaves on thyroid function in dairy cows.] *Veterinarski Arhiv* 1967, 37, 208-218.

16 MOCSY, J. [Poisoning of horses by old sugar beet tops.] *Allatorvosok Kozlemenyei* 1936, 33, 23-25.

CHENOPODIACEAE (other plants)

1 HIBBS, C.M. Cyanide and nitrate toxicoses of cattle. *Veterinary and Human Toxicology* 1979, 21, 401-403.

2 LIEBENOW, H. [Solanum nigrum L. and other weeds as nitrate-containing plants — their nitrate content.] *Wissenschaftliche Zeitschrift der Humboldt-Universität zu Berlin* 1970, 19, 73-80.

3 MADDEN, F.J. The effect of fat hen (Chenopodium album) on young lambs in dry conditions. *Institute of Inspectors of Stock of New South Wales Year Book* 1943, 25.

4 HERWEIJER, C.H.; HOUTER, L.F. DEN. Poisoning due to fat hen (Chenopodium album) in sheep. *Netherlands Journal of Veterinary Science* 1971, 4, 52-54.

5 PEARCE, O.D. Drought in the West. (Brassica campestris and Chenopodium album poisoning in cattle). *Veterinary Record* 1975, 97, 60.

6 ANONYMOUS. Oxalate poisoning in cows (Chenopodium album). *New Zealand Department of Agriculture. Annual Report for 1950-51,* 53-54.

7 GRZYBOWSKI, M.D. A peculiar, pellagra-like skin sensitisation to light in starving persons. *British Journal of Dermatology* 1948, 60, 410-415.

8 SEBASTYŃSKI, T. [A case of a pellagra-like condition after consumption of Chenopodium.] *Polski Tygodnik Lekarski* 1960, 15, 688-689.

9 SCHEUER-KARPIN, R. Poisoning by food plants. *Lancet* 1948, I, 574-575.

COMPOSITAE *Senecio*

1 FORBES, J.C. Ragwort survey in north-east Scotland. The Scottish Agricultural Colleges Research and Development Note No. 5, 1982.

2 WARREN, F.L. Senecio alkaloids. In: *The Alkaloids. Chemistry and Physiology.* Edited by R.H.F. Manske. Academic Press, New York and London. 1970, Vol. XII, 245-331.

3 MATTOCKS, A.R. Toxicity of pyrrolizidine alkaloids. *Nature, London* 1968, 217, 723-728.

4 TILT, S.E. Ragwort toxicosis in a heifer. *Canadian Veterinary Journal* 1969, 10, 302-306.

5 STOCKMAN, S. Poisoning of cattle with British ragwort. *Journal of Comparative Pathology and Therapeutics* 1917, 30, 131-134.

6 DUBY, G.D. Tansy ragwort: a toxic threat to livestock. *Modern Veterinary Practice* 1975, 56, 185-188.

7 LEWANDOWSKI, L.; KUTROWSKI, W. [Senecio jacobaea poisoning in heifers.] *Medycyna Weterynaryjna* 1957, 15, 518.

8 PEARSON, E.G. Clinical manifestations of tansy ragwort poisoning. *Modern Veterinary Practice* 1977, 58, 421-424.

9 ELCOCK, L.; OEHME, F.W. Senecio poisoning in horses: a summary. *Veterinary and Human Toxicology* 1982, 24, 122-123.

10 FORD, E.J.H. Clinical aspects of ragwort poisoning in horses. *Veterinary Annual* 1973, 14, 86-88.

11 MORTIMER, P.H.; WHITE, E.P. Toxicity of some composite (Senecio) weeds. In: *Proceedings of the 28th New Zealand Weed and Pest Control Conference 1975*, 88-91.

12 HARDING, J.D.J.; LEWIS, G.; DONE, J.T.; ALLCROFT, R. Experimental poisoning by Senecio jacobaea in pigs. *Pathologia Veterinaria* 1964, 1, 204-220.

13 DEAN, R.E.; WINWARD, A.H. An investigation into the possibility of tansy ragwort poisoning of black-tailed deer. *Journal of Wildlife Diseases* 1974, 10, 166-169.

14 PIERSON, M.L.; CHEEKE, P.R.; DICKINSON, E.O. Resistance of the rabbit to dietary pyrrolizidine (Senecio) alkaloid. *Research Communications in Chemical Pathology and Pharmacology* 1977, 16, 561-564.

15 SWICK, R.A. Senecio jacobaea: toxicity and effects on mineral metabolism in animals. *Dissertation Abstracts International* 1982, 43, 3B.

16 McGINNESS, J.P. Senecio jacobaea as a cause of hepatic encephalopathy. *California Veterinarian* 1980, 34, 20-22.

17 JOHNSON, A.E. Tolerance of cattle to tansy ragwort (Senecio jacobaea). *American Journal of Veterinary Research* 1978, 39, 1542-1544.

18 HOOPER, P.T. Spongy degeneration in the central nervous system of domestic animals. III. Occurrence and pathogenesis — hepatocerebral disease caused by hyperammonaemia. *Acta Neuropathologica* 1975, 31, 343-351.

19 FORSYTH, A.A. British Poisonous Plants. HMSO, London, UK. Ministry of Agriculture, Fisheries and Food Bulletin 161, 1968, 97-101 (amended 1979, 98-102).

20 GOPINATH, C.; FORD, E.J.H. The effect of ragwort (Senecio jacobaea) on the liver of the domestic fowl (Gallus domesticus): a histopathological and enzyme histochemical study. *British Poultry Science* 1977, 18, 137-141.

21 BUCKMASTER, G.W.; CHEEKE, P.R.; SHULL, L.R. Pyrrolizidine alkaloid poisoning in rats: protective effects of dietary cysteine. *Journal of Animal Science* 1976, 43, 464-473.

22 DICKINSON, J.O.; COOKE, M.P.; KING, R.R.; MOHAMED, P.A. Milk transfer of pyrrolizidine alkaloids in cattle. *Journal of the American Veterinary Medical Association* 1976, 169, 1192-1196.

23 MIRANDA, C.L.; CHEEKE, P.R.; GOEGER, D.E.; BUHLER, D.R. Effect of consumption of milk from goats fed Senecio jacobaea on hepatic drug metabolising enzyme activities in rats. *Toxicology Letters* 1981, 8, 343-347.

24 DEINZER, M.L.; THOMSON, P.A.; BURGETT, D.M.; ISAACSON, D.L. Pyrrolizidine alkaloids: their occurrence in honey from tansy ragwort (Senecio jacobaea L.). *Science, USA* 1977, 195, 497-499.

25 HOWES, F.N. Plants and Beekeeping. Faber and Faber, London, UK. 1979, 25.

26 MINISTRY OF AGRICULTURE, FISHERIES AND FOOD. Weed control — Ragwort. AW51. HMSO, London, UK. 1976 (amended 1978).

27 IRVINE, H.M.; FORBES, J.C.; DRAPER, S.R. Effect of 2,4-D on the water-soluble carbohydrate content of ragwort (Senecio jacobaea L.) leaves. *Weed Research* 1977, 17, 169-172.

COMPOSITAE (other plants)

1 THIVIERGE, G. Granular stomatitis in dogs due to burdock. *Canadian Veterinary Journal* 1973, 14, 96-97.

2 STOJANOVIĆ, D. [Burdock — cause of mortality in a pheasantry in the Požarevac region.] *Veterinarski Glasnik* 1971, 25, 707.

3 CORDY, D.R. Centaurea species and equine nigropallidal encephalomalacia. In: *Effects of Poisonous Plants on Livestock.* Edited by R.F. Keeler, K.R. Van Kampen and L.F. James. Academic Press, New York and London. 1978, 327-336.

4 CLAPHAM, A.R.; TUTIN, T.G.; WARBURG, E.F. Flora of the British Isles. Cambridge University Press, Cambridge, UK. 2nd Edition, 1962, 880.

5 BUBIEŃ, Z.; WACHNIK, Z.; ZUCHOWSKI, A. [Chicory root poisoning in heifers.] *Medycyna Weterynaryjna* 1962, 18, 603-605.

6 FRITZSCH, R. [Food poisoning in cattle from fodder plants: sunflower, beet leaves, Glyceria aquatica.] *Monatshefte für Veterinärmedizin* 1966, 21, 327-331.

7 TOMOV, A. [Poisoning of cattle with wild Helianthus species.] *Veterinariya, Moscow* 1965, 42, No. 2, 113.

8 GARBULIŃSKI, T.; BUBIEŃ, Z.; WEGRZYNOWICZ, R.; KOTZ, J. [Toxicity of helanin from Inula helenium, for laboratory animals.] *Zeszyty Naukowe Wyzszej Szkoly Rolniczej we Wroclawiu, Weterynaria* 1963, 15, 207-214.

9 ULBRICH, M.; LORENZ, H.; RITTENBACH, P.; ROSSOW, N.; VOIGT, O. [Inula conyza as a cause of mass poisoning among cattle.] *Monatshefte für Veterinärmedizin* 1966, 21, 896-902.

10 VOCKRODT, H. [Plant poisoning in farm animals (Senecio jacobaea and Inula conyza) and its prevention.] *Monatshefte für Veterinärmedizin* 1973, 28, 59-62.

11 MEADLY, G.R.W. Weeds of Western Australia. Stinkwort (Inula graveolens Desf.). *Journal of the Department of Agriculture, Western Australia* 1965, 6, 434-437.

12 MacADAM, J.F. Some poisonous plants of the north-west (of New South Wales). *Agricultural Gazette, New South Wales* 1966, 77, 73-78.

13 URROZ, I.G.; MERLO, I.; LAKSMAN, G.M.; GALLO, G.G. [Toxicity of milk thistle (Silybum marianum) for cattle.] *Revista de la Facultad de Ciencias Veterinarias de La Plata* 1960, 2, 93-103.

14 REYNOSO CASTRO, H.W.; SELFERO AUDICO, N. [Poisoning of cattle by the thistle Silybum marianum: use of methylene blue in high concentration.] *Gaceta Veterinaria* 1963, 25, 429-434.

15 STUART, B.P.; COLE, R.J.; GOSSER, H.S. Cocklebur (Xanthium strumarium, L. var. strumarium) intoxication in swine: review and redefinition of the toxic principle. *Veterinary Pathology* 1981, 18, 368-383.

16 KINGSBURY, J.M. Poisonous Plants of the United States and Canada. Prentice-Hall Inc., New Jersey, USA. 1964, 440-442.

17 RÎPEANU, M. [Some important cases of poisoning in animals.] *Revista de Zootehnie şi Medicină Veterinară* 1963, 13, No. 12, 67-68.

18 KRUSTEV, E. [An outbreak of Xanthium strumarium L. poisoning in pigs.] *Izvestiya na Instituta za Nezarazni Bolesti i Zookhigiena, Sofia* 1962, 2, 133-135.

19 HIBBS, C.M. Cyanide and nitrate toxicoses of cattle. *Veterinary and Human Toxicology* 1979, 21, 401-403.

20 FORSYTH, A.A. British Poisonous Plants. HMSO, London, UK. Ministry of Agriculture, Fisheries and Food Bulletin 161. 1968, 97 (amended 1979, 98).

CONVOLVULACEAE

1 AZARYAN, Kh.A. [Cuscuta poisoning in horses and control measures.] *Veterinariya, Moscow* 1955, 32, No. 6, 75-76.

2 IBRAGIMOV, Kh.Z.; KHABIEV, M.S.; BABAEV, P.B.; TOVMASYAN, D.A. [Plant poisoning of farm animals in Uzbekistan.] Izdatel'stvo "Fan", Tashkent, USSR. 1979, 59-61.

3 Poisons Unit. New Cross (Guy's) Hospital, London, UK. Personal communication.

4 TAMPION, J. Dangerous Plants. David and Charles, Newton Abbot, UK. 1977. 35.

CRASSULACEAE

1 CLARKE, E.G.C.; CLARKE, M.L. Veterinary Toxicology. Baillière Tindall, London, UK. 1975, 294.

2 CORNEVIN, C. Des Plantes Vénéneuses. Librairie de Firmin-Didot, Paris, France. 1887, 400-402.

3 McBARRON, E.J. Medical and Veterinary Aspects of Plant Poisons in New South Wales. Department of Agriculture, New South Wales, Australia. 1976, 127.

CRUCIFERAE

1 MINISTRY OF AGRICULTURE, FISHERIES AND FOOD. Poisoning of animals in Britain (1975-1977). *Animal Disease Report* 1978, 2 (2), 9-12.

2 TOOKEY, H.L.; VANETTEN, C.H.; DAXENBICHLER, M.E. Glucosinolates. In: *Toxic Constituents of Plant Foodstuffs.* Edited by I.E.. Liener. Academic Press, New York and London. 2nd Edition. 1980, 103-142.

3 VANETTEN, C.H.; TOOKEY, H.L. Chemistry and biological effects of glucosinolates. In: *Herbivores. Their Interaction with Secondary Plant Metabolites.* Edited by G.A. Rosenthal and D.H. Janzen. Academic Press, New York and London. 1979, 471-500.

4 CROSBY, D.G. Natural toxic background in the food of man and his animals. *Journal of Agricultural and Food Chemistry* 1969, 17, 532-538.

5 HILL, R. A review of the 'toxic' effects of rapeseed meals with observations on meal from improved varieties. *British Veterinary Journal* 1979, 135, 3-16.

6 JOSEFSSON, E.; APPELQVIST, I.-Å. Glucosinolates in seed of rape and turnip rape as affected by variety and environment. *Journal of the Science of Food and Agriculture* 1968, 19, 564-570.

7 WHITTLE, P.J.; SMITH, R.H.; McINTOSH, A. Estimation of S-methylcysteine sulphoxide (kale anaemia factor) and its distribution among brassica forage and root crops. *Journal of the Science of Food and Agriculture* 1976, 27, 633-642.

8 COTE, F.T. Rape poisoning in cattle. *Canadian Journal of Comparative Medicine* 1944, 8, 38-41.

9 SCHOFIELD, F.W. The constant occurrence of macrocytic anemia in cattle feeding on rape. *Report of the Ontario Veterinary College* 1947, No. 29, 122-125.

10 BÄCKGREN, A.W.; JÖNSSON, G. Blood and bone marrow studies in cattle feeding on Brassica species. *Acta Veterinaria Scandinavica* 1969, 10, 309-318.

11 GREGOR, A. Rye-grass staggers. Rape poisoning. Feeding of beet tops. Dietetic haematuria. Selenium poisoning. *Report of Proceedings, Conference on Metabolic Disorders and Other Problems Related to Grassland and Fodder Crops and Innovations in Animal Husbandry.* British Veterinary Association, London, UK. 1952, 132-141.

12 STAMP, J.T.; STEWART, J. Haemolytic anaemia with jaundice in sheep. *Journal of Comparative Pathology and Therapeutics.* 1953, 63, 48-52.

13 PERRETT, D.R. Suspected rape poisoning in cattle. *Veterinary Record* 1947, 59, 674.

14 HUNGERFORD T.G. Diseases of Livestock. McGraw-Hill Book Co., Sydney, Australia. 8th Edition, 1975, 1117.

15 CRAWSHAW, H.A. Rape blindness. *Veterinary Record* 1953, 65, 254.

16 DALTON, P.J. Rape blindness. *Veterinary Record* 1953, 65, 298.

17 O'DRISCOLL, J. Rape poisoning in cattle. *Irish Veterinary Journal* 1958, 12, 82.

18 HUEY, I.B. Rape poisoning in cattle. *Irish Veterinary Journal* 1958, 12, 83.

19 MICHAEL, D.T. Rape or cole: some observations on its management in relation to the health of sheep grazing on it. *Veterinary Record* 1953, 65, 231-232.

20 GRIFFITH, G. ap; JOHNSTON, T.D. The nitrate-nitrogen content of herbage. III. The mineral nitrate content of rape and kale. *Journal of the Science of Food and Agriculture* 1961, 12, 348-352.

21 BRUERE, A.N. Nitrite/nitrate poisoning on second-growth rape. *New Zealand Veterinary Journal* 1956, 4, 128.

22 CONNOR, H.E. The Poisonous Plants in New Zealand. E.C. Keating, Government Printers, Wellington, New Zealand. 1977, 67-69.

23 RUSSEL, A.J.F. A note on goitre in lambs grazing rape (Brassica napus). *Animal Production* 1967, 9, 131-133.

24 HALL, S.A. Lysis of hepatic reticulin. An unusual lesion in laying fowls, possibly associated with rapeseed meal. *Veterinary Record* 1972, 91, 495.

25 JACKSON, N. Toxicity of rapeseed meal and its use as a protein supplement in the diet of two hybrid strains of caged laying hens. *Journal of the Science of Food and Agriculture* 1969, 20, 734-740.

26 FENWICK, G.R.; CURTIS, R.F. Rapeseed meal and its use in poultry diets. A review. *Animal Feed Science and Technology* 1980, 5, 255-298.

27 MARANGOS, A.; HILL, R. The use of rapeseed meal as a protein supplement in poultry and pig diets. *Veterinary Record* 1975, 96, 377-380.

28 BUTLER, E.J.; PEARSON, A.W.; FENWICK, G.R. Problems which limit the use of rapeseed meal as a protein source in poultry diets. *Journal of the Science of Food and Agriculture* 1982, 33, 866-875.

29 ANONYMOUS. Toxic effects of rapeseed meal. Report of the Houghton Poultry Research Station, Huntingdon, UK. 1979-1980, 77-79.

30 PEARSON, A.W.; BUTLER, E.J.; CURTIS, R.F.; FENWICK, G.R.; HOBSON-FROHOCK, A.; LAND, D.G. Rapeseed meal and egg taint: demonstration of the metabolic defect in male and female chicks. *Veterinary Record* 1979, 104, 318-319.

31 PEARSON, A.W.; GREENWOOD, N.M.; BUTLER, E.J.; FENWICK. G.R. Low glucosinolate rapeseed meals and egg taint. *Veterinary Record* 1980, 106, 560.

32 WHEELER, J.L.; PARK, R.J.; SPURWAY, R.A.; FORD, A.L. Variation in the effects of forage rape on meat flavour in sheep. *Journal of Agricultural Science, UK* 1974, 83, 569-571.

33 SEIGLER, D.S. Toxic seed lipids. In: *Herbivores. Their Interaction with Secondary Plant Metabolites*. Edited by G.A. Rosenthal and D.H. Janzen. Academic Press, New York and London. 1979, 449-470.

34 MINISTRY OF AGRICULTURE, FISHERIES AND FOOD. Kale as a feeding stuff. 1975 Advisory Leaflet, No. 408 (amended), 1-5.

35 MINISTRY OF AGRICULTURE, FISHERIES AND FOOD. Bulky feeds for dairy cows. 1977 Advisory Leaflet, No. 524 (revised), 1-16.

36 THOMPSON, K.F. Forage kales. In: *The Future of Brassica Fodder Crops*. Edited by J.F.D. Greenhalgh and M. Hamilton. Occasional Publication, Rowett Research Institute 1971, No. 2, 31-38.

37 COPPOCK, J.T. An Agricultural Atlas of England and Wales. Faber and Faber Ltd., London, UK. 2nd Edition, 1976, 104-105.

38 GREENHALGH, J.F.D. Kale anaemia. *Proceedings of the Nutrition Society* 1969, 28, 178-183.

39 SMITH, R.H. Kale poisoning: the brassica anaemia factor. *Veterinary Record* 1980, 107, 12-15.

40 VanETTEN, C.H.; TOOKEY, H.L. Chemistry and biological effects of glucosinolates. In: *Herbivores, Their Interaction with Secondary Plant Metabolites*. Edited by G.A. Rosenthal and D.H. Janzen. Academic Press, New York and London. 1979, 471-500.

41 PAXMAN, P.J.; HILL, R. The goitrogenicity of kale and its relation to thiocyanate content. *Journal of the Science of Food and Agriculture* 1974, 25, 329-337.

42 VanETTEN, C.H.; DAXENBICHLER, M.E.; WOLFF, I.A. Natural glucosinolates (thioglucosides) in foods and feeds. *Journal of Agricultural and Food Chemistry* 1969, 17, 483-491.

43 McDONALD, R.C.; MANLEY, T.R.; BARRY, T.N.; FORSS, D.A.; SINCLAIR, A.G. Nutritional evaluation of kale (Brassica oleracea) diets.. 3. Changes in plant composition induced by soil fertility practices, with special reference to SMCO and glucosinolate concentrations. *Journal of Agricultural Science* 1981, 97, 13-23.

44 CLEGG, F. Haemoglobinuria of cattle associated with the feeding of kale and other brassicae species. *Proceedings, IVth International Meeting of the World Association for Buiatrics, Zurich, Switzerland, 4-9 August 1966,* 184-195.

45 MacWILLIAMS, P.S.; SEARCY, G.P.; BELLAMY, J.E.C. Bovine parturient hemoglobinuria: a review of the literature. *Canadan Veterinary Journal* 1982, 23, 309-312.

46 GREENHALGH, J.F.D.; AITKEN, J.N.; GUNN, J.B. Kale anaemia. III. A survey of kale feeding practices and anaemia in cattle on dairy farms in England and Scotland. *Research in Veterinary Science* 1972, 13, 15-21.

47 SMITH, R.H.; KAY, M.; MATHESON, N.A.; LAWSON, W. S-methylcysteine sulphoxide, the ruminant kale anaemia factor. *Journal of the Science of Food and Agriculture* 1978, 29, 414-416.

48 WHITTLE, P.J.; SMITH, R.H.; McINTOSH, A. Estimation of S-methylcysteine sulphoxide (kale anaemia factor) and its distribution among brassica forage and root crops. *Journal of the Science of Food and Agriculture* 1976, 27, 633-642.

49 MAXWELL, M.H. Production of a Heinz body anaemia in the domestic fowl after ingestion of dimethyl disulphide: a haematological and ultrastructural study. *Research in Veterinary Science* 1981, 30, 233-238.

50 WRIGHT, E.; SINCLAIR, D.P. The goitrogenic effect of thousand-headed kale on adult sheep and rabbits. *New Zealand Journal of Agricultural Research* 1958, 1, 477-485.

51 WILLIAMS, H.L.; HILL, R.; ALDERMAN, G. The effects of feeding kale to breeding ewes. *British Veterinary Journal* 1965, 121, 2-17.

52 WRIGHT, E.; SINCLAIR, D.P. The concentration of radioiodine by the foetal thyroid gland and its relation to congenital goitre in sheep. *New Zealand Journal of Agricultural Research* 1959, 2, 933-937.

53 HUNGERFORD, T.G. Diseases of Livestock. McGraw-Hill Book Co., Sydney, Australia. 8th Edition, 1975, 151 and 408.

54 PAXMAN, P.J.; HILL, R. Thiocyanate content of kale. *Journal of the Science of Food and Agriculture* 1974, 25, 323-328.

55 SINCLAIR, D.P.; ANDREWS, E.W. Goitre in new-born lambs. *New Zealand Veterinary Journal* 1954, 2, 72-79.

56 BLOOD, D.C.; HENDERSON, J.A.; RADOSTITS, O.M. Veterinary Medicine. Baillière Tindall, London, UK. 5th Edition, 1979, 880-883.

57 DAVID, J.S.E. The effect of prolonged kale feeding on the thyroid glands of sheep. *Journal of Comparative Pathology* 1976, 86, 235-241.

58 BOYD, H.; REED, H.C.B. Investigations into the incidence and cause of infertility in dairy cattle — influence of kale feeding, milk production and management factors associated with 'farming intensity'. *British Veterinary Journal* 1961, 117, 192-200.

59 MELROSE, D.R.; BROWN, B.B. Some observations on the possible effect of kale feeding on fertility in dairy cattle. *Journal of Reproduction and Fertility* 1962, 4, 232.

60 CLEGG, F.G.; EVANS, R.K. Haemoglobi-naemia of cattle associated with the feeding of brassicae species. *Veterinary Record* 1962, 74, 1169-1176.

61 MALLARD, C. [Toxicity of Cruciferae and pregnancy disorders in a herd of goats.] *Bulletin des Groupements Techniques Vétérinaires* 1981, No. 3, 23-25.

62 PICKARD, D.W.; CRIGHTON, D.B. An investigation into the possible oestrogenic effect of kale. *British Veterinary Journal* 1967, 123, 64-69.

63 DEAS, D.W.; MELROSE, D.R.; REED, H.C.B.; VANDEPLASSCHE, M.; PIDDUCK, H. Other non-infectious abnormalities. In: *Fertility and Infertility in Domestic Animals.* Edited by J.A. Laing. Baillière Tindall, London, UK. 3rd Edition, 1979, 137-159.

64 WRIGHT, E. Goitrogen of milk produced on kale. *Nature, London* 1958, 181, 1602-1603.

65 CLEMENTS, F.W.; WISHART, J.W. A thyroid-blocking agent in the etiology of endemic goiter. *Metabolism* 1956, 5, 623-639.

66 BACHELARD, H.S.; McQUILLAN, M.T.; TRIKOJUS, V.M. Studies on endemic goitre. III. An investigation of the anti-thyroid activities of isothiocyanates and derivatives with observations on fractions of

milk from goitrous areas. *Australian Journal of Biological Sciences* 1963, 16, 177-191.

67 LANSON, R.K.; ABDULLA, A. Effect of feeding mustard seed to immature chickens and laying hens. *Poultry Science* 1963, 42, 1283-1284.

68 NIKOLAEV, K. [Toxicological studies on Sinapis arvensis L. I. The amount of active principle in the plant. II. Fowls. III. Sheep.] *Izvestiya Veterinarniya Institut Nezarazni Bolestii Zookhigiena, Sofia* 1962, 2, 101-105; 1963, 3, 91-96, 97-101.

69 GALLIE, J.G.E.; PATERSON, J.D. Charlock poisoning of lambs. *Veterinary Record* 1945, 57, 198-199.

70 KOVALEV, A.A. [Poisoning of horses by 'field mustard' Sinapis arvensis.] *Sovetskaya Veterinariya* 1937, No. 10, 28-31.

71 MIHAILOV, M. [Charlock (Sinapis arvensis) poisoning in horses.] *Veterinarski Glasnik* 1961, 15, 681-683.

72 MAKARYAN, O.A. [Poisoning of cattle with Sinapis arvensis (charlock).] *Veterinariya, Moscow* 1973, No. 11, 95-96.

73 FORSYTH, A.A. British Poisonous Plants. HMSO, London, UK. Ministry of Agriculture, Fisheries and Food Bulletin 161, 1968, 41-42 (amended 1979, 42-43).

74 JAHN, S.; SEFFNER, W. [Results of feeding sheep on mustard cake.] *Archiv für Tierernährung* 1962, 12, 11-16.

75 EATON, G. Suspected poisoning of bullocks by white mustard. *Veterinary Record* 1941, 53, 146.

76 HOLMES, R.G. A case of suspected poisoning of dairy cows by white mustard seeds (Sinapis alba). *Veterinary Record* 1965, 77, 480-481.

77 ALIKUTTY, K.M. Mustard seed toxicity in cattle. *Indian Veterinary Journal* 1976, 53, 962-964.

78 TROXLER, J. [Fatal poisoning of 19 heifers by white mustard (Sinapis alba L.).] *Schweizer Archiv für Tierheilkunde* 1981, 123, 495-497.

79 TAMPION, J. Dangerous Plants. David & Charles, Newton Abbot, UK. 1977, 163.

80 NIKOLAEV, K. [Toxicity of the wild radish, Raphanus raphanistrum.] *Veterinarnomeditsinski Nauki, Sofia* 1964, 1 (10), 31-35.

81 TROUCHE. [Poisoning in a flock of lambs by wild radish (Raphanus raphanistrum).] *Revue Vétérinaire,* 1936, 88, 682-683.

82 WHITTLE, P.J.; SMITH, R.H.; McINTOSH, A. Estimation of S-methylcysteine sulphoxide (kale anaemia factor) and its distribution among brassica forage and root crops. *Journal of the Science of Food and Agriculture* 1976, 27, 633-642.

83 CLEGG, F.G.; EVANS, R.K. Haemoglobinaemia of cattle associated with the feeding of brassicae species. *Veterinary Record* 1962, 74, 1169-1176.

84 GREENHALGH, J.F.D. Problems of animal disease. In: *The Future of Brassica Fodder Crops.* Edited by J.F.D. Greenhalgh and M. Hamilton. Occasional Publication, Rowett Research Institute 1971, No. 2, 56-64.

85 SMITH, R.H. Kale and brassica poisoning. *Veterinary Annual* 1977, 17, 28-33.

86 YOUNG, N.E.; AUSTIN, A.R.; ORR, R.J.; NEWTON, J.E.; TAYLOR, R.J. A comparison of a hybrid stubble turnip (cv. Appin) with other cruciferous catch crops for lamb fattening. 2. Animal performance and toxicological evaluation. *Grass and Forage Science* 1982, 37, 39-46.

87 O'HARA, P.J.; FRAZER, A.J. Nitrate poisoning in cattle grazing crops. *New Zealand Veterinary Journal* 1975, 23, 45-53.

88 DEBACKERE, M.; HOORENS, J.; HAUSTRAETE, K.H. [Poisoning of cows by linseed cake contaminated with rape and turnip seed.] *Vlaams Diergeneeskundig Tijdschrift* 1966, 35, 393-399.

89 WEBB, L.J. Guide to the medicinal and poisonous plants of Queensland. Commonwealth Scientific and Industrial Research Organisation, Australia. Bulletin 232, 1948.

CUCURBITACEAE

1 CORNEVIN, C. Des Plantes Vénéneuses. Librairie de Firmin-Didot, Paris, France. 1887, 360-363.

2 FORSYTH, A.A. British Poisonous Plants. HMSO, London, UK. Ministry of Agriculture, Fisheries and Food Bulletin 161, 1968, 72-73 (amended 1979, 73-74).

3 KYLE, R.A.M. Oxford, UK. Personal communication.

4 DERIVAUX, J.; LIÉGEOIS, F. Toxicologie Vétérinaire. Vigot Frères, Paris, France. 1962, 232-233.

5 RÎPEANU, M. [Observations on some important cases of poisoning in animals.] *Revista de Zootehnie și Medicină Veterinară* 1963, 13, No. 12, 67-68.

6. JORDAN, M. A Guide to Wild Plants. Millington Books, London, U.K. 1976, 192-194.

CUPRESSACEAE

1 LONG, H.C. Plants Poisonous to Live Stock. Cambridge University Press, Cambridge, UK. 1917, 73.

2 MacDONALD, J. Macrocarpa poisoning. *New Zealand Veterinary Journal* 1956, 4, 30.

3 GOULD, C.M. Cypress poisoning. *Veterinary Record* 1962, 74, 743.

4 MASON, R.W. Foetal cerebral leucomalacia associated with Cupressus macrocarpa abortion in cattle. *Australian Veterinary Journal* 1974, 50, 419.

5 BARTÍK, M.; PISKAČ, A. (Editors) Veterinary Toxicology. Elsevier, Amsterdam, Netherlands. 1981, 220-223.

6 BENTZ, H. Nutztiervergiftungen. Erkennung und Verhütung. VEB Gustav Fischer Verlag, Jena, Germany. 1969, 327.

7 FORSYTH, A.A. British Poisonous Plants. HMSO, London, UK. Ministry of Agriculture, Fisheries and Food Bulletin 161, 1968, 29 (amended 1979, 31).

CYPERACEAE

1 SCHAUENBERG, P.; PARIS, F. Guide to Medicinal Plants. Lutterworth Press, Guildford and London, UK. 1977, 199.

2 ROSCA, V.; PAVEL, A. [Hydrocyanic acid poisoning of cattle with sedges of the genus Carex.] *Revista de Zootehnie și Medicină Veterinară* 1969, 19 (11), 81-85.

DIOSCOREACEAE

1 CORNEVIN, C. Des Plantes Vénéneuses. Librairie de Firmin-Didot, Paris, France. 1887, 127-131.

2 BLACKWELL, W.E. Horses poisoned by bryony. *Veterinary Record* 1931, 11, 911-912.

3 VALE, J.A.; MEREDITH, T.J. Poisonous plants. *Hospital Update* 1980 (June), 543-555.

DIPSACACEAE

1 MOIR, J. Poisoned by devil's-bit. *Veterinary Record* 1899, 11, 523-524.

DROSERACEAE

1 CLEMENTS, L.O.; WEAVERS, E.D. Dermatophilus congolensis in lambs. *Irish Veterinary Journal* 1980, 34, 65-67.

2 TAMPION, J. Dangerous Plants. David and Charles, Newton Abbot, UK. 1977, 165.

ERICACEAE

1 SCOTT, P.M.; COLDWELL, B.B.; WIBERG, G.S. Grayanotoxins, occurrence and analysis in honey and a comparison of toxicities in mice. *Food and Cosmetics Toxicology* 1971, 9, 179-184.

2 MacGREGOR, J.L. Poisoning of bees by rhododendron nectars. *British Bee Journal* 1960, 88, 76-78.

3 HOWES, F.N. Plants and Beekeeping. Faber & Faber, London, UK. 1979, 23-24.

4 BOLTON, J.F. Rhododendron poisoning. *Veterinary Record* 1955, 67, 138-139.

5 HIGNETT, P.G. A case of presumed rhododendron poisoning in sheep. *Veterinary Record* 1951, 63, 346-347.

6 BRAHM, E.; BUNTENKOTTER, S.; SIMANOWSKI, W. [Poisoning of llamas, alpacas, goats and wolves by Ericaceae at Dortmund Zoo.] *Erkrankungen der Zootiere. Verhandlungsbericht des XV Internationalen Symposiums* 1973, 125-130.

7 KOHANAWA, M.; IKEDA, K.; OGUMA, K.; SASAKI, N. [Emetic effects of grayanotoxin isolated from Rhododendron hymenanthes, Makino on goats.] *Annual Report of the National Veterinary Assay Laboratory, Japan* 1973, 10, 53-57.

8 GHENNE, P.; MEES, G. [Rhododendron poisoning in a goat.] *Annales de Médecine Vétérinaire* 1968, 112, 25-29.

9 MILNES, J.N. Rhododendron poisoning in the goat. *Veterinary Record* 1953, 65, 211.

10 MASHETER, J.W.H. Rhododendron "poisoning" in cattle. *Veterinary Journal* 1941, 97, 223-225.

11 WOODS, S.B. Personal communication.

12 PUROHIT, K. Rhododendron poisoning in animals. *Indian Veterinary Journal* 1960, 37, 631-633.

13 BOGATKO, W. [Poisoning of nutria with Rhododendron.] *Medycyna Weterynaryjna* 1968, 24, 417-418.

14 MATSCHULLAT, G. [Rhododendron poisoning in sheep.] *Praktische Tierarzt* 1974, 55, 624, 626.

15 ARENA, J.M. Pretty poisonous plants. *Veterinary and Human Toxicology* 1979, 21, 108-111.

EUPHORBIACEAE *Ricinus*

JELINKOVA, V.; VESELY, Z. [Toxicity of castor beans.] *Veterinární Medicína* 1960, 5, 827-838.

2 CORWIN, A.H. Toxic constituents of the castor bean. *Journal of Medicinal and Pharmaceutical Chemistry* 1961, 4, 483-496.

3 LIN, T.T.-S.; LI, S.S.-L. Purification and physicochemical properties of ricins and agglutinins from Ricinus communis. *European Journal of Biochemistry* 1980, 105, 453-459.

4 LIST, G.R.; SPENCER, G.F.; HUNT, W.H. Toxic weed contaminants in soybean processing. *Journal of the American Oil Chemists' Society* 1979, 56, 706-710.

5 WALLER, G.R.; EBNER, K.E.; SCROGGS, R.A.; DAS GUPTA, B.R.; CORCORAN, J.B. Studies on the toxic action of ricin. *Proceedings of the Society for Experimental Biology and Medicine* 1966, 121, 685-691.

6 KNIGHT, B. Ricin — a potent homicidal poison. *British Medical Journal* 1979, 1, 350-351.

7 TIANO, F. [Castor oil cake poisoning in the dog.] *Notes de Toxicologie Vétérinaire* 1977, No. 2, 109-111.

8 GEARY, T. Castor bean poisoning. *Veterinary Record* 1950, 62, 472-473.

9 LENSCH, J. [Ricin poisoning in cattle.] *Tierärztliche Praxis* 1966, 21, 21-22.

10 SEIGLER, D.S. Toxic seed lipids. In: *Herbivores. Their Interaction with Secondary Plant Metabolites*. Edited by G.A. Rosenthal and D.H. Janzen. Academic Press, New York and London. 1979, 449-470.

11 FOX, M.W. Castor seed residue poisoning in dairy cattle. *Veterinary Record* 1961, 73, 885-886.

12 MEL'NIK, I.L.; KOLTUN, E.M. [Castor oil cake (Ricinus), a cause of illness in newborn calves.] *Veterinariya, Moscow* 1973, No. 1, 98-99.

13 ANDERSON, T.S. Castor poisoning in Ayrshire cattle. *Veterinary Record* 1948, 60, 28.

14 CLEMENS, E. [Toxicity and tolerance of Ricinus seed oil meal by different animals.] *Landwirtschaftliche Forschung* 1963, Sonderheft 17, 202-211.

15 LAPCEVIĆ, E.; KOZIĆ, Lj.; PAUNOVIĆ, S. [The clinical picture of castor bean poisoning in the horse.] *Veterinarski Glasnik* 1960, 14, 883-886.

16 McCUNN, J.; ANDREW, H.; CLOUGH, G.W. Castor-bean poisoning in horses. *Veterinary Journal* 1945, 101, 136-138.

17 ANONYMOUS. Castor-oil bean toxicity. *Veterinary Record* 1982, 111, 172.

18 KRIEGER-HUBER, S. [Fatal poisoning by ricin in dogs following intake of the biological

fertiliser "Oscorna animalin".] *Kleintierpraxis* 1980, 25, 281-286.

19 GOLOSNITSKII, A.K.; KOZYREV, V.M. [Changes in the blood of horses poisoned with Ricinus communis seeds.] *Trudy Novocherkasskogo Zootekhnichesko-Veterinarnogo Instituta* 1961, 13, 104-108.

20 ALBIN, R.C.; HARBAUGH, F.G.; ZINN, D.W. Castor bean meal of three ricin levels for cattle. *Journal of Animal Science* 1968, 27, 288.

21 CLARKE, E.G.C.; JACKSON, J.H. The use of immune serum in the treatment of ricin poisoning. *British Veterinary Journal* 1956, 112, 57-62.

22 LAMPE, K.F. Systemic plant poisoning in children. *Pediatrics* 1974, 54, 347-351.

23 O'LEARY, S.B. Poisoning in man from eating poisonous plants. *Archives of Environmental Health* 1964, 9, 216-242.

24 SCOTT, H.G. Poisonous plants and animals. In: *Food-borne Infections and Intoxications.* Edited by H. Riemann. Academic Press, New York and London, 1969, 543-564.

25 SPYKER, D.A.; SAUER, K.; KELL, S.O.; GUERRANT, R.L. A castor bean poisoning and a widely available bioassay for ricin. *Veterinary and Human Toxicology* 1982, 24, 293.

26 COOPER, W.C.; PERONE, V.B.; SCHEEL, L.D.; KEENAN, R.G. Occupational hazards from castor bean pomace: tests for toxicity. *American Industrial Hygiene Association Journal* 1964, 25, 431-438.

27 JENKINS, F.P. Allergenic and toxic components of castor bean meal: review of the literature and studies of the inactivation of these components. *Journal of the Science of Food and Agriculture* 1963, 14, 773-780.

28 LAMPE, K.F.; FAGERSTRÖM, R. Plant Toxicity and Dermatitis. Williams and Wilkins Co., Baltimore, USA. 1968, 62.

EUPHORBIACEAE (other plants)

1 SHARAF, A.E.A. A pharmacological study of the Egyptian plant, Euphorbia peplus. *Veterinary Journal* 1948, 104, 313-318.

2 SHARAF, A.E.A. Chemical investigation of the Egyptian plant, Euphorbia peplus. *British Veterinary Journal* 1949, 105, 128-135.

3 FORSYTH, A.A. British Poisonous Plants. HMSO, London, UK. Ministry of Agriculture, Fisheries and Food Bulletin 161, 1968, 74-75 (amended 1979, 75-76).

4 VLACHOS, P.; POULOS, L.; KOUTSELI-NIS, A.; PAPADATOS, K. Euphorbia poisoning (case reports). *IRCS Medical Science: Library Compendium* 1978, 6, 104.

5 MITCHELL, J.; ROOK, A. Botanical Dermatology. Plants and Plant Products Injurious to the Skin. Greengrass Ltd., Vancouver, Canada. 1979, 269.

6 CALNAN, C.D. Petty spurge (Euphorbia peplus). *Contact Dermatitis* 1975, 1, 128.

7 CHEVALIER, H. [Study of the main plant poisonings in Maine-Anjou.] Thesis, École Nationale Vétérinaire d'Alfort, France. 1974, 11-15.

8 POLIDORI, F.; MAGGI, M. [Nutritional problems in animals. Some cases of Mercurialis annua poisoning in cattle. Experimental studies on differences in the toxicity of the fresh and dried plant.] *Nuova Veterinaria* 1954, 30, 146-150.

9 LONG, H.C. Plants Poisonous to Live Stock. Cambridge University Press, Cambridge, UK. 1917, 67-69.

10 BAKER, J.R.; FAULL, W.B. Dog's mercury (Mercurialis perennis L.) poisoning in sheep. *Veterinary Record* 1968, 82, 485-489.

11 LANDAU, M.; EGYED, M.N.; FLESH, D. Mercurialis annua poisoning in housed sheep. *Refuah Veterinarith* 1973, 30, 131-135.

12 SENF, W.; SEFFNER, W. [Mercurialis annua poisoning in sheep.] *Monatshefte für Veterinärmedizin* 1965, 20, 622-625.

13 DELATOUR, P.; JEAN-BLAIN, C. [Mercurialis poisoning in cattle.] *Notes de Toxicologie Vétérinaire* 1977, No. 2, 65-68.

14 ANONYMOUS. [Mercurialis poisoning in cattle.] *Notes de Toxicologie Vétérinaire* 1979, No. 6, 348-349.

15 BOKORI, J.; KOVÁCS, F.; HARASZTI, E. [Mercurialis annua poisoning in horses.] *Magyar Allatorvosok Lapja* 1955, 10, 191-196.

16 HARTLEY, W.J.; HAKIOGLU, F. Investigation of an outbreak of icterohaemoglobinuria in goats. *Pendik Veteriner Kontrol Arastirma Enstitusi Dergisi* 1970, 2, No. 2, 67-89.

17 Poisons Unit. New Cross (Guy's) Hospital, London, UK. Personal communication.

18 FORSYTH, A.A. British Poisonous Plants. HMSO, London, UK. Ministry of Agriculture, Fisheries and Food Bulletin 161, 1968, 75-76 (amended 1979, 76-77).

FAGACEAE

1 COLLAHITE, J.W.; PIGEON, R.F.; CAMP, B.J. The toxicity of gallic acid, pyrogallol, tannic acid and Quercus havardi in the rabbit. *American Journal of Veterinary Research* 1962, 23, 1264-1267.

2 WEBER-KIRCHNER, C. [Acorn poisoning in cattle. Observations on naturally affected animals and on two experimental animals.] Inaugural Dissertation, Tierärztliche Hochschule, Hannover, Germany. 1978, 88pp.

3 BROUGHTON, J.E. Acorn poisoning. *Veterinary Record* 1976, 99, 403-404.

4 DANIELS, M.G. Acorn poisoning. *Veterinary Record* 1976, 99, 465-466.

5 LLEWELLYN, C.A. A case of chronic oak poisoning. *Veterinary Record* 1962, 74, 1238.

6 FORSYTH, A.A. British Poisonous Plants. HMSO, London, UK. Ministry of Agriculture, Fisheries and Food Bulletin 161, 1968, 81-83 (amended 1979, 82-84).

7 PANCIERA, R.J. Oak poisoning in cattle. In: *Effects of Poisonous Plants on Livestock.* Edited by R.F. Keeler, K.R. Van Kampen and L.F. James. Academic Press, New York and London. 2nd Edition, 1978, 499-506.

8 DOLLAHITE, J.W. Shin oak (Quercus havardi) poisoning in cattle. *Southwestern Veterinarian* 1960-1961, 14, 198-201.

9 MINISTRY OF AGRICULTURE, FISHERIES AND FOOD. Poisoning of animals in Britain. *Animal Disease Report* 1978, 2, No. 2, 9-12.

10 SLAUGHTER, T.S. On acorn poisoning in cattle. *Veterinary Medicine and Small Animal Clinician* 1964, 59, 227-230.

11 DIXON, P.M.; McPHERSON, E.A.; ROWLAND, A.C.; MacLENNAN, W. Acorn poisoning in cattle. *Veterinary Record* 1979, 104, 284-285.

12 EDWARDS, C.M. Some observations on plant poisoning in grazing animals. *Veterinary Record* 1949, 61, 864-865.

13 WAGNER, H. [Fatal poisoning of sheep by green acorns.] *Berliner und Münchener Tierärztliche Wochenschrift* 1935, 51, 452-453.

14 TUDOR, G. [Green acorn poisoning in sheep.] *Revista de Zootehnie şi Medicină Veterinară* 1971, 21, No. 8, 60-62.

15 WHARMBY, M.J. Acorn poisoning. *Veterinary Record* 1976, 99, 343.

16 BATU, A.; NADAS, Ü. G.; GÜREL, A. [Experiments on the use of calcium hydroxide for the treatment and prevention of oak leaf poisoning in rabbits.] *Pendik Veteriner Bakteriyoloji ve Seroloji Enstitusu Dergisi* 1978, 10, 93-100.

17 DOLLAHITE, J.W.; HOUSHOLDER, G.T.; CAMP, B.J. Effect of calcium hydroxide on the toxicity of post oak (Quercus stellata) in calves. *Journal of the American Veterinary Medical Association* 1966, 148, 908-912.

18 CORNEVIN, C. Des Plantes Vénéneuses. Librairie de Firmin-Didot, Paris, France. 1887, 137-139.

19 BOHOSIEWICZ, M. [Veterinary toxicology.] Panstwowe Wydawnictwo Rolnicze i Leśne, Warsaw, Poland. 1970, 214.

20 VÖLKER, R. Lehrbuch der Toxikologie für Tierärzte. (Fröhner). Ferdinand Enke Verlag, Stuttgart, Germany. 6th Edition, 1950, 325-326.

21 COOPER, P. Poisoning by Drugs and Chemicals, Plants and Animals. Alchemist Publications, London, UK. 3rd Edition, 1974, 102.

FUMARIACEAE

1 KINGSBURY, J.M. Poisonous Plants of the United States and Canada. Prentice-Hall, Inc., New Jersey, USA. 1964, 154-156.

2 BLACK, O.F.; EGGLESTON, W.W.; KELLY, J.W.; TURNER, H.C. Poisonous properties of Bikukulla cucullaria (Dutchman's breeches) and B. canadensis (squirrel-corn). *Journal of Agricultural Research* 1923, 23, 69-77.

3 ARENA, J.M. Pretty poisonous plants. *Veterinary and Human Toxicology* 1979, 21, 108-111.

GERANIACEAE

1 HURST, E. The Poison Plants of New South Wales. Snelling Printing Works Pty Ltd., 52-54 Bay Street, Sydney, Australia. 1942, 200-201.

2 FORD, G.E. Photosensitivity due to Erodium spp. *Australian Veterinary Journal* 1965, 41, 56.

3 CONNOR, H.E. The Poisonous Plants in New Zealand. E.C. Keating, Government Printer, Wellington, New Zealand. 1977, 81-82.

GRAMINEAE

1 SIDHU, K.S.; HARGUS, W.A.; PFANDER, W.H. Metabolic inhibitors in fractions of orchardgrass (Dactylis glomerata L.) detected by in vitro rumen fermentation technique. *Proceedings of the Society for Experimental Biology and Medicine* 1967, 124, 1038-1041.

2 BREEZE, R.G.; PIRIE, H.M.; SELMAN, I.E.; WISEMAN, A. Fog fever (acute pulmonary emphysema) in cattle in Britain. *Veterinary Bulletin* 1976, 46, 243-251.

3 ROBERTS, H.E.; BENSON, J.A.; JONES, D.G.H. "Fog fever" (acute bovine pulmonary emphysema) in Mid-Wales, 1971: features of occurrence. *Veterinary Record* 1973, 92, 558-561.

4 SELMAN, I.E.; WISEMAN, A.; PIRIE, H.M.; BREEZE, R.G. Fog fever in cattle: clinical and epidemiological features. *Veterinary Record* 1974, 95, 139-146.

5 HAMMOND, A.C.; CARLSON, J.R.; BREEZE, R.G. Monensin and the prevention of tryptophan-induced acute bovine pulmonary edema and emphysema. *Science, USA* 1978, 201, 153-155.

6 KÖHLER, H. [Calcinosis in cattle and the current state of research.] *Deutsche Tierärztliche Wochenschrift* 1977, 84, 98-100.

7 SPEDDING, C.R.W.; DIEKMAHNS, E.C. (Editors). Grasses and legumes in British agriculture. Bulletin 49 Commonwealth Bureau of Pastures and Field Crops. Commonwealth Agricultural Bureaux, Farnham Royal, UK. 1972, 273.

8 RÎPEANU, M. [Observations on some cases of poisoning in animals.] *Revista de Zootehnie și Medicină Veterinară* 1963, 13, No. 12, 63-64.

9 BYFORD, M.J. Ryegrass staggers: what causes it — and how to control it through pasture management. *New Zealand Journal of Agriculture* 1979, 139 (6), 33, 35.

10 SHREEVE, B.J.; PATTERSON, D.S.P.; ROBERTS, B.A.; MacDONALD, S.M.; WOOD, E.N. Isolation of potentially tremorgenic fungi from pasture associated with a condition resembling ryegrass staggers. *Veterinary Record* 1978, 103, 209-210.

11 MENNA, M.E. DI; MANTLE, P.G. The role of penicillia in ryegrass staggers. *Research in Veterinary Science* 1978, 24, 347-351.

12 GALLAGHER, R.T.; WHITE, E.P.; MORTIMER, P.H. Ryegrass staggers: isolation of potent neurotoxins lolitrem A and lolitrem B from staggers-producing pastures. *New Zealand Veterinary Journal* 1981, 29, 189-190.

13 CLEGG, F.C.; WATSON, W.A. Ryegrass staggers in sheep. *Veterinary Record* 1960, 72, 731-733.

14 RUSSELL, C.A. 'Rye grass staggers'. *Veterinary Record* 1975, 97, 295.

15 SORGDRAGER, H. [Ryegrass staggers among sheep in the Netherlands.] *Tijdschrift voor Diergeneeskunde* 1978, 103, 500-501.

16 CLARKE, M.L.; HARVEY, D.G.; HUMPHREYS, D.J. Veterinary Toxicology. Baillière Tindall, London, UK. 2nd Edition, 1981, 224.

17 BUSH, L.P.; BURTON, H.; BOLING, J.A. Activity of tall fescue alkaloids and analogues in in vitro rumen fermentation. *Journal of Agricultural and Food Chemistry* 1976, 24, 869-872.

18 LONG, H.C. Plants Poisonous to Live Stock. Cambridge University Press, Cambridge, UK. 1917, 82-84.

19 KINGSBURY, J.M. Poisonous Plants of the United States and Canada. Prentice-Hall Inc., New Jersey, USA. 1964, 484-486.

20 AINSWORTH, G.C.; AUSTWICK, P.K.C. Fungal Diseases of Animals. Commonwealth Agriculture Bureaux, Farnham Royal, UK. 1st Edition, 1959, 52.

21 WATT, J.M.; BREYER-BRANDWIJK, M.G. Medicinal and Poisonous Plants of Southern and Eastern Africa. E. & S. Livingstone Ltd., Edinburgh and London, UK. 2nd Edition, 1962, 475-476.

22 STEYN, D.G. The Toxicology of Plants in South Africa. Central News Agency Ltd, South Africa. 1934, 493-497.

23 CUNNINGHAM, I.J. Non-toxicity to animals of ryegrass endophyte fungi and other endophyte fungi of New Zealand grasses. *New Zealand Journal of Agricultural Research*, 1958, 1, 489-497.

24 URBAIN, A.; NOUVEL, J. [Darnel poisoning of wild animals in captivity.] *Bulletin de l'Académie Vétérinaire de France* 1939, 12, 77-82.

25 DAVIES, E.G.; ASHTON, W.M. Coumarin and related compounds of Anthoxanthum puelli and Melilotus alba and dicoumarol formation in spoilt sweet vernal and sweet clover hay. *Journal of the Science of Food and Agriculture* 1964, 15, 733-738.

26 SCHEEL, C.D. The toxicology of sweet clover and coumarin anticoagulants. In: *Mycotoxic Fungi, Mycotoxins, Mycotoxicoses. An Encyclopedic Handbook.* Edited by T.D. Wyllie and L.G. Morehouse. Marcel Dekker Inc., New York, USA. Vol. 2, 1978, 121-142.

27 PRITCHARD, D.G.; MARKSON, L.M.; BRUSH, P.J.; SAWTELL, J.A.A.; BLOXHAM, P.A. Haemorrhagic syndrome of cattle associated with the feeding sweet vernal (Anthoxanthum odoratum) hay containing dicoumarol. *Veterinary Record* 1983, 113, 78-84.

28 MACAULIFFE, T.G. Rachitogenic effect of diets containing rye for broiler chicks. *Dissertation Abstracts International* 1977, 38, 2447B.

29 ANTONIOU, T.C. Identification, isolation, mode of action and partial characterisation of an anti-nutritional factor in rye grain. *Dissertation Abstracts International* 1980, 41, 524B.

30 FERNANDEZ, R.; LUCAS, E.; McGINNIS, J. Fractionation of a chick growth depressing factor from rye. *Poultry Science* 1973, 52, 2252-2259.

31 ORSKOV, E.R. Whole grain feeding for ruminants. *Veterinary Record* 1980, 106, 399-401.

32 ELAM, C.J. Acidosis in feedlot cattle: practical observations. *Journal of Animal Science* 1976, 43, 898-901.

33 HUBER, T.L. Physiological effects of acidosis on feedlot cattle. *Journal of Animal Science* 1976, 43, 902-909.

34 McMANUS, W.R.; LEE, G.J.; ROBINSON, V.N.E. Micro-lesions of rumen papillae of sheep fed diets of wheat grain. *Research in Veterinary Science* 1977, 22, 135-137.

35 LEE, G.J. Changes in composition and pH of digesta along the gastrointestinal tract of sheep in relation to scouring induced by wheat engorgement. *Australian Journal of Agricultural Research* 1977, 28, 1075-1082.

36 NAGARAJA, T.J.; BARTLEY, E.E.; FINA, L.R.; ANTHONY, H.D. Relationship of rumen gram-negative bacteria and free endotoxin to lactic acidosis in cattle. *Journal of Animal Science* 1978, 47, 1329-1337.

37 MULLEN, P.A. Intensive beef production — barley beef. *Veterinary Bulletin* 1972, 42, 119-124.

38 SIMONSSON, A.; BJORKLUND, N.E. Some effects of the fineness of ground barley on gastric lesions and gastric contents in growing pigs. *Swedish Journal of Agricultural Research* 1978, 8, 97-106.

39 DOBSON, K.J.; DAVIES, R.L.; CARGILL, C.F. Ulceration of the pars oesophagia in pigs. *Australian Veterinary Journal* 1978, 54, 601-602.

40 IBRAHIM, T.M.; SHAKER, M.; KAMEL, S.H. Cyanide content in growing corn. *Veterinary Medical Journal, Giza* 1969, 16, 127-134.

41 DUNLOP, R.H. Pathogenesis of ruminant lactic acidosis. *Advances in Veterinary Science and Comparative Medicine* 1972, 16, 259-302.

42 CLARKE, E.G.C.: CLARKE, M.L. Veterinary Toxicology. Baillière Tindall, London, UK. 1975, 318-320.

43 FRIGG, M.; BRUBACHER, G. Biotin deficiency in chicks fed a wheat-based diet. *International Journal for Vitamin and Nutrition Research* 1976, 46, 314-321.

HIPPOCASTANACEAE

1 CONNOR, H.E. The Poisonous Plants in New Zealand. E.C. Keating, Government Printer, Wellington, New Zealand, 1977, 96.

2 SCOTT, H.G. Poisonous Plants and Animals. In: Food-borne Infections and Intoxications. Edited by H. Riemann. Academic Press, New York and London. 1969, 543-604.

3 REYNARD, G.B.; NORTON, J.B.S. Poisonous plants of Maryland in relation to livestock. *University of Maryland Agricultural Experiment Station Technical Bulletin A10*, 1942, 270.

4 MUENSCHER, W.C. Poisonous Plants of the United States. Macmillan, New York, USA. 1939, 157-159.

5 LAMPE, K.F.; FAGERSTRÖM, R. Plant Toxicity and Dermatitis. Williams and Wilkins Co., Baltimore, USA. 1968, 23.

HYDRANGEACEAE

1 HURST, E. The Poison Plants of New South Wales. Snelling Printing Works Pty Ltd., 52-54 Bay Street, Sydney, Australia. 1942, 138.

2 HARDIN, J.W.; ARENA, J.M. Human Poisoning from Native and Cultivated Plants. Duke University Press, North Carolina, USA. 2nd Edition, 1974, 78-79.

HYPERICACEAE

1 PACE, N.; MacKINNEY, G. Hypericin, the photodynamic pigment from St. John's wort. *Journal of the American Chemical Society* 1941, 63, 2570-2574.

2 ARAYA, O.S.; FORD, E.J.H. An investigation of photosensitisation caused by ingestion of St. John's wort (Hypericum perforatum) by calves. *Journal of Comparative Pathology* 1981, 91, 135-141.

3 MARSH, D. Toxic effect of St. John's wort (Hypericum perforatum) on cattle and sheep. United States Department of Agriculture Technical Bulletin No. 202, 1930, 23pp.

4 RAY, G. [Note on the toxic effects of leaves of Hypericum crispum.] *Recueil de Médecine Vétérinaire* 1914, 68, 39-42.

5 CUNNINGHAM, I.J. Photosensitivity diseases in New Zealand. V. Photosensitisation by St. John's wort (Hypericum perforatum). *New Zealand Journal of Science and Technology* 1947, 29A, 207-213.

6 DODD, S. St. John's wort and its effects on livestock. *Agricultural Gazette of New South Wales,* 1920, 31, 265-272.

7 CLARE, N.T. Photosensitisation in Diseases of Domestic Animals. Review Series No. 3, Commonwealth Bureau of Animal Health. Commonwealth Agricultural Bureaux, Farnham Royal, UK. 1952, 11-15.

8 HOLMES, J.W.H. Simultaneous cases of photosensitisation. *Veterinary Record* 1963, 75, 1223-1224.

9 SALGUES, R. [New chemical and toxicological studies on the genus Hypericum L. (Tourn).] *Qualitas Plantarum et Materiae Vegetabiles* 1961, 8, 38-64.

IRIDACEAE

1 CORNEVIN, C. Des Plantes Vénéneuses. Librairie de Firmin-Didot, Paris, France. 1887, 131.

2 HENSLOW, G. Poisonous Plants in Field and Garden. Society for Promoting Christian Knowledge, 1901. p.165.

3 KINGSBURY, J.M. Deadly Harvest. George Allen and Unwin Ltd., London, UK. 1967, 114.

4 JORDAN, M. A Guide to Wild Plants. Millington Books Ltd., London, UK. 1976, 225-226.

5 BOHOSIEWICZ, M. Toksykologia Weterynaryjna, Panstwowe Wydawnictwo Rolnicze i Leśne, Warsaw, Poland. 1970, 311

6 BRUCE, E.A. Iris poisoning of calves. *American Veterinary Journal* 1919-1920, 56, New Series 9, 72-74.

7 BODDIE, G.F. Toxicological problems in veterinary practice. *Veterinary Record* 1947, 59, 471-486.

8 FORSYTH, A.A. British Poisonous Plants. HMSO, London, UK. Ministry of Agriculture, Fisheries and Food Bulletin 161, 1968, 107-108 (amended 1979, 108-109).

9 LAMPE, K.F.; FAGERSTRÖM, R. Plant Toxicity and Dermatitis. Williams and Wilkins Co., Baltimore, USA. 1968, 35-36.

10 SCHAUENBERG, P.; PARIS, F. Guide to Medicinal Plants. Lutterworth Press, Guildford and London, UK. 1977, 238.

JUNCACEAE

1 ALBISTON, H.E. The joint leaf rush (Juncus holoschoenus): a cyanogenetic plant. *Australian Veterinary Journal* 1937, 13, 200.

2 MOGG, A.O.D. Vlei poisoning. *South African Journal of Science* 1927, 24, 269-277.

3 MINISTRY OF AGRICULTURE, FISHERIES AND FOOD. Grass and Grassland. HMSO, London, UK. 1966, Bulletin No. 154, 15.

4 MINISTRY OF AGRICULTURE, FISHERIES AND FOOD. Grass and Grassland. HMSO, London, UK. 1966, Bulletin No. 154, 90.

5 FORSYTH, A.A. British Poisonous Plants. HMSO, London, UK. Ministry of Agriculture, Fisheries and Food Bulletin 161, 1968, 106 (amended 1979, 106-107).

JUNCAGINACEAE

1 CONN, E.E. Cyanogenic glycosides. *Journal of Agricultural and Food Chemistry* 1969, 17, 519-526.

2 CONN, E.E. Cyanogenesis, the production of hydrogen cyanide by plants. In: *Effects of Poisonous Plants on Livestock.* Edited by R.F. Keeler, K.R. Van Kampen and L.F. James. Academic Press, New York and London. 1978, 301-310.

3 KINGSBURY, J.M. Poisonous Plants of the United States and Canada. Prentice-Hall Inc., New Jersey, USA. 1964, 501-503.

4 ANONYMOUS. 16 plants poisonous to livestock in Western States. United States Department of Agriculture Farmer's Bulletin No. 2106, 1958, 2-4.

5 HIBBS, C.M. Cyanide and nitrate toxicoses of cattle. *Veterinary and Human Toxicology* 1979, 21, 401-403.

6 JUBB, K.V.F.; KENNEDY, P.C. Pathology of Domestic Animals. Vol. 2. Academic Press, New York and London. 2nd Edition, 1970, 383-384.

7 CLAWSON, A.B.; MORAN, E.A. Toxicity of arrowgrass for sheep and remedial treatment. United States Department of Agriculture Technical Bulletin No. 580, 1937, 16pp.

8 BURROWS, G.E. Cyanide intoxication in sheep: therapeutics. *Veterinary and Human Toxicology* 1981, 23, 22-27.

LABIATAE

1 JORDAN, M. A Guide to Wild Plants. Millington Books Ltd., London, UK. 1976, 101-103.

2 HUGHES, R.E.; ELLERY, P.; HARRY, T.; JENKINS, V.; JONES, E. The dietary potential of the common nettle. *Journal of the Science of Food and Agriculture* 1980, 31, 1279-1286.

3 WATT, J.M.; BREYER-BRANDWIJK, M.G. The Medicinal and Poisonous Plants of Southern and Eastern Africa. E. & S. Livingstone Ltd., Edinburgh and London, UK. 2nd Edition, 1962, 1042-1045.

4 ANONYMOUS. Stinging nettle (Urtica sp.) and dogs. *Veterinary and Human Toxicology* 1982, 24, 247.

5 HAZSLINSZKY, B. VON. [Poisoning of horses by Glechoma.] *Deutsche Tierärztliche Wochenschrift* 1935, 43, 708-709.

6 NICOLAU, A. VON; BÂRZĂ, H.; DUCA, H.; CRETEANU, C.; MAY, H.; POPOVICIU, A. [Acute emphysema of the lungs in horses caused by ingestion of ground ivy (Glechoma hederacea).] *Monatshefte für Veterinärmedizin* 1956, 11, 534-538.

7 RICHTER, H.E. [Damage caused by the etheric oils of Mentha longifolia (abortion in cow).] *Wiener Tierärztliche Monatsschrift* 1966, 53, 201-202.

8 FORSYTH, A.A. British Poisonous Plants. HMSO, London, UK. Ministry of Agriculture, Fisheries and Food Bulletin 161, 1968, 96 (amended 1979, 97).

9 FROLKIN, M. [Poisoning of horses and pigs with seeds of hemp-nettle (Galeopsis).] *Veterinariya, Moscow* 1965, 42 (9), 68.

LEGUMINOSAE

1 JAMES, L.F.; KEELER, R.F.; JOHNSON, A.E.; WILLIAMS, M.C.; CRONIN, E.H.; OLSEN, J.D. Plants poisonous to livestock in the Western States. United States Department of Agriculture, Agriculture Information Bulletin No. 415, 1980, 41-43.

2 JAMES, L.F.; JOHNSON, A.E. Some major plant toxicities of the Western United States. *Journal of Range Management* 1976, 29, 356-363.

3 JAMES, L.F.; VAN KAMPEN, K.R. Effect of protein and mineral supplementation on potential locoweed (Astragalus spp) poisoning in sheep. *Journal of the American Veterinary Medical Association* 1974, 164, 1042-1043.

4 SHERWOOD, R.T.; SHAMMA, M.; MONIOT, J.L.; KROSCHEWSKY, J.R. Flavone C-glycosides from Coronilla varia. *Phytochemistry* 1973, 12, 2275-2278.

5 SHENK, J.S.; WANGSNESS, P.J.; LEACH, R.M.; GUSTINE, D.L.; GOBBLE, J.L.; BARNES, R.F. Relationship between ʃ-nitropropionic acid content of crown vetch and toxicity in nonruminant animals. *Journal of Animal Science* 1976, 42, 616-621.

6 GUSTINE, D.L.; MOYER, B.G.; WANGSNESS, P.J.; SHENK, J.S. Ruminal metabolism of 3-nitropropanoyl-D-glucopyranoses from crown vetch. *Journal of Animal Science* 1977, 44, 1107-1111.

7 KÖHLER, H. [Examination of Galega species for their toxin content by biological methods. I. Toxicity of goat's rue (Galega officinalis) for warm-blooded animals.] *Biologisches Zentralblatt* 1969, 88, 165-177.

8 PUYT, J.D.; FALIU, L.; KECK, G.; GEDFRAIN, J.C.; PINAULT, L.; TAINTURIER, D. Fatal poisoning of sheep by Galega officinalis (French honeysuckle). *Veterinary and Human Toxicology* 1981, 23, 410-411.

9 FALIU, L.; PUYT, J.D.; TAINTURIER, D. [Goat's rue (Galega officinalis), a very dangerous legume for sheep.] *Recueil de Médecine Vétérinaire* 1981, 157 419-426.

10 RÎPEANU, M. [Observations on some important cases of poisoning in animals.] *Revista de Zootehnie şi Medicină Veterinară* 1963, 13(12), 61-69.

11 CONNOR, H.E. The Poisonous Plants in New Zealand. E.C. Keating, Government Printer, Wellington, New Zealand. 1977, 107.

12 MORQUER, R.; RIVAS, P.; ANDRAL, L. [Galega officinalis: a dangerous plant for livestock.] *Revue de Médecine Vétérinaire* 1952, 103, 327-342.

13 JAFFÉ, W.G. Hemagglutinins (lectins). In: *Toxic Constituents of Plant Foodstuffs*. Edited by I.E. Liener. Academic Press, New York and London. 2nd Edition, 1980, 73-102.

14 DUFFUS, C.M.; SMITH, P.M. Legumes and their toxins. *Span* 1981, 24, 63-65.

15 ROMBOLI, I.; FINZI, A. [The antithyroid factors in soya.] *Rivista di Zootecnica e Veterinaria* 1974, No. 2, 123-137.

16 FEDELI AVANZI, C. [Thyroid-inhibiting effects of soya beans.] *Agricoltura Italiana, Pisa* 1972, 72, 293-296.

17 LIENER, I.E.; KAKADE, M.I. Protease inhibitors. In: *Toxic Constituents of Plant Foodstuffs*. Edited by I.E. Liener. Academic Press, New York and London. 2nd Edition, 1980, 7-71.

18 HOVE, E.L.; KING, S. Composition, protein quality and toxins of seeds of the grain legumes Glycine max, Lupinus spp., Phaseolus spp., Pisum sativum and Vicia faba. *New Zealand Journal of Agricultural Research* 1978, 21, 457-462.

19 BOOTH, A.N.; ROBBINS, D.J.; RIBELIN, W.E.; DEEDS, F. Effect of raw soybean meal and amino acids on pancreatic hypertrophy. *Proceedings of the Society for Experimental Biology and Medicine* 1960, 104, 681-683.

20 SAXENA, H.C.; JENSEN, L.S.; McGINNIS, J.; LAUBER, J.K. Histophysiological studies on chick pancreas as influenced by feeding raw soybean meal. *Proceedings of the Society for Experimental Biology and Medicine* 1963, 112, 390-393.

21 STOCKMAN, S. Cases of poisoning in cattle by feeding a meal from soya bean after extraction of the oil. *Journal of Comparative Pathology and Therapeutics* 1916, 29, 95-107.

22 STEWART, G.H.G.; LAWRENCE, J.A. An outbreak of hepatosis dietetica in Rhodesia. *Rhodesian Veterinary Journal*, 1978, 8, 80-86.

23 MOUNTS, T.L.; DUTTON, H.J.; EVANS, C.D.; COWAN, J.C. Chick edema factor: removal from soybean oil. *Journal of the American Oil Chemists' Society* 1976, 53, 105-107.

24 KINGSBURY, J.M. Poisonous Plants of the United States and Canada. Prentice-Hall Inc., New Jersey, USA. 1964, 320-322.

25 BORNSTEIN, S.; LIPSTEIN, B. The influence of age of chicks on their sensitivity to raw soybean oil meal. *Poultry Science* 1963, 42, 61-70.

26 FINZI, A.; ROMBOLI, I. [Congenital blindness in chicks as a result of prolonged administration of raw soya bean meal to laying hens.] *Rivista Italiana delle Sostanze Grasse* 1972, 49, 252-253.

27 COOPER, P. Poisoning by Drugs and Chemicals, Plants and Animals. Alchemist Publications, London, UK. 3rd Edition, 1974, 69-70.

28 FORSYTH, A.A. British Poisonous Plants. HMSO, London, UK. Ministry of Agriculture, Fisheries and Food Bulletin 161, 1968, 60-61 (amended 1979, 62-63).

29 AUCHTERLONE, L. Laburnum poisoning. *Veterinary Record* 1948, 60, 633.

30 CONNOLLY, F. Laburnum poisoning in cattle. *Irish Veterinary Journal* 1949, 3, 266-268.

31 CLARKE, M.L.; CLARKE, E.G.C.; KING, T. Fatal Laburnum poisoning in a dog. *Veterinary Record* 1971, 88, 199-200.

32 LEYLAND, A. Laburnum (Cytisus laburnum) poisoning in two dogs. *Veterinary Record* 1981, 109, 287.

33 CORNEVIN, D. Des Plantes Vénéneuses. Librarie de Firmin-Didot, Paris, France. 1887, 288-307.

34 BRAMLEY, A.; GOULDING, R. Laburnum "poisoning". *British Medical Journal* 1981, 283, 1220-1221.

35 MITCHELL, R.G. Laburnum poisoning in children. Report on ten cases. *Lancet* 1951, II, 57-58.

36 Poisons Unit, New Cross (Guy's) Hospital, London, UK. Personal communication.

37 RICHARDS, H.G.H.; STEPHENS, A. A fatal case of laburnum seed poisoning. *Medical Science and the Law* 1970, 10, 260-266.

38 FORRESTER, R.M. "Have you eaten laburnum?" *Lancet* 1979, I, 1073.

39 PADMANABAN, G. Lathyrogens. In: *Toxic Constituents of Plant Foodstuffs*. Edited by I.E. Liener. Academic Press, New York and London. 2nd Edition, 1980, 239-263.

40 LAMBEIN, F.; VOS, B. DE. Lathyrism in young chicks induced by isoxazolin-5-ones from Lathyrus odoratus seedlings. *Archives Internationales de Physiologie et de Biochimie* 1981, 89 (2), B66-B67.

41 BARROW, M.V.; SIMPSON, C.F.; MILLER, E.J. Lathyrism: a review. *Quarterly Journal of Biology* 1974, 49, 101-128.

42 ROY, D.N. Toxic amino acids and proteins from Lathyrus plants and other leguminous species: a literature review. *Nutrition Abstracts and Reviews, Series A* 1981, 51, 691-707.

43 LEVENE, C.I. Collagen and lathyrism. *Proceedings of the Royal Society of Medicine* 1966, 59, 757-758.

44 ANONYMOUS. Lathyrism — an ancient disease, odoratism — an experimental model. *Nutrition Reviews* 1959, 17, 272-274.

45 DASTUR, D.K.; IYER, C.G. Lathyrism versus odoratism. *Nutrition Reviews* 1959, 17, 33-36.

46 FORSYTH, A.A. British Poisonous Plants. HMSO, London, UK. Ministry of Agriculture, Fisheries and Food Bulletin 161, 1968, 62-63 (amended 1979, 64-65).

47 SUGG, R.S.; SIMMS, B.T.; BAKER, K.G. Studies of toxicity of wild winter peas (Lathyrus hirsutus) for cattle. *Veterinary Medicine* 1944, 39, 308-311.

48 GIBBONS, W.J. Forage poisoning. Part Two. *Modern Veterinary Practice* 1959, 40 (16), 43-47.

49 ANONYMOUS. Lathyrism in sheep. *Surveillance* 1981, 8, 22.

50 CONNOR, H.E. The Poisonous Plants in New Zealand. E.C. Keating, Government Printer, Wellington, New Zealand. 1977, 105.

51 GREATOREX, J.C. Some unusual cases of plant poisoning in animals. *Veterinary Record* 1966, 78, 725-727.

52 KINGSBURY, J.M. Poisonous Plants of the United States and Canada. Prentice-Hall, New Jersey, USA. 1964, 326-331.

53 PRODANOV, P.; ZHELEZOVA, B. [Studies on the cyanogenic properties of Lotus corniculatus (birdsfoot trefoil) in Bulgaria.] *Izvestiya na Instituta po Sravnitelna Patologiya na Domashnite Zhivotni, Sofia* 1960, 8, 281-287.

54 DOBES, F.; JŮZA, J. [Investigation of the HCN content of leaves, flowers and pods of birdsfoot trefoil (Lotus corniculatus.] *Rostlinná Výroba* 1972, 18, 1097-1104.

55 BIRK, Y.; PERI, I. Saponins. In: *Toxic Constituents of Plant Foodstuffs*. Edited by I.E. Liener. Academic Press, New York and London. 2nd Edition. 1980, 161-182.

56 DOUGHERTY, R.W.; CHRISTENSEN, R.B. In vivo absorption of hydrocyanic acid of plant juice origin. *Cornell Veterinarian* 1953, 43, 481-486.

57 SHKLYAR, B.L. [Hydrocyanic acid poisoning by birdsfoot trefoil (Lotus corniculatus).] *Veterinariya, Moscow* 1956, 33(6), 79.

58 RICHTER, H.E. [Influence of certain indigenous Austrian plants on milk quality. II. Taint and smell.] *Wiener Tierärztliche Monatsschrift* 1964, 51, 266-280.

59 GLADSTONES, J.S. Lupins as crop plants. *Field Crop Abstracts* 1970, 23, 123-148.

60 HOVE, E.L.; KING, S. Trypsin inhibitor contents of lupin seeds and other grain legumes. *New Zealand Journal of Agricultural Research* 1979, 22, 41-42.

61 SCHULTZ, G.; ELGHAMRY, M.I. Isolation of biochanin A from Lupinus termis and estimation of its estrogenic activity. *Naturwissenschaften* 1971, 58, 98.

62 GARDINER, M.R. Lupinosis. *Advances in Veterinary Science* 1967, 11, 85-138.

63 KEELER, R.F. Lupin alkaloids from teratogenic and nonteratogenic lupins. III. Identification of anagyrine as the probable teratogen in feeding trials. *Journal of Toxicology and Environmental Health* 1976, 1, 889-898.

64 KEELER, R.F. Alkaloid teratogens from Lupinus, Conium, Veratrum and related genera. In: *Effects of Poisonous Plants on Livestock*. Edited by R.F. Keeler, K.R. Van Kampen and L.F. James. Academic Press, New York and London. 1978, 397-408.

65 CRAIGMILL, A.L.; CROSBY, D.; KILGORE, W.; POPPEN, N.; HEDRICK, K. Passage of toxic alkaloids into goats milk. *Proceedings of the Third International Conference on Goat Production and Disease, Tucson, Arizona, 1982.* Dairy Goat Journal Publishing Co., Scottsdale, Arizona, USA. 1982, 567.

66 GARDINER, M.R.; PETTERSON, D.S. Pathogenesis of mouse lupinosis induced by a fungus (Cytospora sp.) growing on dead lupins. *Journal of Comparative Pathology* 1972, 82, 5-13.

67 WARMELO, K.T. VAN; MARASAS, W.F.O.; ADELAAR, T.F.; KELLERMAN, T.S.; RENSBERG, I.B.J. VAN; MINNE, J.A. Experimental evidence that lupinosis of sheep is a mycotoxicosis caused by the fungus Phomopsis leptostromiformis (Kühn) Bubák. *Journal of the South African Veterinary Medical Association* 1970, 41, 235-247.

68 WOOD, P.McR.; BROWN, A.G.P.; PETTERSON, D.S. Production of lupinosis mycotoxin by Phomopsis russiana. *Australian Journal of Experimental Biology and Medical Science* 1973, 51, 557-558.

69 ZÜRN, F.A. [Mass outbreak of disease in sheep caused by consumption of infected lupins.] *Vorträge für Thierärzte* 1879, Series II, 7, 3-29.

70 ALLEN, J.G. An evaluation of lupinosis in cattle in Western Australia. *Australian Veterinary Journal* 1981, 57, 212-215.

71 Poisons Unit, New Cross (Guy's) Hospital, London, UK. Personal communication.

72 NORTH, P.M. Poisonous Plants and Fungi. Blandford Press, London, UK. 1967, 127-128.

73 MORRISON, J. Lucerne (Medicago sativa). In: *Grasses and Legumes in British Agriculture.* Edited by C.R.W. Spedding and E.C. Diekmahns. Commonwealth Agricultural Bureaux, Farnham Royal, UK. 1972, 387-403.

74 BYRNE, K.V. Dermatitis in white pigs due to photosensitisation. *Australian Veterinary Journal* 1937, 13, 74-75.

75 AUSTIN, A.R.; RESTALL, D. Variation in blood coagulation in animals fed legume forages. Grassland Research Institute, Maidenhead, UK. Annual Report 1980 (published 1981), 103.

76 SCHEEL, C.D. The toxicology of sweet clover and coumarin anticoagulants. In: *Mycotoxic Fungi, Mycotoxins, Mycotoxicoses. An Encyclopedic Handbook.* Edited by T.D. Wyllie and L.G. Morehouse. Marcel Dekker Inc., New York, USA. Vol. 2, 1978, 121-142.

77 RADOSTITS, O.M.; SEARCY, G.P.; MITCHALL, K.G. Moldy sweet clover poisoning in cattle. *Canadian Veterinary Journal* 1980, 21, 155-158.

78 CONNOR, H.E. The Poisonous Plants in New Zealand. E.C. Keating, Government Printer, Wellington, New Zealand. 1977, 117-118.

79 DUFFUS, C.M.; SMITH, P.M. Legumes and their toxins. *Span* 1981, 24, 63-65.

80 ROY, D.N. Toxic amino acids and proteins from Lathyrus plants and other leguminous species: a literature review. *Nutrition Abstracts and Reviews, Series A* 1981, 51, 691-707.

81 PUSZTAI, A. Nutritional toxicity of the kidney bean (Phaseolus vulgaris). *Rowett Research Institute Annual Report of Studies in Animal Nutrition and Allied Sciences* 1980, 36, 110-118.

82 PUSZTAI, A.; CLARKE, E.M.W.; GRANT, G.; KING, T.P. The toxicity of Phaseolus vulgaris lectins. Nitrogen balance and immunochemical studies. *Journal of the Science of Food and Agriculture* 1981, 32, 1037-1046.

83 NOAH, N.D.; BENDER, A.E.; REAIDI, G.B.: GILBERT, R.J. Food poisoning from raw red kidney beans. *British Medical Journal* 1980, 281, 236-237.

84 ANONYMOUS. Unusual outbreak of food poisoning. *British Medical Journal* 1976, 2, 1268.

85 JAFFÉ, W.G. Hemagglutinins (lectins). In: *Toxic Constituents of Plant Foodstuffs.* Edited by I.E. Liener. Academic Press, New York and London. 2nd Edition, 1980, 73-102.

86 HAIDVOGL, M.; FRITSCH, G.; GRUBBAUER, H.M. [Poisoning by raw garden beans (Phaseolus vulgaris and Phaseolus coccineus) in children.] *Pädiatrie und Pädologie* 1979, 14, 293-296.

87 SALMON, W.D.; SEWELL, W.E. Lameness in hogs produced by Austrian pea (Pisum arvense). 47th Annual Report of the Agricultural Experiment Station, Polytechnic Institute, Auburn, Alabama, USA. 1936, 17-18.

88 WHITING, F.; CONNELL, R.; PLUMMER, P.J.G.; CLARK, R.D. Incoordination (cerebellar ataxia) among lambs from ewes fed peavine silage. *Canadian Journal of Comparative Medicine and Veterinary Science* 1957, 21, 77-84.

89 KIENHOLZ, E.W.; JENSEN, L.S.; McGINNIS, J. Evidence for chick growth inhibitors in several legume seeds. *Poultry Science* 1962, 41, 367-371.

90 MORRISON, F.B. Feeds and Feeding. Morrison Publishing Company, Iowa, USA. 1959, 328-329.

91 KINGSBURY, J.M. Poisonous Plants of the United States and Canada. Prentice-Hall, Inc., New Jersey, USA. 1968, 351-353.

92 KELLER, H.; DEWITZ, W. [Poisoning of nine horses by the bark of false acacia (Robinia pseudoacacia).] *Deutsche Tierärztliche Wochenschrift* 1969, 76, 115-116.

93 ZAREMBA, S.; DONIEC, H. Histological changes in the chick liver following phytohaemagglutinin administration. *Folia Biologica, Krakow* 1977, 25, 55-61.

94 LAMPE, K.F.; FAGERSTRÖM, R. Plant Toxicity and Dermatitis. Williams and

Wilkins Co., Baltimore, USA. 1968, 71.

95 BARTÍK, M.; PISKAČ, A. (Editors) Veterinary Toxicology. Elsevier, Amsterdam, Netherlands. 1981, 250.

96 SCHAUENBERG, P.; PARIS, F. Guide to Medicinal Plants. Lutterworth Press, Guildford and London, UK. 1977, 50.

97 NICHOLSON, J.A. Lander's Veterinary Toxicology. Baillière, Tindall and Cox, London, UK. 1945, 216.

98 MORRISON, J. White clover (Trifolium repens). In: *Grasses and Legumes in British Agriculture*. Edited by C.R.W. Spedding and E.C. Diekmahns. Commonwealth Agricultural Bureaux, Farnham Royal, UK. 1972, 347-369.

99 MORRISON, J. Red clover (Trifolium pratense). In: *Grasses and Legumes in British Agriculture*. Edited by C.R.W. Spedding and E.C. Diekmahns. Commonwealth Agricultural Bureaux, Farnham Royal, UK. 1972, 370-386.

100 COX, R.I. Plant estrogens affecting livestock in Australia. In: *Effects of Poisonous Plants on Livestock*. Edited by R.F. Keeler, K.R. Van Kampen and L.F. James. Academic Press, New York and London. 1978, 451-464.

101 SABA, N.; DRANE, H.M.; HEBERT, C.M.; HOLDSWORTH, R.J. Seasonal variation in oestrogenic activity, coumestrol and formononetin content of white clover. *Journal of Agricultural Science* 1974, 83, 505-510.

102 WARD, W.R. The aetiology of 'ringwomb' or partial dilatation of the cervix. *Veterinary Annual* 1975, 15, 75-78.

103 WHITMAN, R.J. Herbivore feeding and cyanogenesis in Trifolium repens L. *Heredity* 1973, 30, 241-245.

104 GURNEY, M.P.; JONES, W.T.; MERRALL, M.; REID, C.S.W. Cyanide poisoning in cattle: two unusual cases. *New Zealand Veterinary Journal* 1977, 25, 128-130.

105 FORSYTH, A.A. British Poisonous Plants. HMSO, London, UK. Ministry of Agriculture, Fisheries and Food Bulletin 161, 1968, 62 (amended 1979, 64).

106 AUSTIN, A.R.; RESTALL, D. Variation in blood coagulation in animals fed legume forages. Grassland Research Institute, Maidenhead, UK. Annual Report 1980 (published 1981), 103.

107 FINCHER, M.G.; FULLER, H.K. Photosensitisation-trifoliosis-light sensitisation. *Cornell Veterinarian* 1942, 32, 95-98.

108 MORRILL, C.C. Clover sickness, or trifoliosis. *North American Veterinarian* 1943, 24, 731-732.

109 SCHOFIELD, F.W. Liver disease of horses (big liver) caused by the feeding of Alsike clover. Veterinary College, Ontario Department of Agriculture, Circular No. 52, 1933, 1-4.

110 BLOOD, D.C.; HENDERSON, J.A.; RADOSTITS, O.M. Veterinary Medicine. Baillière Tindall, London, UK. 5th Edition, 1979, 993-995.

111 SMITH, A. Other legumes. In: *Grasses and Legumes in British Agriculture*. Edited by C.R.W. Spedding and E.C. Diekmahns. Commonwealth Agricultural Bureaux, Farnham Royal, UK. 1972, 414-422.

112 RUBY, E.S.; BEASLEY, J.; STEPHENSON, E.L. Prussic acid poisoning in common vetch (Vicia sativa) seed. *Proceedings of the Arkansas Academy of Sciences* 1955, 18-20.

113 CONN, E.E. Cyanogenic glycosides. *Journal of Agricultural and Food Chemistry* 1969, 17, 519-526.

114 HIBBS, C.M. Cyanide and nitrate toxicoses of cattle. *Veterinary and Human Toxicology* 1979, 21, 401-403.

115 RESSLER, C. Isolation and identification from common vetch of the neurotoxin β-cyano-L-alanine, a possible factor in neurolathyrism. *Journal of Biological Chemistry* 1962, 237, 733-735.

116 VÖLKER, R. Lehrbuch der Toxikologie für Tierärzte. (Fröhner). Ferdinand Enke Verlag, Stuttgart, Germany. 6th Edition, 1950, 272-273.

117 ARSCOTT, G.H.; HARPER, J.A. Evidence for a difference in toxicity between common and hairy vetch seed for chicks. *Poultry Science* 1964, 43, 271-273.

118 HARPER, J.A.; ARSCOTT, G.H. Toxicity of common and hairy vetch seed for poults and chicks. *Poultry Science* 1962, 41, 1968-1974.

119 CLAUGHTON, W.P.; CLAUGHTON, H.D. Vetch seed poisoning. *Auburn Veterinarian* 1954, 10, 125-126.

120 PANCIERA, R.J. Hairy vetch (Vicia villosa Roth) poisoning in cattle. In: *Effects of Poisonous Plants on Livestock.* Edited by R.F. Keeler, K.R. Van Kampen and L.F. James. Academic Press, New York and London. 1978, 555-563.

121 KERR, L.A.; EDWARDS, W.C. Hairy vetch poisoning of cattle. *Veterinary Medicine and Small Animal Clinician* 1982, 77, 257-258.

122 CLAPHAM, A.R.; TUTIN, T.G.; WARBURG, E.F. Flora of the British Isles. University Press, Cambridge, UK. 1962, 359.

123 AHERNE, F.X.; LEWIS, A.J.; HARDIN, R.T. An evaluation of faba beans (Vicia faba) as a protein supplement for swine. *Canadian Journal of Animal Science* 1977, 57, 321-328.

124 STRYCZEK, J. [Outbreak of Vicia faba poisoning in swine.] *Medycyna Weterynaryjna* 1981, 37, 549.

125 MAGER, J.; CHEVION, M.; GLASER, G. Favism. In: *Toxic Constituents of Plant Foodstuffs.* Edited by I.E. Liener. Academic Press, New York and London. 2nd Edition, 1980, 265-294.

126 SENIOR, B.; BRAUDO, J.L. Favism. Report of a case occurring in Johannesburg. *South African Medical Journal* 1955, 29, 1264-1266.

127 GESSNER, O. Die Gift- und Arzneipflanzen von Mitteleuropa. Carl Winter, Heidelberg, Germany. 1953, 667.

128 GARDNER, C.A.; BENNETTS, H.W. The Toxic Plants of Western Australia. West Australian Newspapers Periodicals Division, Perth, Australia. 1956, 114.

129 GESSNER, O. Die Gift- und Arzneipflanzen von Mitteleuropa. Carl Winter, Heidelberg, Germany. 1953, 318-319.

130 CORNEVIN, C. Des Plantes Vénéneuses. Librairie de Firmin-Didot, Paris, France. 1887, 309-310.

131 LAMPE, K.F. Pharmacology of poisonous plants of Florida. *Journal of the Florida Medical Association* 1978, 65, 171-174.

132 LAMPE, K.F.; FAGERSTRÖM, R. Plant Toxicity and Dermatitis. Williams and Wilkins, Baltimore, USA. 1968, 19.

133 KINGSBURY, J.M. Poisonous Plants of the United States and Canada. Prentice-Hall, Inc., New Jersey, USA. 1964, 364.

LILIACEAE

1 FINCH, J.M. Autumn crocus libelled (correspondence). *Veterinary Record* 1977, 100, 226.

2 DELATOUR, P. Colchicum autumnale. *Notes de Toxicologie Vétérinaire* 1977, No. 1, 23-24.

3 DEBARNOT, A. [Colchicum autumnale (meadow saffron) poisoning.] Thesis, Ecole Nationale Vétérinaire, Alfort, Paris, France. 1968, 66pp.

4 TRIBUNSKII, M.P. [Colchicum autumnale poisoning in lambs.] *Veterinariya, Moscow* 1970, 6, 71-72.

5 SCHULZ, O. VON; HOMMEL, H. [Colchicum autumnale poisoning in cattle.] *Monatshefte für Veterinärmedizin* 1975, 30, 333-334.

6 ADAMESTEANU, I.; ADAMESTEANU, C.; SALANTIU, V.; GHERGARIU, S.; PRECUP, O. [Clinical and pathological features of Colchicum autumnale poisoning in cattle.] *Revista de Zootehnie şi Medicină Veterinară,* 1966, 16 (7), 58-61.

7 SHERGIN, YU. K.; TRIBUNSKII, M.P. [Pathology of Colchicum (Kesselring variety) poisoning in lambs.] *Veterinariya, Moscow* 1971, 5, 88-89.

8 RICHTER, H.E. [Influence of certain Austrian plants on milk quality. I. Excretion of plant poisons in milk.] *Wiener Tierärztliche Monatsschrift* 1963, 50, 692-699.

9 HILL, F.W.G. Malabsorption in dogs induced with oral colchicine. *British Veterinary Journal* 1972, 128, 372-378.

10 KASIM, M.; LANGE, H. [Toxicological diagnosis of Colchicum autumnale poisoning in ruminants. Method for determining colchicine.] *Archiv für Experimentelle Veterinärmedizin* 1973, 27, 601-603.

11 HARDIN, J.W.; ARENA, J.M. Human Poisoning from Native and Cultivated Plants. Duke University Press, Durham, North Carolina, USA. 1969, 35-36.

12 LAMPE, K.F.; FAGERSTRÖM, R. Plant Toxicity and Dermatitis. Williams and Wilkins, Baltimore, USA. 1968, 79-86.

13 SCOTT, H.G. Poisonous plants and animals. In: *Food-borne Infections and Intoxications.* Edited by H. Riemann. Academic Press, New York and London. 1969, 543-604.

14 O'LEARY, S.B. Poisoning in man from eating poisonous plants. *Archives of Environmental Health* 1964, 9, 216-242.

15 LAMPE, K.F. Systemic plant poisoning in children. *Pediatrics* 1974, 54, 347-351.

16 Poisons Unit, New Cross (Guy's) Hospital, London, UK. Personal communication.

17 RAISON, A.V. Poisons in your back yard. *Canadian Pharmaceutical Journal* 1968, 101, 4-8.

18 COOPER, P. Poisoning by Drugs and Chemicals, Plants and Animals. Alchemist Publications, London, UK. 3rd Edition, 1974, 64.

19 FORSYTH, A.A. British Poisonous Plants. HMSO, London, UK. Ministry of Agriculture, Fisheries and Food Bulletin 161, 1968, 103-104 (amended 1979, 104-105).

20 THURSBY-PELHAM, R.H.C. Suspected Scilla nonscripta (bluebell) poisoning in cattle. *Veterinary Record* 1967, 80, 709-710.

21 MITCHELL, J.; ROOK, A. Botanical Dermatology. Plants and Plant Products Injurious to the Skin. Greengrass Ltd., Vancouver, Canada. 1979, 445.

22 NIEUWLAND, I.C.H. [The use of bulbs as cattle feed.] *Tijdschrift voor Diergeneeskunde* 1941, 68, 359-368.

23 HARDIN, J.W.; ARENA, J.M. Human Poisoning from Native and Cultivated Plants. Duke University Press, Durham, North Carolina, USA. 1969, 38.

24 MITCHELL, J.; ROOK, A. Botanical Dermatology. Plants and Plant Products Injurious to the Skin. Greengrass Ltd., Vancouver, Canada. 1979, 443.

25 CEH, L.; HAUGE, J.G. Alveld-producing saponins. I. Chemical studies. *Acta Veterinaria Scandinavica* 1981, 22, 391-402.

26 ENDER, F. [Aetiological studies on 'alveld' — a disease involving photosensitisation and icterus in lambs.] *Nordisk Veterinaermedicin* 1955, 7, 329-377.

27 ENDER, F. Aetiological studies on 'alveld', a disease in lambs caused by grazing Narthecium ossifragum. *Proceedings of the Eighth International Grasslands Congress, Reading, UK.* 1960, 664-667.

28 LAKSESVELA, B.; DISHINGTON, I.W.; PESTALOZZI, M.; OVERÅS, H.; HAMAR, T.O. [Alveld (photosensitisation due to Narthecium ossifragum) in lambs.] *Norsk Veterinaertidsskrift* 1977, 89, 199-209.

29 SANDERS, K.J. Loss of ears in lambs. *Veterinary Record* 1981, 109, 320.

30 LAMONT, H.G. Loss of ears in lambs. *Veterinary Record* 1981, 109, 368.

31 FORD, E.J.H. A preliminary investigation of photosensitisation in Scottish sheep. *Journal of Comparative Pathology and Therapeutics* 1964, 74, 37-44.

32 ANONYMOUS. *Glasshouse Crops and Horticultural Trades Journal* 1977, 182 (7), 12.

33 VAHRMEIJER, J. Poisonous Plants of Southern Africa. Tafelberg Publishers Ltd., Cape Town, South Africa. 1981, 20.

34 MARETIĆ, Z.; RUSSELL, F.E.; LADAVAC, J. Tulip bulb poisoning. *Periodicum Biologorum* 1978, 80 (Supplement 1), 141-143.

LINACEAE

1 BURTON, D.; HANENSON, I.B. Plant toxins. In: *Quick Reference to Clinical Toxicology.* Edited by I.B. Hanenson. J.B. Lippincott, Philadelphia, USA. 1980, 242-251.

2 JAMES, L.F.; JOHNSON, A.E. Some major plant toxicities of the Western United States. *Journal of Range Management* 1976, 29, 356-363.

3 BISHARA, H.N.; WALKER, H.F. The vitamin B_6 status of pigs given a diet containing linseed meal. *British Journal of Nutrition* 1977, 37, 321-331.

4 McBARRON, E.J. Medical and Veterinary Aspects of Plant Poisons in New South Wales. Department of Agriculture, New South Wales. 1976. 179.

5 BRIOUX, C.; RICHART, A. [Hydrocyanic acid in linseed cake. Toxicity of some oilseed cakes.] *Bulletin de l'Académie Vétérinaire de France* 1928, 1 (New Series), 134-146.

6 VILLET, C. [Alimentary toxicology of linseed cake in cattle.] Thesis. Ecole Nationale Vétérinaire de Lyon, France. 1965. 69pp.

7 PERROT, M. [Poisoning of sheep by linseed cake.] *Recueil de Médecine Vétérinaire* 1928, 104, 15-18.

8 COLIN, M.A.M. [Toxicity of linseed cake for sheep.] Thesis. Ecole Nationale Vétérinaire d'Alfort, France. 1937. 51pp.

9 MORRISON, F.B. Feeds and Feeding. Morrison Publishing Co., Iowa, USA. 22nd Edition, 1959, 485-489.

10 FORSYTH, A.A. British Poisonous Plants. HMSO, London, UK. Ministry of Agriculture, Fisheries and Food Bulletin 161, 1968, 57 (amended 1979, 57).

LOBELIACEAE

1 CORNEVIN, C. Des Plantes Vénéneuses. Librairie de Firmin-Didot, Paris, France. 1887. 486-487.

2 DOLLAHITE, J.W.; ALLEN, T.J. Poisoning of cattle, sheep and goats with Lobelia and Centaurium species. *Southwestern Veterinarian* 1962, 15, 126-130.

3 MITCHELL, J.; ROOK, A. Botanical Dermatology. Plants and Plant Products Injurious to the Skin. Greengrass Ltd., Vancouver, Canada, 1979, 150-151.

LORANTHACEAE

1 SAMUELSSON, G. Phytochemical and pharmacological studies on Viscum album L. IV. Countercurrent distribution studies on viscotoxin. *Svensk Farmaceutisk Tidskrift* 1961, 65, 209-222.

2 SAMUELSSON, G.; PETTERSSON, B.M. The amino acid sequence of viscotoxin B from the European mistletoe (Viscum album L. Loranthaceae). *European Journal of Biochemistry* 1971, 21, 86-89.

3 GREATOREX, J.C. Some unusual cases of plant poisoning in animals. *Veterinary Record* 1966, 78, 725-727.

4 CHAPRON, M.H. [Probable poisoning of a dog by mistletoe.] *Revue de Pathologie Comparée et d'Hygiene Génerale* 1936, 36, 400.

5 JEAN-BLAIN, C. [Mistletoe.] *Notes de Toxicologie Vétérinaire* 1977, No. 1, 21-22.

6 CORNEVIN, C. Des Plantes Vénéneuses. Librairie de Firmin-Didot, Paris, France. 1887, 163-164.

7 STANDRING, G.; GOULDING, R. Poisonous plants. *Nursing Times* 1969, August 7, 1009-1011.

8 HARVEY, J.; COLIN-JONES, D.G. Mistletoe hepatitis. *British Medical Journal* 1981, 282, 186-187.

9 COLIN-JONES, D.G.; HARVEY, J.. Mistletoe hepatitis. *British Medical Journal* 1982, 284, 744-745.

MALVACEAE

1 DODD, S.; HENRY, M. Staggers or shivers in live stock. *Journal of Comparative Pathology and Therapeutics* 1922, 35, 41-61.

2 GORDON, McL. H. Some field observations on various diseases of sheep. *Australian Veterinary Journal* 1936, 12, 29-31.

3 HENNING, M.W. Krimpsiekte. 11th and 12th Reports of the Director of Veterinary Education and Research, Onderstepoort, South Africa, 1926, 331-365.

4 MARSH, C.D.; CLAWSON, A.B.; ROE, G.C. Four species of range plants not poisonous to livestock. United States Department of Agriculture, Technical Bulletin No. 93, 1928. 9pp.

5 CONNOR, H.E. The Poisonous Plants in New Zealand. E.C. Keating, Government Printer, Wellington, New Zealand. 1977, 124.

6 MacFARLANE, J.J.; SHENSTONE, F.S.; VICKERY, J.R. Malvalic acid and its structure. *Nature, London* 1957, 179, 830-831.

7 SHENSTONE, F.S.; VICKERY, J.R. A biologically active fatty-acid in Malvaceae. *Nature, London* 1956, 177, 94.

8 SHENSTONE, F.S.; VICKERY, J.R. Substances in plants of the order Malvale causing pink whites in stored eggs. *Poultry Science* 1959, 38, 1055-1070.

OLEACEAE

1 FORSYTH, A.A. British Poisonous Plants. HMSO, London, UK. Ministry of Agriculture, Fisheries and Food Bulletin 161, 1968, 85-86 (amended 1979, 86).

2 REEVES, R.J.C. Cattle poisoning from ash leaves and fruits. *Veterinary Record* 1966, 79, 580.

3 MITCHELL, J.; ROOK, A. Botanical Dermatology. Plants and Plant Products Injurious to the Skin. Greengrass Ltd., Vancouver, Canada. 1979, 493.

4 FORSYTH, A.A. British Poisonous Plants. HMSO, London, UK. Ministry of Agriculture, Fisheries and Food Bulletin 161, 1968, 85-86 (amended 1979, 86-87).

5 TURNER, T.W. Some interesting cases. *Veterinary Record* 1904, 17, 319-320.

6 ANONYMOUS. Accidental poisonings of stock. *New Zealand Journal of Agriculture* 1939, 59, 429-431.

7 REYNARD, G.B.; NORTON, J.B.S. Poisonous plants of Maryland in relation to livestock. University of Maryland Agricultural Experiment Station. Technical Bulletin No. A10, 1942, 273.

8 Poisons Unit. New Cross (Guy's) Hospital, London, UK. Personal communication.

9 MITCHELL, J.; ROOK, A. Botanical Dermatology. Plants and Plant Products Injurious to the Skin. Greengrass Ltd., Vancouver, Canada. 1979, 494.

OROBANCHACEAE

1 CORNEVIN, C. Des Plantes Vénéneuses. Librairie de Firmin-Didot, Paris, France. 1887, 504-505.

2 KAMEL, S.H. [Chemical and toxicological study of an Egyptian plant: Orobanche minor Sutton.] *Revue d'Élevage et de Médecine Vétérinaire des Pays Tropicaux* 1956, 9, 43-48.

3 LONG, H.C. Plants Poisonous to Live Stock. Cambridge University Press, Cambridge, UK. 1917, 95.

OXALIDACEAE

1 MATHAMS, R.H.; SUTHERLAND, A.K. The oxalate content of some Queensland pasture plants. *Queensland Journal of Agricultural Science* 1952, 9, 317-334.

2 BULL, L.B. Poisoning of sheep by soursobs (Oxalis cernua): chronic oxalic acid poisoning. *Australian Veterinary Journal* 1929, 5, 60-69.

3 WALKER, D.J. Poisoning of sheep by Oxalis corniculata. Institute of Inspectors of Stock of New South Wales 1939, 49-52.

4 LONG, H.C. Plants Poisonous to Live Stock. Cambridge University Press, Cambridge, UK. 1917, 23.

PAEONIACEAE

1 GUSYNIN, I.A. [The toxicology of poisonous plants.] Gosudarstvennoe Izdatel'stvo Sel'skokhozyaistvennoi Literatury, Moscow, USSR. 3rd Edition, 1955, 255.

2 SCHILLING, R.; SPEAKER, J. Incidence of plant poisonings in Philadelphia noted as poison information calls. *Veterinary and Human Toxicology* 1980, 22, 148-150.

PAPAVERACEAE

1 CORNEVIN, C. Des Plantes Vénéneuses. Librairie de Firmin-Didot, Paris, France. 1887, 234-237.

2 LAGNEAU, F.; GALLARD, P. [Poisoning of cattle by poppies (Papaver somniferum).] *Recueil de Médecine Vétérinaire* 1946, 122, 310-313.

3 LÉZY. [Poisoning of cattle by poppy capsules (Papaver somniferum).] *Recueil de Médecine Vétérinaire* 1946, 122, 23-24.

4 MALMANCHE, I. DE. Suspected Papaver nudicaule (Iceland poppy) poisoning in two horses. *New Zealand Veterinary Journal* 1970, 18, 96.

5 TERBLANCHE, M.; ADELAAR, T.F. A note on the toxicity of Papaver nudicaule L. (Iceland poppy). *Journal of the South African Veterinary Medical Association* 1964, 35, 383-384.

6 McLENNAN, G.C. Poisoning of sheep by ingestion of Iceland poppies (Papaver nudicaule). *Australian Veterinary Journal* 1929, 5, 117.

7 McLENNAN, G.C. Iceland poppy poisoning. *Australian Veterinary Journal* 1930, 6, 40.

8 ANONYMOUS. Poisoning with Iceland poppies (Papaver nudicaule). Annual Report, New Zealand Department of Agriculture 1960, 190.

9 FORSYTH, A.A. British Poisonous Plants. HMSO, London, UK. Ministry of Agriculture, Fisheries and Food Bulletin 161, 1968, 40 (amended 1979, 42).

10 SCHAUENBERG, P.; PARIS, F. Guide to Medicinal Plants. Lutterworth Press, Guildford and London, UK. 1977, 29.

11 REEKS, H.C. Poisoning of cattle by common celandine. *Journal of Comparative Pathology and Therapeutics* 1903, 16, 367-371.

12 VÖLKER, R. Lehrbuch der Toxikologie für Tierärzte. (Fröhner). Ferdinand Enke Verlag, Stuttgart, Germany. 6th Edition, 1950, 286.

PHYTOLACCACEAE

1 KINGSBURY, J.M. Poisonous Plants of the United States and Canada. Prentice-Hall Inc., New Jersey, USA. 1964, 225-227.

2 WATT, J.M.; BREYER-BRANDWIJK, M.G. The Medicinal and Poisonous Plants of Southern and Eastern Africa. E. & S. Livingstone Ltd., Edinburgh and London, UK. 2nd Edition, 1962, 834-841.

3 SCOTT, H.G. Poisonous plants and animals. In: *Foodborne Infections and Intoxications*. Edited by H. Riemann. Academic Press, New York and London. 1969, 543-604.

4 HANSEN, A.A. The poisonous plant situation in Indiana. *American Veterinary Journal* 1924, 66, 351-362.

5 PATTERSON, F.D. Pokeweed causes heavy losses in swine herd. *Veterinary Medicine* 1929, 24, 114.

6 BARNETT, B.D. Toxicity of pokeberries (fruit of Phytolacca americana Large) for turkey poults. *Poultry Science* 1975, 54, 1215-1217.

7 CATTLEY, R.C.; BARNETT, B.D. The effect of pokeberry ingestion on immune response in turkeys. *Poultry Science* 1977, 56, 246-248.

8 DUNCAN, A.A. Inkweed is a potentially dangerous weed. *New Zealand Journal of Agriculture* 1962, 105, 17, 19.

9 O'LEARY, S.B. Poisoning in man from eating poisonous plants. *Archives of Environmental Health* 1964, 9, 216-242.

10 LAMPE, K.F.; FAGERSTRÖM, R. Plant Toxicity and Dermatitis. Williams and Wilkins, Baltimore, USA. 1968, 32.

11 ANONYMOUS. Pokeweed poisoning — Passiac County. *Communication, Food Production and Inspection Branch, Agriculture, Canada* 1981, 28, 25.

12 BARKER, B.E.; FARNES, P. Histochemistry of blood cells treated with pokeweed mitogen. *Nature, London* 1967, 214, 787-789.

PINACEAE

1 STEVENSON, A.H.; JAMES, L.F.; CALL, J.W. Pine-needle (Pinus ponderosa) — induced abortion in range cattle. *Cornell Veterinarian* 1972, 62, 519-524.

2 ANONYMOUS. Plants poisonous to livestock in the Western States. United States Department of Agriculture Information Bulletin No. 415, 1980, 57.

POLYGONACEAE

1 CLARE, N.T. Photosensitisation in Diseases of Domestic Animals. Review Series No. 3, Commonwealth Bureau of Animal Health. Commonwealth Agricultural Bureaux, Farnham Royal, UK. 1952, 15-16.

2 CLARE, N.T. Photosensitisation in animals. *Advances in Veterinary Science* 1955, 2, 182-211.

3 WATT, J.M.; BREYER-BRANDWIJK, M.G. The Medicinal and Poisonous Plants of Southern and Eastern Africa. E. & S. Livingstone Ltd., Edinburgh and London, UK. 3rd Edition, 1962, 857-859.

4 FORSYTH, A.A. British Poisonous Plants. HMSO, London, UK. Ministry of Agriculture, Fisheries and Food Bulletin 161, 1968, 79-80 (amended 1979, 80-81).

5 KINGSBURY, J.M. Poisonous Plants of the United States and Canada. Prentice-Hall Inc., New Jersey, USA. 1964, 228-230.

6 SALGUES, R. [Polygonaceae. Chemical and toxicological studies.] *Qualitas Plantarum et Materiae Vegetabiles* 1961, 8, 367-395.

7 GUSYNIN, I.A. [The Toxicology of Poisonous Plants.] Gosudarstvennoe Izdatel'stvo Sel'skokhozyaistvennoi Literatury, Moscow, USSR. 1955, 236-237.

8 CHEREMISINOV, G.A. [Persistence of photodynamic substances in white sheep fed on buckwheat.] *Veterinariya, Moscow* 1956, No. 6, 78.

9 PRIOUZEAU, M.M. [Fagopyrism in cattle.] *Recueil de Médecine Vétérinaire* 1942, 118, 160-168.

10 CONNOR, H.E. The Poisonous Plants in New Zealand. E.C. Keating, Government Printer, Wellington, New Zealand. 1977, 139-141.

11 COWARD, T.G. Acute, fatal poisoning in sheep due to ingestion of common sorrel (Rumex acetosa). *Veterinary Record* 1949, 46, 765-766.

12 CRAIG, J.F.; KEHOE, D. Investigations as to the poisonous nature of common sorrel (Rumex acetosa Linn.) for cattle. *Journal of Comparative Pathology and Therapeutics* 1921, 34, 27-47.

13 CORNEVIN, C. Des Plantes Vénéneuses. Librairie de Firmin-Didot, Paris, France. 1887, 150-151.

14 NAUDIN, L. [Poisoning of a goat by rhubarb leaves.] *Recueil de Médecine Vétérinaire* 1932, 109, 91-92.

15 BUCHANAN, J.M. Three cases of poisoning by plants. *Veterinary Record* 1933, 13, 927.

16 HANSEN, A.A. Indiana plants injurious to livestock. Purdue University Agricultural Experiment Station Circular No. 175, 1930, 24.

17 ROBB, H.F. Death from rhubarb leaves due to oxalic acid poisoning. *Journal of the American Medical Association* 1919, 73, 627-628.

18 LEFFMAN, H. Death from rhubarb leaves due to oxalic acid poisoning. *Journal of the American Medical Association* 1919, 73, 928-929.

19 ANONYMOUS. Poisoning by rhubarb leaves. *Lancet* 1917, i, 847.

20 FASSETT, D.W. Oxalates. In: *Toxicants Occurring Naturally in Foods*. National Academy of Sciences, Washington, USA. 2nd Edition, 1973, 346-362.

21 FORSYTH, A.A. British Poisonous Plants. HMSO, London, UK. Ministry of Agriculture, Fisheries and Food Bulletin 161, 1968, 79 (amended 1979, 80).

22 KNIGHT, P.R. Suspected nitrite toxicity in horses associated with the ingestion of wireweed (Polygonum aviculare). *Australian Veterinary Practitioner* 1979, 9, 175-177.

23 LLOYD, M. Central Veterinary Laboratory, Weybridge, Surrey, UK. Personal communication.

PRIMULACEAE

1 CORNEVIN, C. Des Plantes Vénéneuses. Librairie de Firmin-Didot, Paris, France. 1887, 429-430.

2 WATT, J.M.; BREYER-BRANDWIJK, M.G. Medicinal and Poisonous Plants of Southern and Eastern Africa. E. & S. Livingstone Ltd., Edinburgh and London, UK. 1962, 870.

3 REYNARD, G.B.; NORTON, J.B.S. Poisonous plants of Maryland in relation to livestock. University of Maryland Agricultural Experiment Station, Technical Bulletin A10, 1942, 292.

4 FORSYTH, A.A. British Poisonous Plants. HMSO, London, UK. Ministry of Agriculture, Fisheries and Food Bulletin 161, 1968, 84-85 (amended 1979, 85-86).

5 PULLAR, E.M. Studies on five suspected poisonous plants. *Australian Veterinary Journal* 1939, 15, 19-23.

6 SCHNEIDER, D.J. Fatal ovine nephrosis caused by Anagallis arvensis. *Journal of the South African Veterinary Association* 1978, 49, 321-324.

7 MITCHELL, J.; ROOK, A. Botanical Dermatology. Plants and Plant Products Injurious to the Skin. Greengrass Ltd., Vancouver, Canada. 1979, 544.

RANUNCULACEAE

1 SABER, A.H.; MAHRAN, G.H.; EL-ALFY, T.S. Phytochemical investigation of Ranunculus sceleratus L. growing in Egypt. *Journal of Pharmaceutical Sciences U.A.R.* 1968, 9, 35-45.

2 MAHRAN, G.H.; SABER, A.H.; EL-ALFY, T.S. Spectrophotometric determination of protoanemonin, anemonin and ranunculin in Ranunculus sceleratus Linne. *Journal of Pharmaceutical Sciences U.A.R.* 1968, 9, 73-81.

3 SHEARER, G.D. Some observations on the poisonous properties of buttercups. *Veterinary Journal* 1938, 94, 22-32.

4 MIRKOVIC, M. [Some cases of poisoning in cattle by Ranunculaceae.] *Jugoslovenski Veterinarski Glasnik* 1936, 16, 544-545.

5 FORSYTH, A.A. British Poisonous Plants. HMSO, London, UK. Ministry of Agriculture, Fisheries and Food Bulletin 161, 1968, 32-39 (amended 1979, 33-40).

6 MOORE, R.H.S. Poisoning by old man's beard (Clematis vitalba). *Veterinary Record* 1971, 89, 569-570.

7 THERREIN, H.P.; HIDIROGLOU, M.; CHARETTE, L.A. Note on the toxicity of tall buttercup (Ranunculus acris L.) to cattle. *Canadian Journal of Animal Science* 1962, 42, 123-124.

8 HIDIROGLOU, M.; KNUTTI, H.J. The effects of green tall buttercup on the growth and health of beef cattle and sheep. *Canadian Journal of Animal Science* 1963, 43, 68-71.

9 TEHON, L.R.; MORRILL, C.C.; GRAHAM, R. Illinois plants poisonous to livestock. Illinois College of Agriculture Extension Service Bulletin 599, 1946, 37-40.

10 WINTERS, J.B. Severe urticarial reaction in a dog following ingestion of tall field buttercup. *Veterinary Medicine and Small Animal Clinician* 1976, 71, 307.

11 GUNNING, O.V. Suspected buttercup poisoning in a Jersey cow. *British Veterinary Journal* 1949, 105, 393.

12 RAMISZ, A. [Poisoning of two cows by the celery-leaved buttercup (Ranunculus sceleratus).] *Medycyna Weterynaryjna* 1971, 27, 411-412.

13 RÎPEANU, M. [Observations on some important cases of poisoning in animals.] *Revista de Zootehnie şi Medicină Veterinară*, 1963, 13(12), 61-69.

14 PIEKARZ, J. [Buttercup poisoning in a horse.] *Medycyna Weterynaryjna* 1981, 37, 658.

15 BLASZYK, P. [Disease of cattle after application of growth regulators to pasture.] *Gesunde Pflanzen* 1969, 21, 33-36.

16 RAISON, A.V. Poisons in your backyard. *Canadian Pharmaceutical Journal* 1968, 101, 4-8.

17 GERBAUD, O. [Aconites.] *Notes de Toxicologie Vétérinaire* 1980, No. 8, 453-456.

18 CORNEVIN, C. Des Plantes Vénéneuses. Librairie de Firmin-Didot, Paris, France. 1887, 211-220.

19 COOPER, P. Poisoning by Drugs and Chemicals, Plants and Animals. Alchemist Publications, London, UK. 3rd Edition, 1974, 4-5.

20 WILLIAMS, M.C.; CRONIN, E.H. Five poisonous range weeds — when and why they are dangerous. *Journal of Range Management* 1968, 19, 274-279.

21 JAMES, L.F.; KEELER, R.F.; JOHNSON, A.E.; WILLIAMS, M.C.; CRONIN, E.H.; OLSEN, J.D. Plants Poisonous to Livestock in the United States. United States Department of Agriculture, Agriculture Information Bulletin No. 415, 1980, 31-34.

22 NATION, P.N.; BENN, M.H.; ROTH, S.H.; WILKENS, J.L. Clinical signs and studies of the site of action of purified larkspur alkaloid methyllycaconitine, administered parenterally to calves. *Canadian Veterinary Journal* 1982, 23, 264-266.

23 MILNE, J.A. A case of Delphinium poisoning in rams. *New Zealand Veterinary Journal* 1966, 14, 127.

24 ELPHICK, E.E. Sheep poisoned as a result of eating larkspur (Delphinium consolidum). *Veterinary Record* 1931, 43, 512-513.

25 Poisons Unit. New Cross (Guy's) Hospital, London, UK. Personal communication.

26 BERSELLI, L. [Green hellebore poisoning in cattle.] *Nuova Veterinaria* 1936, 14, 197-198.

27 JOHNSON, C.T.; ROUTLEDGE, J.K. Suspected Hellaborus viridis poisoning of cattle. *Veterinary Record* 1971, 89, 202.

28 CHOMEL, B.; JAUSSAUD, P.; PRAVE, M. [Differential diagnosis between infectious diseases and poisonings producing nervous disorders.] *Revue de Médecine Vétérinaire* 1981, 132, 195-202.

RHAMNACEAE

1 VÖLKER, R. Lehrbuch der Toxikologie für Tierärzte. (Fröhner). Ferdinand Enke Verlag, Stuttgart, Germany. 6th Edition, 1950, 300.

2 SÖDERMARK, N. [Frangula poisoning in cattle.] *Skandinavisk Veterinärtidskrift* 1942, 32, 458.

3 CORNEVIN, C. Des Plantes Vénéneuses. Librairie de Firmin-Didot, Paris, France. 1887, 274.

4 LAMPE, K.F.; FAGERSTRÖM, R. Plant Toxicity and Dermatitis. Williams and Wilkins Co., Baltimore, USA. 1968, 56, 58.

5 COOPER, P. Poisoning by Drugs and Chemicals, Plants and Animals. Alchemist Publications, London, UK. 3rd Edition, 1974, 106.

ROSACEAE

1 CONN, E.E. Cyanogenesis, the production of hydrogen cyanide, by plants. In: *Effects of Poisonous Plants on Livestock*. Edited by R.F. Keeler, K.R. Van Kampen and L.F. James. Academic Press, New York and London. 1978, 301-310.

2 MORAN, F.A. Cyanogenetic compounds in plants and their significance in animal industry. *American Journal of Veterinary Research* 1954, 15, 171-176.

3 JEAN-BLAIN, C. [Cherry laurel.] *Notes de Toxicologie Vétérinaire* 1978, No. 4, 222-223.

4 HIBBS, C.M. Cyanide and nitrate toxicoses of cattle. *Veterinary and Human Toxicology* 1979, 21, 401-403.

5 ROBB, W.; CAMPBELL, D. Poisoning of sheep by the consumption of laurel leaves. *Veterinary Record* 1941, 53, 93-95.

6 WILSON, D.R.; GORDON, W.J.. Laurel poisoning in sheep. *Veterinary Record* 1941, 53, 95-97.

7 CARDASSIS, J.; GIANNAKOULAS, D. Hydrocyanic acid poisoning from plum stones in pigs. *Hellenike Kteniatrike, Thessaloniki*, 1961, 4, 136-141.

8 AUSTVOLL, A. Plumstones in pig swill. *Veterinary Record* 1954, 66, 681.

9 MUENSCHER, W.C. Poisonous Plants of the United States. Macmillan, New York, USA. 1939, 109-113.

10 GLODEK, S. [Plum poisoning in cows and pigs.] *Medycyna Weterynaryjna* 1965, 21, 44. .

11 THOLHUYSEN, L.J.Th. [Lethal intoxication of two heifers by bitter almonds.] *Tijdschrift voor Diergeneeskunde* 1960, 85, 1243-1244.

12 LASCH, E.E.; EL RAGHDA, S. Multiple cases of cyanide poisoning by apricot kernels in children from Gaza. *Pediatrics* 1981, 68, 5-7.

13 KINGSBURY, J.M. Poisonous Plants of the United States and Canada. Prentice-Hall Inc., New Jersey, USA. 1964, 364-370.

14 COOPER, P. Poisoning by Drugs and Chemicals, Plants and Animals. Alchemist Publications, London, UK. 3rd Edition. 1974, 185-186.

15 MAJAK, W.; McDIARMID, R.E.; HALL, J.W. The cyanide potential of Saskatoon serviceberry (Amelanchier alnifolia) and chokecherry (Prunus virginiana). *Canadian Journal of Animal Science* 1981, 61, 681-686.

16 HANSEN, A.A. The poison plant situation in Indiana. *American Veterinary Journal* 1924, 66, 351-362.

17 STAUFFER, V.D. Hydrocyanic acid poisoning from chokecherry leaves. *Journal of the American Veterinary Medical Association* 1970, 157, 1324.

18 Poisons Unit. New Cross (Guy's) Hospital. London, UK. Personal communication.

19 ST. JOHN, T.N. Urine discolouration. *Veterinary Record* 1976, 99, 21.

SALICACEAE

1 Poisons Unit. New Cross (Guy's) Hospital, London, UK. Personal communication.

SCROPHULARIACEAE

1 ARENA, J.M. A guide to poisonous plants. *Veterinary and Human Toxicology* 1979, 21, 108-111.

2 COOPER, P. Poisoning by Drugs and Chemicals, Plants and Animals. Alchemist Publications, London, UK. 3rd Edition, 1974, 85.

3 CORRIGALL, W.; MOODY, R.R.; FORBES, J.C. Foxglove (Digitalis purpurea) poisoning in farmed red deer (Cervus elephus). *Veterinary Record* 1978, 102, 119-122.

4 McCLEAN, A. Suspected foxglove poisoning in sheep. *Veterinary Record* 1966, 79, 817-818.

5 BARNIKOL, H.; HOFFMANN, W. [Digitalis poisoning in pigs.] *Tierärztliche Umschau* 1973, 28, 612-614, 616.

6 PARKER, W.H. Foxglove (Digitalis purpurea) poisoning in turkeys. *Veterinary Record* 1951, 63, 416.

7 GERBAUD, O. [Foxglove, Digitalis purpurea.] *Notes de Toxicologie Vétérinaire* 1980, No. 8, 450-452.

8 LAMPE, K.F. Systemic plant poisoning in children. *Pediatrics* 1974, 54, 347-351.

9 DICKSTEIN, E.S.; KUNKEL, F.W. Digitalis purpurea poisoning in man. *American Journal of Medicine* 1980, 69, 167-169.

10 LEE, T.C. Van Gogh's vision. Digitalis intoxication? *Journal of the American Medical Association* 1981, 245, 727-729.

11 EWART, R.H. Poisoning in young cattle by a member of the Scrophulariaceae. *Veterinary Record* 1937, 49, 1514.

SOLANACEAE

1 FODOR, G. Tropane alkaloids. In: *Chemistry of Alkaloids*. Edited by S.W. Pelletier. Van Nostrand Reinhold Company, New York, USA. 1970, 431-467.

2 Merck Index, Merk & Co. Inc., Rahway, New Jersey, USA. 9th Edition, 1976, p.117.

3 GERBAUD, O. [Belladonna.] *Notes de Toxicologie Vétérinaire* 1980, No. 9, 540-543.

4 SCOTT, H.G. Poisonous plants and animals. In: *Food-borne Infections and Intoxications*. Edited by H. Riemann, Academic Press, New York and London, 1969, 561.

5 FORSYTH, A.A. British Poisonous Plants. HMSO, London, UK. Ministry of Agriculture, Fisheries and Food Bulletin 161, 1968, 88-90 (amended 1979, 89-90).

6 SMITH, H.C.; TAUSSIG, R.A.; PETERSON, P.C. Deadly nightshade poisoning in swine. *Journal of the American Veterinary Medical Association* 1956, 129, 116-117.

7 OGILVIE, D.D. Atropine poisoning in the goat. *Veterinary Record* 1935, 15, 1415-1417.

8 SAWIN, P.B.; GLICK, D. Atropinesterase, a genetically determined enzyme in the rabbit. *Proceedings of the National Academy of Science* 1943, 29, 55-59.

9 Poisons Unit. New Cross (Guy's) Hospital, London, UK. Personal communication.

10 TESTASECCA, D.; CAPUTI, C.; PAVONI, P.A. [A case of poisoning by belladonna berries.] *Clinica Terapeutica, Rome* 1978, 86, 277-280.

11 McBARRON, E.J. Medical and Veterinary Aspects of Plant Poisons in New South Wales. Department of Agriculture, New South Wales, Australia. 1976, 83.

12 KEHAR, N.D.; RAU, K.G. Poisoning of livestock by Datura stramonium. *Indian Journal of Veterinary Science* 1944, 14, 112-114.

13 HIGHTOWER, C.E. Plants that kill and cure. *Veterinary and Human Toxicology* 1979, 21, 360-361.

14 BARNEY, G.H.; WILSON, B.J. A rare toxicity syndrome in ponies. *Veterinary Medicine* 1963, 58, 419-421.

15 SINGH, R.C.P.; SINGH, R.P. A suspected case of Datura poisoning in a cow. *Indian Veterinary Journal* 1971, 48, 194-196.

16 WATT, J.M.; BREYER-BRANDWIJK, M.G. Medicinal and Poisonous Plants of Southern and Eastern Africa. E. & S. Livingstone Ltd., Edinburgh and London, UK. 1962, 946-953.

17 ANONYMOUS. Datura stramonium poisoning in sheep. Edinburgh School of Agriculture Annual Report 1978, 129-130.

18 EL DIRDIRI, N.I.; WASFI, I.A.; ADAM, S.E.I.; EDDS, G.T. Toxicity of Datura stramonium to sheep and goats. *Veterinary and Human Toxicology* 1981, 23, 241-246.

19 BEHRENS, H.; HORN, M. [Tolerance of pigs to Datura stramonium seeds.] *Praktische Tierarzt* 1962, 2, 43-44.

20 LEIPOLD, W.; OEHME, F.W.; COOK, J.E. Congenital arthrogryposis associated with ingestion of jimsonweed by pregnant sows. *Journal of the American Veterinary Medical Association* 1973, 162, 1059-1060.

21 LIST, G.R.; SPENCER, G.F. Fate of jimsonweed seed alkaloids in soybean processing. *Journal of the American Oil Chemists' Society* 1976, 53, 535-536.

22 FANGAUF, R.; VOGT, H. [Toxicity trials in laying hens and chicks with Datura stramonium seeds, a common contaminant of soya bean consignments.] *Archiv für Geflügelkunde* 1961, 25, 167-171.

23 HESSELBARTH. [Results of feeding experiments in cattle and pigs with Datura stramonium feeds.] *Praktische Tierarzt* 1962, No. 7, 266-267 and No. 8, 304-305.

24 WORTHINGTON, T.R.; NELSON, E.P.; BRYANT, M.J. Toxicity of thornapple (Datura stramonium L.) seeds to the pig. *Veterinary Record* 1981, 108, 208-211.

25 Poisons Unit. New Cross (Guy's) Hospital, London, UK. Personal communication.

26 SCHILLING, R.; SPEAKER, J. Incidence of plant poisonings in Philadelphia noted as poisons information calls. *Veterinary and Human Toxicology* 1980, 22, 148-150.

27 SIEGEL, R.K. Herbal intoxication, psychoactive effects from herbal cigarettes, tea and capsules. *Journal of the American Medical Association* 1976, 236, 473-476.

28 CRANE E. (Editor). Honey: A comprehensive survey. William Heinemann Ltd., London, UK. 1975, 204.

29 SENGER, E.; BAROUX, D. [Cases of poisoning after consumption of maize.] *Notes de Toxicologie Vétérinaire* 1980, No. 8, 468-474.

30 SCHAUENBERG, P.; PARIS, F. Guide to Medicinal Plants. Lutterworth Press, Guilford and London, UK. 1977, 39.

31 CORNEVIN, C. Des Plantes Vénéneuses. Librairie de Firmin-Didot, Paris, France. 1887, 470-473.

32 MIĘDZOBRODZKI, K. [Poisoning in cows with henbane (Hyoscyamus niger).] *Medycyna Weterynaryjna* 1962, 18, 536-537.

33 GUSYNIN, I.A. [Toxicology of Poisonous Plants.] Gosudarstvennoe Izdatel'stvo Sel'skokhozyaistvennoi Literatury, Moscow, USSR. 1955, 61-62.

34 WELSBY, J.R. Henbane poisoning. *Veterinary Record* 1903, 16, 181.

35 Merck Index, Merck & Co., Rahway, New Jersey, USA, 9th Edition, 1976, 647.

36 FORSYTH, A.A. British Poisonous Plants. HMSO, London, UK. Ministry of Agriculture, Fisheries and Food Bulletin 161, 1968, 87-88 (amended 1979, 88-89).

37 LONG, H.C. Plants Poisonous to Live Stock. Cambridge University Press, Cambridge, UK. 1917, 51-52.

38 Poisons Unit. New Cross (Guy's) Hospital, London, UK. Personal communication.

39 ALTMANN, H. Poisonous Plants and Animals. Chatto & Windus, London, UK. 1980, 82-83.

40 FORSYTH, A.A. British Poisonous Plants. HMSO, London, UK. Ministry of Agriculture, Fisheries and Food Bulletin 161, 1968, 92-93 (amended 1979, 93-94).

41 CROWE, M.W. Skeletal abnormalities in pigs associated with tobacco. *Modern Veterinary Practice* 1969, 50 (13), 54-55.

42 KEELER, R.F.; SHUPE, J.L.; CROWE, M.W.; OLSON, A.; BALLS, L.D. Nicotiana glauca-induced congenital deformities in calves: clinical and pathologic aspects. *American Journal of Veterinary Research* 1981, 42, 1231-1234.

43 McBARRON, E.J. Medical and Veterinary Aspects of Plant Poisons in New South Wales. Department of Agriculture, New South Wales, Australia. 1976, 91.

44 McKEY, D. The distribution of secondary compounds within plants. In: *Herbivores. Their Interaction with Secondary Plant Metabolites.* Edited by G.A. Rosenthal and D.H. Janzen. Academic Press, New York and London. 1979, 55-133.

45 CORNEVIN, C. Des Plantes Vénéneuses. Librairie de Firmin-Didot, Paris, France. 1887, 455.

46 CRAIG, J.F.; KEHOE, D. Plant poisoning. *Veterinary Record* 1925, 38, 793-825.

47 YATES, G. Poisoning by woody nightshade. *Veterinary Record* 1915, 28, 269-270.

48 BARRATT, M. [Poisoning by bittersweet.] *Journal de Médecine Vétérinaire et de Zootechnie, Lyons* 1926, 72, 545-552.

49 Poisons Unit. New Cross (Guy's) Hospital, London, UK. Personal communication.

50 ALEXANDER, R.F.; FORBES, G.B.; HAWKINS, E.S. A fatal case of solanine poisoning. *British Medical Journal* 1948, 2, 518-519.

51 SENGER, E.; BAROUX, D. [Herbicides and resistance — toxicological significance.] *Notes de Toxicologie Vétérinaire* 1980, No. 8, 444-445.

52 WELLER, R.F.; PHIPPS, R.H. A review of black nightshade (Solanum nigrum L.). *Protection Ecology* 1979, 1, 121-139.

53 KEELER, R.F. Alkaloid teratogens from Lupinus, Conium, Veratrum and related genera. In: *Effects of Poisonous Plants on Livestock.* Edited by R.F. Keeler, K.R. Van Kampen and L.F. James. Academic Press, New York and London. 1978, 397-408.

54 LIEBENOW, H. [Solanum nigrum L. as a nitrate-containing plant and the determination of its alkaloid content.] *Wissenschaftliche Zeitschrift der Humboldt-Universität zu Berlin* 1970, 19, 59-71.

55 BROBERG, G. Observations of the action of extracts of Glium lotoides on the miracidia of Fasciola gigantica and Schistosoma mansoni. *Suomen Eläinlääkärilehti* 1980, 86, 146-147.

56 CORNEVIN, C. Des Plantes Vénéneuses. Librairie de Firmin-Didot, Paris, France. 1887, 456.

57 Encyclopaedia Britannica 1929, 16, 447.

58 HUBBS, J.C. Belladonna poisoning in pigs. *Veterinary Medicine* 1947, 42, 428-429.

59 FORSYTH, A.A. British Poisonous Plants. HMSO, London, UK. Ministry of Agriculture, Fisheries and Food Bulletin 161, 1968, 92 (amended 1979, 91-92).

60 FAWCETT, R.S.; JENNINGS, V.M. Today's weed. Black nightshade (Solanum nigrum L.). *Weeds Today* 1979, 10, 21.

61 GUNNING, O.V. Poisoning in goats by black nightshade (Solanum nigrum). *British Veterinary Journal* 1949, 105, 473-474.

62 KWATRA, M.S.; HOTHI, D.S.; SINGH, A.; CHAWLA, R.S. Arteriosclerosis with metastatic calcification in Corriedale sheep in Punjab. *Atherosclerosis* 1974, 19, 521-528.

63 SENGER, E.; BAROUX, D. [Cases of poisoning after consumption of maize.] *Notes de Toxicologie Vétérinaire* 1980, No. 8, 468-474.

64 WATT, J.M.; BREYER-BRANDWIJK, M.G. The Medicinal and Poisonous Plants of Southern and Eastern Africa. E. & S. Livingstone Ltd., Edinburgh and London, UK. 1962, 996-1000.

65 JADHAU, S.J.; SALUNKHE, D.K. Formation and control of chlorophyll and glycoalkaloids in tubers of Solanum tuberosum L. and evaluation of glycoalkaloid toxicity. *Advances in Food Research* 1975, 21, 307-354.

66 CHAUBE, S.; SWINYARD, C.A. Teratological and toxicological studies of alkaloidal and phenolic compounds from Solanum tuberosum L. *Toxicology and Applied Pharmacology* 1976, 36, 227-237.

67 COXON, D.T. The glycoalkaloid content of potato berries. *Journal of the Science of Food and Agriculture* 1981, 32, 412-414.

68 NICHOLSON, J.W.G.; YOUNG, D.A.; McQUEEN, R.E.; DE JONG, H.; WOOD, F.A. The feeding potential of potato vines. *Canadian Journal of Animal Science* 1978, 58, 559-569.

69 OGILVIE, D.D. Solanin poisoning in pigs. *Veterinary Record* 1943, 55, 249.

70 LEWANDOWSKI, L.; BĄK, T.; MIĘDZOBRODSKI, K. [Solanine poisoning in swine.] *Zeszyty Naukowe Wyzszej Szkoly Rolniczej we Wroclawiu, Zootechnika* 1963, 11, 203-207.

71 BUCZEK, A.; MAJERAN, W. [A rare complication after solanin poisonings in pigs.] *Medycyna Weterynaryjna* 1969, 25, 507-508.

72 MILLIGAN, J.B. Suspected potato poisoning in cattle. *Veterinary Record* 1941, 53, 512.

73 KOTOWSKI, K. [Cases of poisoning in cattle due to excessive feeding with potatoes.] *Medycyna Weterynaryjna* 1967, 23, 736-737.

74 FORSYTH, A.A. British Poisonous Plants. HMSO, London, UK. Ministry of Agriculture, Fisheries and Food Bulletin 161, 1968, 92-93 (amended 1979, 92-93).

75 BOLIN, F.M. Green potatoes can kill sheep. *North Dakota Farm Researh* 1962, 22 (7), 15.

76 GUNNING, O.V. Suspected potato poisoning in a mare. *British Veterinary Journal* 1950, 106, 32-33.

77 BLOUNT, W.P. Potato poisoning in the adult dog. *Veterinary Record* 1928, 43, 924-925.

78 TEMPERTON, H. The effects of feeding green and sprouted potatoes to laying pullets. *Veterinary Record* 1943, 55, 359.

79 KLINE, B.E.; ELBE, H.; DAHLE, N.A.; KUPCHAN, S.M. Toxic effect of potato sprouts and of solanine fed to pregnant rats. *Proceedings of the Society for Experimental Biology and Medicine* 1961, 107, 807-809.

80 WILLIMOTT, S.G. An investigation of solanine poisoning. *Analyst* 1933, 58, 431-438.

81 WILSON, G.S. A small outbreak of solanine poisoning. *Monthly Bulletin of the Ministry of Health and the Public Health Laboratory Service* 1958, 17, 207-210.

82 McMILLAN, M.; THOMPSON, J.C. An outbreak of suspected solanine poisoning in schoolboys. *Quarterly Journal of Medicine* 1979, New Series 48, 190, 227-243.

83 RENWICK, J.H. Anencephaly and spina bifida are usually preventable by avoidance of a specific but unidentified substance present in some potato tubers. *British Journal of Preventive and Social Medicine* 1972, 26, 67-88.

84 BROWN, D.; KEELER, R.F. Structure-activity relation of steroid teratogens. 2. N-substituted jervines. *Journal of Agricultural and Food Chemistry* 1978, 26, 564-566.

TAXACEAE

1 WILLIAMSON, R. The Great Yew Forest, the Natural History of Kingsley Vale. Macmillan, London, UK. 1978.

2 ALDEN, C.L.; FOSNAUGH, C.J.; SMITH, J.B.; MOHAN, R. Japanese yew poisoning of large domestic animals in the Midwest. *Journal of the American Veterinary Medical Association* 1977, 170, 314-316.

3 PUYT, J.D.; FALIU, L.; JEAN-BLAIN, C. [Yew. Poisonous plant no. 2.] *Point Vétérinaire* 1982, 13, 86-87.

4 ORR, A.B. Poisoning in domestic animals and birds. *Veterinary Record* 1952, 64, 339-343.

5 KÖHLER, H.; GRÜNBERG, W. [Yew poisoning in a kangeroo.] *Archiv für Experimentelle Veterinärmedizin* 1960, 14, 1149-1162.

6 JORDAN, W.J. Yew (Taxus baccata) poisoning in pheasants (Phasianus colchicus). *Tijdschrift voor Diergeneeskunde* 1964, 89, Suppl. No. 1, 187-188.

7 ANONYMOUS. [Yew.] *Notes de Toxicologie Vétérinaire* 1977, No. 3, 157-158.

8 KNOWLES, I.W. Yew poisoning in cattle. *Veterinary Record* 1949, 61, 421-422.

9 BOUTHIÈRE, G.; DELATOUR, P.; JEAN-BLAIN, C.; LORGUE, G.; RANCIEN, P. [Collective poisoning of cattle by yew.] *Bulletin de la Société des Sciences Vétérinaires et de Médecine Comparée de Lyon* 1973, 75, 163-164.

10 SZABADOS, A. [Severe cases of poisoning in horses due to Taxus baccata.] *Magyar Allatorvosok Lapja* 1976, 31, 69.

11 LOWE, J.E.; HINTZ, H.P.; SCHRYVER, H.F.; KINGSBURY, J.M. Taxus cuspidata (Japanese yew) poisoning in horses. *Cornell Veterinarian* 1970, 60, 36-39.

12 KYLE, R.A.M. Oxford, UK. Personal communication.

13 FORSYTH, A.A. British Poisonous Plants. HMSO, London, UK. Ministry of Agriculture, Fisheries and Food Bulletin 161, 1968, 29-31 (amended 1979, 31-33).

14 Poisons Unit. New Cross (Guy's) Hospital, London, UK. Personal communication.

15 SCHULTE, T. [Fatal poisoning by yew (Taxus baccata).] *Archives of Toxicology* 1975, 34, 153-158.

THYMELAEACEAE

1 NICHOLSON, J.A. Lander's Veterinary Toxicology. Baillière, Tindall and Cox, London, UK. 3rd Edition, 1945, 273-276.

2 GUSYNIN, I.A. [The toxicology of poisonous plants.] Gosudarstvennoe Izdatel'stvo Sel'skokhozyaistvennoi Literatury, Moscow, USSR. 3rd Edition, 1955, 176-177.

3 FORSYTH, A.A. British Poisonous Plants. HMSO, London, UK. Ministry of Agriculture, Fisheries and Food Bulletin 161, 1968, 66-67 (amended 1979, 66-68).

4 KINGSBURY, J.M. Deadly Harvest. George Allen & Unwin, London, UK. 1967, 36-37.

5 CORNEVIN, C. Des Plantes Vénéneuses. Librairie de Firmin-Didot, Paris, France. 1887, 160-163.

6 Poisons Unit. New Cross (Guy's) Hospital, London, UK. Personal communication.

TRILLIACEAE

1 DERIVAUX, J.; LIÉGEOIS, F. Toxicologie Vétérinaire, Vigot Frères, Paris, France. 1962, 254.

2 GUSYNIN, I.A. [The toxicology of poisonous plants.] Gosudarstvennoe Izdatel'stvo Sel'skokhozyaistvennoi Literatury, Moscow, USSR. 1955, 202-203.

3 SCHURZ, J. [Herb paris.] *Kosmos* 1976, 72, 236-237.

UMBELLIFERAE

1 MINISTRY OF AGRICULTURE, FISHERIES AND FOOD. Poisoning of Animals in Britain. *Animal Disease Report* 1978, 2, No. 2, 9-12.

2 KEELER, R.F.; BALLS, L.D.; SHUPE, J.L.; CROWE, M.W. Teratogenicity and toxicity of coniine in cows, ewes and mares. *Cornell Veterinarian* 1980, 70, 19-26.

3 KUBIK, M.; REJHOLEC, J.; ZACHO-VAL, J. [Outbreak of hemlock poisoning in cattle.] *Veterinarstvi* 1980, 30, 157-158.

4 TUDOR, G.; ANTON, E.; DIACONESCU, G. [Conium maculatum (hemlock) poisoning in sheep.] *Revista de Zootehnie și Medicină Veterinară* 1969, 19 (11), 74-80.

5 COPITHORNE, B. Suspected poisoning of goats by hemlock (Conium maculatum). *Veterinary Record* 1937, 49, 1018-1019.

6 MacDONALD, H. Hemlock poisoning in horses. *Veterinary Record* 1937, 49, 1211-1212.

7 ANONYMOUS. Unusual case of hemlock poisoning in swine. *California Veterinarian* 1951, 5(2), 26.

8 RICHTER, H.E. [Poisoning by hemlock, Conium maculatum.] *Wiener Tierärztliche Monatsschrift* 1964, 51, 404-407.

9 EDMONDS, L.D.; SELBY, L.A.; CASE, A.A. Poisoning and congenital malformations associated with consumption of poison hemlock by sows. *Journal of the American Veterinary Medical Association* 1972, 160, 1319-1324.

10 DYSON, D.A.; WRATHALL, A.E. Congenital deformities in pigs possibly associated with exposure to hemlock (Conium maculatum). *Veterinary Record* 1977, 100, 241-242.

11 KEELER, R.F. Coniine, a teratogenic principle from Conium maculatum producing congenital malformations in cattle. *Clinicial Toxicology* 1974, 7, 195-206.

12 KEELER, R.F.; BALLS, L.D. Teratogenic effects in cattle of Conium maculatum and Conium alkaloids and analogs. *Clinical Toxicology* 1978, 12, 49-64.

13 MILNE, J. Fatal poisoning in a horse by Oenanthe crocata — the water dropwort. *Veterinary Record* 1945, 57, 30.

14 WILSON, A.L.; JOHNSTON, W.G.; McCUSKER, M.B.; BANNATYNE, C.C. Hemlock water dropwort (Oenanthe crocata) poisoning in cattle. *Veterinary Record* 1958, 70, 587-590.

15 ANGER, J.-P.; ANGER, F.; CHAUVEL, Y.; GIRRE, R.L.; CURTES, N.; CURTES, J.-P. [Fatal poisoning by hemlock water dropwort (Oenanthe crocata).] *European Journal of Toxicology* 1976, 9, 119-125.

16 MITCHELL, M.I.; ROUTLEDGE, P.A. Hemlock water dropwort poisoning — a review. *Clinical Toxicology* 1978, 12, 417-428.

17 Poisons Unit. New Cross (Guy's) Hospital, London, UK. Personal communication.

18 FORSYTH, A.A. Treatment for poisoning by Oenanthe crocata. *Veterinary Record* 1966, 79, 55.

19 MIĘDZOBRODZKI, K. [Oenanthe aquatica poisoning in heifers.] *Medycyna Weterynaryjna* 1960, 16, 609-610.

20 ASPIOTIS, N.; LAVRENTIADES, G.; ANDREOU, C. [Pharmacodynamic study of the poisonous plant Oenanthe silaifolia.] *Bulletin de l'Académie Vétérinaire de France* 1960, 33, 75-80.

21 CEDERSTAM, R. [Cowbane poisoning.] *Svensk Veterinärtidning* 1976, 28, 1114-1116.

22 PRIOUZEAU, M.M. [Poisoning by cowbane.] *Recueil de Médecine Vétérinaire* 1951, 127, 483-488.

23 DIJKSTRA, R.G.; FALKENA, R. [Cicutoxin poisoning in two ponies.] *Tijdschrift voor Diergeneeskunde* 1981, 106, 1037-1039.

24 NILSSON, N.-S. [Cowbane poisoning, another case.] *Svensk Veterinärtidning* 1977, 29, 725.

25 TATAR, A.; OTLOWSKI, F. [Mass poisoning of cattle with cowbane (Cicuta virosa L.).] *Życie Weterynaryjne* 1967, 42, 137-140.

26 LASKOWSKI, S.; MATYJEK, J.; KOPPICZ, M.; POHORSKI, A. [Cowbane (Cicuta virosa) poisoning.] *Polski Tygodnik Lekarski* 1975, 30, 533-534.

27 STARREVELD, E.; HOPE, C.E. Cicutoxin poisoning (water hemlock). *Neurology* 1975, 25, 730-734.

28 VÖLKER, H.; SCHULZ, O.; ALBRECHT, K.; SIERING, W. [Poisoning by cowbane (Cicuta virosa) in fattening bulls.] *Monatshefte für Veterinärmedizin* 1983, 38, 11-13.

29 LONG, H.C. Plants Poisonous to Live Stock. Cambridge University Press, Cambridge, UK. 1917, 39-40.

30 BARR, A.G.; DAVIES, C.S. An unusual case of poisoning in a sow and litter. *Veterinary Record* 1963, 75, 457.

31 SWART, F.W.J. [Poisoning of goats with fool's parsley.] *Tijdschrift voor Diergeneeskunde* 1975, 100, 989-900.

32 VÖLKER, R. Lehrbuch der Toxikologie für Tierärzte. (Fröhner)., Ferdinand Enke Verlag, Stuttgart, Germany. 6th Edition, 1950, 303-304.

33 OETTINGEN, W.F. VON. Poisoning. W.B. Saunders Co., Philadelphia, USA. 2nd Edition. 1958, 346.

34 ANONYMOUS. The giant hogweed. *Lancet* 1970, II, 32.

35 DREVER, J.C.; HUNTER, J.A.A. Hazards of giant hogweed. *British Medical Journal* 1970, 3, 109.

36 HELLIER, F.F. "Non-accidental injury" and wild parsnips. *British Medical Journal* 1982, 284, 1198.

37 CAMPBELL, A.N.; COOPER, C.E.; DAHL, M.G.C. "Non-accidental injury" and wild parsnips. *British Medical Journal* 1982, 284, 708.

INDEX

Abies 62
Abortion 51, 53, 68, 107, 134, 139
Acacia 155-156
Acetylandromedol 111
Aconite 198-199
Aconitine 198
Aconitum anglicum 198
Aconitum napellus 198-199, 239, photo 31
Acrid Lobelia 173
Actaea spicata 203
Acute haemorrhagic syndrome 57-58
Adonis annua 197
Aesculetin 130
Aesculin 130, 176
Aesculus hippocastanum 129-130
Aethusa cynapium 237, 240
Aflatoxicosis 50
Aflatoxin 49-50, 239
Agaricus arvensis 40
Agaricus campestris 22, 24, 40, 44
Agaricus nivescens 40
Agaricus placomyces 40
Agaricus silvicola 40
Agaricus xanthodermus 40
Aglycone 13
Agrostemma githago 77-78, photo 12
Ajacine 200
Ajaconine 200
Alcohol and fungal poisoning 38-39
Alder Buckthorn 203-204, 240
Alfalfa 151-152
Algae 20
Alkaloids 11-13
Alliaceae 63-65, 257-258
Allium 63-65, 239, 240
Allium cepa 63-65
Allium ursinum 63-65, photo 8
Allium validum 64
Allium vineale 63
Allyl glucosinolate 92, 101, 103
Allyl isothiocyanate 92, 101, 103, 104
Almond 204, 206, 207
Alsike Clover 157
Alveld 167-168
Amanita muscaria 30-32, photo 2
Amanita pantherina 30-32
Amanita phalloides 23-26, photo 5
Amanita rubescens 30

Amanita verna 24, 26
Amanita virosa 24
Amanitin 24
Amaryllidaceae 66, 258
Amatoxins 24-26
American Nightshade 184
Amino acids 20, 146, 161
Amurine 181
Amygdalin 205, 207
Amygdalus communis 204
Anabasine 217
Anagallis arvensis 191-192
Anagyrine 150
Andromedotoxins 111
Anemone 192, 193
Anemone nemorosa 193, photo 32
Anemone pulsatilla 193, 195
Annual Mercury 118-119, 240
Anthoxanthum odoratum 126-127
Anthriscus sylvestris 229
Apoatropine 212
Apple 204, 207
Apricot 207
Aquifoliaceae 67, 258
Aquilegia vulgaris 198, 200
Araceae 67-69, 258-259
Arachis hypogea 140
Araliaceae 69-70, 259
Arctium lappa 87
Arctium minus 87
Arctium pubens 87
Arenaria 77
Armillaria mellea 32, 35
Armoracia rusticana 103-104
Aroin 68
Aronin(e) 68
Arrow Grass 136-138
Artemesia vulgaris 90
Artichoke, Jerusalem 90
Arum maculatum 67-69, photo 9
Ash 176, 240, photo 28
Aspergillus 50-51
Aspergillus flavus 50, 127
Aspergillus fumigatus 51, 127
Aspergillus parasiticus 50
Aspidiaceae 53-55, 255-256
Aspidium 53
Astragalus 141
Astragalus miser 141

Asulam 62
Atriplex patula 83
Atropa bella-donna 211-213, 216, photo 35
Atropine 212, 213, 216
Atropinesterase 7, 212
Autumn Crocus 164
Avena sativa 127-129
Azalea 110, 111

Bacon and Eggs 148
Baneberry 203
Barberry 70
Barley 127-129
Batyl alcohol 61
Bean 153-154
Bear's Foot 201
Beech 122-123
Beet 80-82, 239, 240
Belladonine 212
Benweed 83
Berberidaceae 70, 259
Berberine 70
Berberis vulgaris 70
Beta vulgaris 80-82, 239, 240
Bikukulla 123
Biochanin A 150
Birdsfoot Trefoil 148-149, 240, photo 25
Black Acacia 155
Black Bean 153
Black Bryony 109, photo 17
Black Locust 155
Black Nightshade 219-220, photo 40
Blackthorn 204
Bleeding Heart 123
Blewits 45
Bloat 128, 158, 159
Blue Legs 32
Bluebell 169-170, 239
Blusher 30
Bog Asphodel 166-168, photo 27
Boletus 34, 40-41
Boletus satanas 40-41
Books on poisonous plants 249-250
Boraginaceae 70-72, 259-260
Box 73-74, photo 11
Bracken 55-62, 239, 240, photo 7

Brassica 93-101
Brassica campestris 93-97, 240
Brassica napus 93-97
Brassica oleracea 97-101, 104, photo 15
Bright blindness 59, 60
British Mandrake 105
Brittle Gills 43
Broad Bean 162-163
Broom 156
Broomrape 178
Brown Hay Cap 33
Brussels Sprouts 104
Bryonia dioica 105-106, 239, photo 16
Bryonicine 106
Bryonidin 106
Bryonin(e) 106
Bryony, Black 109, photo 17
Bryony, White 105-106, 239, photo 16
Buckler Fern 53-54
Buckthorn 203-204, 240
Buckwheat 186-187
Bulbous Buttercup 195
Burdock 87
Buttercup 194-198, 240
Buxaceae 73-74, 260
Buxine 73
Buxus sempervirens 73-74, photo 11

Cabbage 104
Caffeic acid 221
Calcinosis 125, 220
Calcium borogluconate 18
Caley Pea 146
Calocybe gambosa 45
Caltha palustris 192, 193-194
Cannabaceae 74-75, 260
Cannabis sativa 74-75
Cantherellus cibarius 37
Caper Spurge 117
Caprifoliaceae 75-77, 260-261
Capsella bursa-pastoris 105, 240
Carboxyatractyloside 89
Carcinogens 55, 56
Cardiac glycosides 15-16, 209
Carduus 90
Carex 108
Carex vulpina 108
Caryophyllaceae 77-78, 261
Castor Oil Plant 113-116, 240
Celandine Poppy 183
Celastraceae 79-80, 261
Celery 4, 19, 238

Celery Leaved Buttercup 196
Celery Leaved Crowfoot 196-197
Centaurea solstitialis 87-88
Cereal grains 127-129
Chaconine 219, 221, 222
Chanterelle 37
Charcoal 10
Charlock 101-102
Chelerythrine 182, 183
Chelidonine 76, 183
Chelidonium majus 183-184, photo 29
Chenopodiaceae 80-83, 261-262
Chenopodium album 82-83, 239
Cherry 204, 206, 207, 208
Cherry Laurel 204-208, photo 34
Chick Pea 146, 147
Chickling Vetch 146
Chickweed 77
Chicory 88
Chincherinchee 170
Chlorogenic acid 221
Chokecherry 207
Cholecalciferol 124
Christmas Rose 202
Chrysanthemum vulgare 90
Cichorium intybus 88
Cicuta virosa 234-236, 239, fig. 3
Cicutoxin 236
Cirsium 90
Citrinin 50-51
Claviceps 46-49
Claviceps purpurea 46-49, 239, 254-255, photo 1
Clematis vitalba 192, 194, photo 33
Clitocybe 31, 36-37
Clitocybe clavipes 38, 39
Clitocybe dealbata 36
Clitocybe nebularis 39
Clitocybe olearia 37
Clitocybe rivulosa 36
Cloud Cap 39
Clouded Agaric 39
Clover 157-160, 240
Club Foot Mushroom 39
Cocklebur 89-90
Cocksfoot 124
Colchiceine 165
Colchicine 165
Colchicum autumnale 164-166, 239, photo 26
Cole 93
Columbine 198, 200
Colza 93

Comfrey 70-72, photo 10
Common Buckthorn 203
Common Buttercup 194-195
Common Elder 75-76
Common Horsetail 52-53
Common Ink Cap 38-39
Common Mallow 175
Common St. John's Wort 131-133, photo 22
Common Vetch 160-162
Common Viper's Bugloss 73
Compositae 83-90, 240, 262-264
Conhydrin 230
Coniceine 230
Coniferae 62
Coniine 230, 237
Conium maculatum 229-232, 239, 240, photo 42 and fig. 1
Conocybe 26
Consolidine 72
Convallamarin 168
Convallaria majalis 168-169
Convallarin 168
Convallotoxin 168
Convicine 161, 163
Convolvulaceae 90-91, 264
Copper Trumpet 37
Coprine 38
Coprinus atramentarius 38-39
Copse Laurel 226
Corn Cockle 77-78, photo 12
Corn Poppy 180
Coronilla varia 141-142
Coronopus 239, 240
Cortinarius 27-28, photo 3
Cortinarius orellanoides 27
Cortinarius orellanus 27
Cortinarius speciosissimus 27-28
Cotoneaster 208
Coumarins 126-127, 152, 221, 227
Cow Parsley 229
Cow Wheat 211
Cowbane 234-236, 239, fig. 3
Crassulaceae 91, 265
Crataegus monogyna 208, 239
Creeping Buttercup 197
Cress 239, 240
Crooked calf disease 150
Crow Garlic 63
Crowfoot 194
Crown Vetch 141-142
Cruciferae 92-105, 265-268
Crustlike Hebeloma 41

Cuckoo Pint 67-69, photo 9
Cucurbitaceae 105-106, 269
Cupressaceae 107, 269
Cupressus 107, 239
Cupressus macrocarpa 107
Cupressus sempervirens 107
Cursed Crowfoot 196
Cuscuta 90
Cuscuta epithymum 90
Cuscuta europaea 90
Cyanides 13-14
Cyanogenic glycosides 13-14, 55-
56, 76, 108, 135, 137-138, 148-149,
158-159, 161, 171-172, 205-207,
224
Cyclamin 191
Cynapine 237
Cynoglossine 71-72
Cynoglossum officinale 72, 239
Cyperaceae 108, 269
Cypress 107, 239
Cytisine 144-145, 156
Cytisus laburnum 144

Dactylis glomerata 124
Daffodil 66
Danewort 77
Daphne laureola 226-227, photo 41
Daphne mezereum 226-227
Daphnetin 227
Daphnetoxin 227
Daphnin(e) 227
Daphnitin 227
Darnel 126
Datura stramonium 213-215, photo 37
Deadly Agaric 24
Deadly Nightshade 211-213, photo
35
Dead Men's Fingers 232
Death Cap 23-26, photo 5
Delphinine 200
Delphinium 199-200
Delphinium 198, 199-200
Delphinium barbeyi 200
Delphinium consolidum 200
Delphinium hybridum 200
Dennstaedtiaceae 55-62, 256-257
Deoxynivalenol 51
Dermocybe 27
Destroying Angel 24
Detoxification 6-7
Devil's Bit Scabious 110

Devil's Boletus 40
Diacetoxyscirpenol 51
Diagnosis 8-9
Dicentra canadensis 123
Dicentra cucullaria 123
Dicentra spectabilis 123
Dicoumarol 127, 152
Digitalin 209
Digitalis purpurea 208-210, photo 36
Digitalosmin 209
Digitonin 209
Digitoxin 209
Dimethyl disulphide 98
Dioscoraceae 109, 269
Dipsacaceae 110, 269
Divicine 161
Dodder 90
Dog's Mercury 118-119, photo 20
Drosera 110
Droseraceae 110, 269
Dryopteris 53-55
Dryopteris borreri 54
Dryopteris filix-mas 53-55
Dung Roundhead 34
Dutch Clover 157
Dutchman's Breeches 123
Dwarf Bay 226
Dwarf Mallow 175

Earthballs 44
Earthnut 140
Easter Rose 202
Echimidine 72
Echinatine 72
Echium lycopis 72-73
Echium plantagineum 72
Echium vulgare 73
Echiumidine 72
Egg Taint 97
Elder 75-76, 212
Emetic 9-10
Emodin 204
Endymion nonscriptus 169-170, 239
Enteque seco 220
Entoloma 41
Entoloma lividum 41
Entoloma sinuatum 41
Enzootic haematuria 57, 58-60
Ephedrine 224
Equisetaceae 52-53, 255
Equisetum 52-53, 239, 240
Equisetum arvense 52-53

Equisetum palustre 52-53
Ergocristine 47
Ergometrine 47
Ergonovine 47
Ergot 46-49, 239, 254-255, photo 1
Ergotamine 47
Ergotism 47-49
Ericaceae 110-112, 269-270
Erodium 124
Erodium cicutarium 124
Erucic acid 93, 97
Euonymin 79
Euonymus europaeus 79-80, photo 13
Euphorbane 117
Euphorbia 116-118
Euphorbia helioscopia 116, 117-118,
photo 19
Euphorbia lathyrus 117
Euphorbia peplus 116, 117
Euphorbiaceae 112-119, 270-272
Euphorbin(e) 117
Euphorbiosteroid 117
Everlasting Pea 146, 147
Evobioside 79
Evomonoside 79
Evonoside 79
Evonymine 79

Fabism(us) 163
Fagaceae 119-123, 272
Fagin 122
Fagopyrin 186
Fagopyrism 187
Fagopyrum esculentum 186-187
Fagus sylvatica 122-123
Fairy Cake Hebeloma 41
Fairy Clubs 43
Fairy Ring Fungus 36
False Blusher 30
False Morel 28-29
Farmer's lung 51
Fat Hen 82-83, 239
Fava Bean 162
Favism 163
Ferns 53-62
Fescue 126
Fescue foot 125, 126
Festuca arundinacea 126
Field Buttercup 194
Field Mushroom 22, 24, 40, 44
Field Pea 154-155
Field Poppy 180-181

Figwort 211
Fir 62
Flax 171
Fly Agaric 30-32, photo 2
Fodder Beet 80
Fog fever 94, 95, 124-125
Fool's Mushroom 24
Fool's Parsley 237, 240
Formononetin 158
Foxglove 208-210, photo 36
Frangula alnus 203-204, 240
Fraxinus excelsior 176, 240, photo 28
French Bean 153
French Honeysuckle 142
French Lilac 142
F-2 toxin 51
Fumariaceae 123, 273
Fungi 22-51, 125, 140, 150, 152, 158, 160, 251-255
Furocoumarins 238
Fusarium 51

Galantamine 66
Galanthus nivalis 66
Galega officinalis 142
Galegin(e) 142
Galeopsis 139-140
Galerina 26
Gallic acid 21
Gallotannins 120
Garden Nightshade 219
Garlic 63, 239, 240
Genistein 156, 158
Geraniaceae 124, 273
Giant Hogweed 237-238
Gitalonin 209
Githagism 78
Gitoxin 209
Glaucine 182
Glaucium flavum 182-183
Glechoma hederacea 139
Globe Flower 197
Glossary 242-248
Glucobrassicanapin 98
Glucobrassicin 98
Glucoiberin 98
Gluconapin 98
Glucopyranoses 141-142
Glucosinolates 14-15, 92, 93, 94, 98, 101, 102, 103-104
Glyceria maxima 125
Glycine max 143-144
Glycosides 13-16

Goat's Rue 142
Goitre 15, 93, 96, 99-100
Goitrins 14, 93
Goitrogenic glycosides 14-15
Goitrogens 14-15, 93, 96, 98, 100-101, 158, 159
Golden Chain 144
Golden Rain 144
Golden Rod 90
Grain 127-129
Gramineae 124-129, 273-275
Grass Pea 146
Grass Vetchling 147
Grayanotoxins 111
Greater Celandine 183-184, photo 29
Green Hellebore 201
Grey Mottle Gill 33, photo 6
Ground Ivy 139
Groundnut 140
Guelder Rose 77
Gymnopilus 32
Gymnopilus junonius 32
Gymnopilus validipes 35
Gyromitra esculenta 28-29
Gyromitrin 28-29

Haematuria 56-57, 58-60
Haemoglobinuria 94-95, 98-99, 105
Haemolytic anaemia 94-95, 98-99, 105
Hairy Tare 160
Hairy Vetch 160
Hairy Vetchling 146
Hallucinogenic fungi 30-36
Hallucinogens 30-36, 91, 213-214, 216
Halphen acid 175
Handsome Clavaria 43
Happy Mushrooms 32
Haricot Beans 153
Hashish 75
Hawthorn 208, 239
Hebeloma 41
Hebeloma crustuliniforme 41
Hedera helix 69-70, 240
Hederasaponins 69
Hederin 69
Helenin(e) 89
Helianthus annuus 88
Helianthus tuberosus 90
Heliosupine 71, 72, 73
Heliotropium 73
Heliotropium europaeum 73

Hellebore 201-202
Helleborein(e) 202
Helleborigenin(e) 202
Helleborin(e) 202
Helleborus 201-202
Helleborus foetidus 201
Helleborus niger 201
Helleborus viridis 201
Helvella 28
Helvellic acid 28
Hemlock 229-232, 239, 240, photo 42 and fig. 1
Hemlock Water Dropwort 232-234, fig. 2
Hemp 74-75
Hemp Nettle 139-140
Henbane 215-217, 240, photo 38
Henbit 140
Heracleum mantegazzianum 237-238
Herb Christopher 203
Herb Paris 228
Hermidin(e) 118
Hippocastanaceae 129-130, 275
History 2-3
Hogweed 237-238
Holcus lanatus 125
Holly 67
Holly Oak 120
Holm Oak 120
Homochelidonine 183
Honey 86, 111, 215, 216
Honey Fungus 32, 35
Honeysuckle 77
Hordeum vulgare 127-129
Horse Bean 162
Horse Chestnut 129-130
Horse Mint 139
Horse Mushroom 40
Horse Radish 103-104
Horsetail 52-53, 239, 240
Hound's Tongue 72, 239
Hyacinth 170
Hyacinthus orientalis 170
Hydrangea 130-131
Hydrangeaceae 130-131, 275
Hydrocyanic acid 13-14, 56, 76, 124, 125, 137-138, 148-149, 161, 171-172, 205-207
Hydroxycoumarin 126-127, 130, 152, 227
Hydroxygalegine 142
Hyoscine 212, 213, 216
Hyoscyamine 212, 213, 215, 216
Hyoscyamus niger 215-217, 240, photo 38

Hypericaceae 131-133, 275
Hypericin(e) 131-132
Hypericum 131-133, photo 22
Hypericum perforatum 131-133, 240
Hypholoma fasciculare 42
Hypocalcaemia 18, 81-82, 179, 188-189

Ibotenic acid 30-31
Iceland Poppy 182
Ilex aquifolium 67
Ilicin 67
Indian Pea 146
Inkberry 184
Ink Cap 38-39
Inocybe 31, 36-37, photo 4
Inocybe fastigiata 36
Inocybe geophylla 37
Inocybe patouillardii 36-37
Inula conyza 88-89
Inula graveolens 89
Inula helenium 89
Ipecacuanha 9-10
Ipomoea purpurea 91
Iridaceae 133-135, 275-276
Iridin 134
Iris foetidissima 134-135, photo 23
Iris pseudacorus 133-135
Irisin(e) 134
Isoaconitine 198
Isoamyleneguanidine 142
Isosparteine 156
Isothiocyanates 14, 92-93, 98
Ivy 69-70, 240

Jacobine 84
Jacoline 86
Jaconine 84
Jerusalem Artichoke 90
Jimsonweed 213-214
Juncaceae 135-136, 276
Juncaginaceae 136-138, 276
Juncus 135-136
Juncus effusus 135
Juncus holoschoenus 135
Juncus inflexus 135-136
Juncus squarrosus 135
Juniper 107-108
Juniperine 107
Juniperus 107-108
Juniperus communis 107-108
Juniperus sabina 107

Kaempferol 55, 56
Kale 97-101, photo 15
Kaley Pea 146
Kalmia 112
Kingcup 193-194
Knotgrass 190

Labiatae 138-140, 276-277
Laburnum 144-145, 240, photo 24
Laburnum alpinum 144
Laburnum anagyroides 144-145, 240, photo 24
Lactarius 42
Lactarius piperatus 42
Lactarius pyrogalus 42
Lacterius torminosus 42
Lactic acidosis 128, 129
Ladino Clover 157
Laminitis 128-129, 158-159
Lamium 140
Lamium amplexicaule 140
Larkspur 198, 199-200
Lathyrism 147-148, 161
Lathyrogens 146-148
Lathyrus 146-148
Lathyrus aphaca 146
Lathyrus hirsutus 146
Lathyrus nissolia 147
Lathyrus odoratus 146, 147
Lathyrus pratensis 146
Lathyrus sativus 146, 147
Lathyrus sylvestris 146
Laudanine 181
Laughing Mushrooms 32
Laxatives 10
Lectins 113, 143, 153-154
Leguminosae 140-164, 277-282
Lepidium 239
Lepiota 26, 29
Lepiota cristata 29
Lepiota procera 29
Lepista 45
Lepista nuda 45
Lepista saeva 45
Lesser Celandine 196
Liberty Cap 33, 35
Ligustrin 177
Ligustrum 176-177
Ligustrum ovalifolium 176-177
Ligustrum vulgare 176-177
Liliaceae 164-171, 282-283
Lily of the Valley 168-169
Linaceae 171-172, 283-284

Linamarase 158, 171
Linamarin 148, 158, 171, 172
Linaria 211
Linatene 172
Linatine 172
Linseed 171-172
Linum catharticum 172
Linum usitatissimum 171-172
Lobelia 173
Lobelia 173
Lobelia berlandieri 173
Lobelia urens 173
Lobeliaceae 173, 284
Locoweed 141
Loliin(e) 126
Lolitrems 126
Lolium 124, 126
Lolium multiflorum 126
Lolium perenne 124, 125-126
Lolium temulentum 126
Lonicera 77
Loranthaceae 173-174, 284
Loranthus 173
Lords and Ladies 67
Lotaustralin 158, 171
Lotus corniculatus 148-149, 240, photo 25
Lotusin(e) 148
Lousewort 211
Lucerne 151-152
Lupanine 150
Lupin 149-151
Lupinidine 156
Lupinine 150
Lupinosis 150-151
Lupinus 149-151
Lupinus arboreus 149
Lupinus polyphyllus 149
Lupinus nootkatensis 149
Lycaconitine 198
Lycoperdon 44
Lycopersicon lycopersicum 223
Lycorine 66
d-Lysergic acid 91

Magic Mushrooms 32, 34-35
Maize 127-129
Male Fern 53-55
Mallow 175
Malva 175
Malva neglecta 175
Malva parviflora 175

Malva sylvestris 175
Malvaceae 175, 284-285
Malvalic acid 175
Mangel 80
Mangel Wurzel 80
Mangold 80
Mangold Wurzel 80
Marasmius oreades 36
Mare's Tail 52
Marijuana 75
Marsh Arrow Grass 136-138
Marsh Horsetail 52-53
Marsh Mallow 175
Marsh Marigold 193
Meadow Buttercup 194-195
Meadow Rue 197
Meadow Saffron 164-166, 239, photo 26
Meadow Vetchling 146
Meat taint 97
Medicago denticulata 151
Medicago hispida 151
Medicago polymorpha 151
Medicago sativa 151-152
Medick 151-152
Melampyrum 211
Melilot 152-153
Melilotus 127, 152-153, 240
Melilotus alba 152
Melilotus altissima 152
Melilotus indica 153
Melilotus officinalis 152
Mentha 139, 240
Mentha longifolia 139
Mercurialine 118
Mercurialis annua 118-119, 240
Mercurialis perennis 118-119, 240, photo 20
Mercury 118-119, 240
Metabolic inhibitors 124
Meteloidine 212
Methaemoglobin 16-17
S-Methyl cysteine sulphoxide 93-94, 98-99, 104-105
Methylamine 118
Methylconiine 230
Methylene blue 17
3-Methylindole 124
Methyllycaconitine 200
Mezerein 227
Mezereinic acid 227
Mezereon 226-227
Microcystis 20

Micropolyspora faeni 51
Milk, plants affecting 239-241
Milk Caps 42
Milk Thistle 89
Milk Vetch 141
Mint 139, 240
Miserotoxin 141
Mistletoe 173-174
Monkeynut 140
Monkshood 198-199, 239, photo 31
Monomethylhydrazine 28
Morchella esculenta 28, 42
Morel 28, 42
Morning Glory 91
Mower's Mushroom 33
Mugwort 90
Muscarine 30-31, 36-37
Muscazine 31
Muscimol 31
Mustard oil 92, 101
Mutter Pea 146
Mycotoxicoses 49-51
Mycotoxins 49-51, 125, 140, 150, 158, 160, 255
Myristic acid 134

Naked Ladies 164
Napelline 198
Narceine 181
Narcissine 66
Narcissus pseudonarcissus 66
Narcotine 181
Narrow Leaved Vetch 160, 161
Narthecin 167
Narthecium ossifragum 166-168, photo 27
Navy Bean 153
Neoglucobrassicin 98
Nettle 138
Nicotiana 217
Nicotiana glauca 217
Nicotiana tabacum 217
Nicotine 217
Nightshade, American 184
Nightshade, Black 219-220, photo 40
Nightshade, Deadly 211-213, photo 35
Nightshade, Garden 219
Nightshade, Woody 217-218, photo 39
Nitrates 16-17, 71, 80-81, 95, 98, 105, 129, 158, 159, 175, 188, 219

Nitriles 92
Nitrites 16-17, 71, 80-81, 95-96, 98, 105, 129, 159, 175, 219
Noratropine 212
Nudaurine 181

Oak 119-121, 240, photo 21
Oats 127-129
Ochratoxin 50-51
Odoratism 147
Oenanthe aquatica 234
Oenanthe crocata 232-234, fig. 2
Oenanthe pimpinelloides 234
Oenanthe silaifolia 234
Oenanthetoxin 232
Oestrogens 100, 124, 143, 150, 151, 158
Old Man's Beard 194
Oleaceae 176-177, 285
Omphalotus olearius 37
Onion 63-65, 239, 240
Opium 181-182
Opium Poppy 181-182
Orache 83
Orellanin(e) 27
Ornithogalum 170
Ornithogalum umbellatum 170
Orobanchaceae 178, 285
Orobanche 178
Orobanche minor 178
Oxalates 17-18, 80, 81, 82, 179, 188-189, 190
Oxalidaceae 178-179, 285
Oxalic acid 17-18, 179
Oxalis 178-179, 239, 240
Oxalis acetosella 178-179
Oxalis corniculata 179
Oxazolidinethione 96

Paeonia 179-180
Paeoniaceae 179-180, 285
Panaeolina foenisecii 33, 35
Panaeolus campanulatus 31
Panaeolus sphinctrinus 33, photo 6
Panaeolus subbalteatus 32-33, 35
Panther Cap 30-32
Papaver 180-183, 240
Papaver dubium 183
Papaver hybridum 183
Papaver nudicaule 182
Papaver rhoeas 180-181

Papaver somniferum 181-182
Papaveraceae 180-184, 285-286
Papaverine 181, 183
Parasol Mushroom 29
Paridin 228
Paris quadrifolia 228
Paristyphin 228
Parsnip 238
Pasque Flower 193, 195
Pastinaca sativa 238
Paterson's Curse 72
Paxillus involutus 42-43
Pea 146-148, 154-155, 240
Peach 204
Peanut 140
Pear 204
Pedicularis 211
Pedunculate Oak 119
Penicillium 51, 126
Peonin 180
Peony 179-180
Pepperwort 239
Peptides 20
Perloline 126
Perosis 96-97
Persicaria 190
Petty Spurge 116, 117
Phallin 24
Phalloidin 24-26
Phallolysin 24
Phallotoxins 24
Phaseolus vulgaris 153-154
Phasin 154, 155
Pheasant's Eye 197
Pholiota 32
Pholiota spectabilis 32
Pholiota squarrosa 43
Phomopsin A 150
Phomopsis leptostromiformis 150
Phoradendron 173
Photosensitisation 18-19, 83, 94,
    95 96, 110, 124, 132-133, 151, 160,
    167-168, 186-187, 238
Phylloerythrin 19, 167
Phytohaemagglutinins113, 143, 153,
    155
Phytolacca americana 184-185
Phytolaccaceae 184-185, 286
Phytolaccatoxin 184
Phytolaccin 184
Phytophthora infestans 221
Picea 62
Pieris 112

Pigeonberry 184
Pilewort 196
Pimpernel 191-192
Pinaceae 186, 286
Pine 186
Pinto Bean 153
Pinus 186
Pinus ponderosa 186
Pisum 154-155, 240
Pisum arvense 154-155
Pisum sativum 154-155
Pithomyces chartarum 160
Plant metabolites, primary 4
Plant metabolites, secondary 4-5
Pleurotus olearius 37
Ploughman's Spikenard 88-89
Plum 204, 206
Poison Vetch 141
Pokeberry 184
Pokeweed 184-185
Pokeweed mitogen 185
Polygonaceae 186-191, 286-287
Polygonum aviculare 190, 191
Polygonum cuspidatum 191
Polygonum hydropiper 190
Polygonum persicaria 190
Pontic Rhododendron 110
Poor Man's Weather Glass 191
Poppy 180-183, 240
Post Oak 121
Potato 220-223, 240
Potato blight 221
Primulaceae 191-192, 287-288
Privet 176-177
Procumbent Yellow Sorrel 179
Progoitrin 93-94, 98
n-Propyl disulphide 63-65
Proteins 20
Protoanemonin 192-193, 197-198
Protopine 123, 181, 182, 183
Prunasin 55-56, 205, 207
Prunus cerasus 204
Prunus domestica 204
Prunus laurocerasus 204-207, photo 34
Prunus persica 204
Prunus serotina 207
Prunus spinosa 204
Prunus virginiana 207
Pseudoconhydrine 230
Psilocin 34
Psilocybe 33
Psilocybe semilanceata 33, 34, 35
Psilocybin 32-36

PSL syndrome 37
Psoralens 238
Pteridium aquilinum 55-62, 240, photo
    7
Pteridophytes 52-62
Puffballs 44
Purging Buckthorn 203
Purging Flax 172
Purple Viper's Bugloss 72-73
Pyracantha 208
Pyrogallol 21
Pyrrolizidine alkaloids 71, 72, 73, 84
Pyrus communis 204
Pyrus malus 204

Quercetin 55-56
Quercus 119-121, 240, photo 21
Quercus ilex 120
Quercus petraea 119-121
Quercus robur 119-121
Quercus stellata 121

Radish 104, 240
Ragwort 83-87, photo 14
Ramaria 43
Ramaria formosa 43
Ramsons 63, photo 8
Ranunculaceae 192-203, 288-289
Ranunculin 192
Ranunculus 192, 194-198, 240
Ranunculus acris 193, 194-195
Ranunculus bulbosus 195
Ranunculus ficaria 196
Ranunculus flammula 196
Ranunculus lingua 197
Ranunculus repens 197
Ranunculus sceleratus 196-197
Rape 93-97
Rape scald 96
Rapeseed meal 93, 96-97
Raphanus raphanistrum 104, 240
Rapistrum rugosum 101
Red Clover 157-160
Red Kidney Bean 153
Red Poppy 180-181
Redshank 190
Redwood 62
Reed Grass 125
Rhamnaceae 203-204, 289
Rhamnus cathartica 203-204, 240
Rhamnus frangula 203

Rheum rhaponticum 189-190
Rhinanthus 211
Rhodanese 14, 206
Rhododendron 110-112, 240, photo 18
Rhododendron ponticum 110-112, 240
Rhodophyllus 41
Rhodotoxin 111
Rhoeadine 180-181
Rhubarb 189-190
Ricin 113-116
Ricine 113
Ricinoleic acid 114
Ricinus communis 113-116, 240
Rickets 127, 129
Ringwomb 158
Robinia pseudoacacia 155-156
Robin(in) 155
Roll Rim 42-43
Rosaceae 204-208, 289-290
Rough Comfrey 71
Rumex 187-189, 240
Rumex acetosa 188-189
Rumex acetosella 187-189, photo 30
Rumicin 188
Rush 135-136
Russian Comfrey 71
Russula 43
Russula emetica 43
Russula fellea 43
Russula nauseosa 43
Rusty Male Fern 54
Rye 127-129
Ryegrass 124, 125-126
Ryegrass staggers 125-126

St. Anthony's Fire 49
St. Anthony's Turnip 195
St. Barnaby's Thistle 87
St. George's Mushroom 45
St. James's Wort 83
St. John's Wort 131-133, 240, photo 22
Salicaceae 208, 290
Salix 208
Salvation Jane 72
Sambucus ebulus 77
Sambucus nigra 75-76, 212
Sambunigrin 76
Sandwort 77
Sanguinarine 182, 183
Saponaria 77
Saponic glycosides 13

Saponins 16, 78, 80, 143, 191
Sarothamnine 156
Sarothamnus scoparius 156
Scabious 110
Scarlet Pimpernel 191-192
Scillaine 66
Scillarens 169
Scillitoxin 66
Scleroderma 44
Scleroderma cepa 44
Sclerotinia 4, 19, 238
Scopolamine 212, 213, 216
Scopolin 221
Scrophularia 210-211
Scrophularia aquatica 210-211, 240
Scrophulariaceae 208-211, 290
Sea Arrow Grass 136-138
Sea Poppy 182
Secale cereale 127-129
Secondary plant metabolites 4-5
Sedanine 91
Sedge 108
Sedridine 91
Sedum acre 91
Senecio cineraria 85
Senecio jacobaea 83-87, photo 14
Senecionine 84
Seneciosis 86
Seneciphylline 84
Sequoia 62
Sessile Oak 119
Sheep's Sorrel 187-189, photo 30
Shepherd's Purse 105, 240
Shepherd's Weatherglass 191
Sickener 43
Sillys 32
Silybum marianum 89
Silymarin 25-26
Sinalbin 102
Sinapine 93
Sinapis alba 102-103
Sinapis arvensis 101-102
Sinigrin 92, 98, 101, 103, 104
Sium latifolium 229
Skewer Wood 79
Sleeping Beauty 178
Sloe 204
SMCO 93-94, 98-99, 104-105
Snowberry 76-77
Snowdrop 66
Soapwort 77
Solanaceae 211-223, 290-293
Solanidine 218, 220

Solanine 218-223
Solanum dulcamara 217-218, photo 39
Solanum malacoxylon 220
Solanum nigrum 219-220, photo 40
Solanum tuberosum 220-223, 240
Solasodine 219
Solidago 90
Sorrel 187-189, 240, photo 30
Sour Dock 188
Sour Grass 187
Soya Bean 143-144
Spanish Broom 156
Sparteine 150, 156
Spartium junceum 156
Spearwort 196, 197
Spindle 79-80, photo 13
Spore print 22
Sporidesmin 160
Spruce 62
Spurge 116-118
Spurge Flax 226
Spurge Laurel 226-227, photo 41
Spurge Olive 226
Staggerweed 83
Star of Bethlehem 170
Stellaria 77
Stinging Nettle 138
Stinking Hellebore 201
Stinking Iris 134, photo 23
Stitchwort 77
Stomach lavage 10
Stonecrop 91
Storksbill 124
Stropharia aeruginosa 44
Stropharia coronilla 44
Stropharia semiglobata 34
Subterranean Clover 158
Subterranean Trefoil 158
Succisa pratensis 110
Sugar Beet 80
Sulphur Tuft 42
Sun Spurge 116, 117, photo 19
Sundew 110
Sunflower 88
Swede 104
Swede Rape 93
Sweet Clover 152-153, 240
Sweet Clover Disease 127
Sweet Pea 146-147
Sweet Vernal Grass 125, 126-127
Symphoricarpos albus 76
Symphoricarpos rivularis 76-77
Symphytum asperrimum 71

Symphytum asperum 71
Symphytum officinale 70-72, photo 10
Symphytum uplandicum 71

Tall Buttercup 194
Tall Larkspur 200
Tamus communis 109, photo 17
Tannic acid 120
Tannins 20-21, 120
Tansy 90
Tansy Ragwort 83
Tare 160
Taxaceae 223-226, 293-294
Taxin(e) 224
Taxiphyllin 224
Taxus 223-226
Taxus baccata 223-226, 240
Taxus cuspidata 223
Temulentine 126
Temuline 126
Teratogens 12, 141, 150, 217, 219,
  222, 232
Tetrahydrocannabinols 74-75
Thalictrum 197
Thiaminase 52. 54-55, 56, 57
Thiamine 52, 53, 54, 55, 56, 57, 61
Thiocyanates 14, 92, 98, 100, 102
Thioglucosidase 14, 92
Thioglucosides 14
Thistle 90
Thorn Apple 213-215, photo 37
Thymelaeaceae 226-227, 294
Toadflax 211
Tobacco 217
Tomato 223
Traveller's Joy 194, photo 33
Treatment, general 9-10
Triacetin 79
Triazotin 79
Tricholoma 45
Tricholoma album 45
Tricholoma gambosum 45
Tricholoma nudum 45
Tricholoma personatum 45
Tricholoma saevum 45
Tricholoma sulphureum 45
Trichothecenes 50-51
Trifoliosis 160
Trifolium 157-160, 240
Trifolium hybridum 157-160
Trifolium pratense 157-160
Trifolium repens 157-160

Trifolium subterraneum 158
Triglochin maritima 136-138
Triglochin palustris 136-138
Triglochinin 137
Trilliaceae 228, 294
Trimethylamine 97, 118
Trisetum flavescens 124, 125
Triticum vulgare 127-129
Trollius 197
Tropacocaine 212
Trypsin inhibitors 143, 150, 153
Tryptophan 124, 125
Tulip 171
Tulipa 171
Tulipalin 171
Tuliposide 171
Tumours 60-61
Turban Fungus 28
Turnip 104, 240
Turnip Rape 93
Turnip Weed 101

Umbelliferae 229-238, 294-295
Umbelliferone 221, 227
Urtica dioica 138

Verdigris Agaric 44
Vetch 160-162
Vetchling 146-148
Viburnin 76
Viburnum lantana 77
Viburnum opulus 77
Vicia 160-162
Vicia angustifolia 160, 161
Vicia faba 162-163
Vicia hirsuta 160
Vicia sativa 160-162
Vicia villosa 160, 162
Vicianin 161
Vicine 161, 163
Viper's Bugloss 72-73
Viscotoxins 174
Viscum album 173-174
Vlei poisoning 135

Wake Robin 67
Wart Wort 183
Water Betony 210-211, 240
Water Figwort 210
Water Parsnip 229

Water Pepper 190
Wax Bean 153
Wayfaring Tree 77
Wheat 127-129
Wheat poisoning 128
White Bean 153
White Bryony 105-106, 239, photo 16
White Clover 157-160
White Mustard 102-103
White Poppy 181
Wild Arum 67
Wild Garlic 63
Wild Hyacinth 169
Wild Onion 64
Wild Pea 146-148
Wild Pepper 226
Wild Radish 104
Willow 208
Wireweed 190
Wistarin 164
Wisteria 164
Wisteria 164
Wolfsbane 198
Wood Anemone 193, photo 32
Wood Laurel 226
Wood Mushroom 40
Wood Sorrel 178-179, 240
Woody Nightshade 217-218, photo
  39
Woolly Milk Cap 42

Xanthium strumarium 89-90
Xanthostrumarin 89
Xylosin 167

Yellow Flag 133-135
Yellow Horned Poppy 182
Yellow Oat Grass 124, 125
Yellow Rattle 211
Yellow Sorrel 179
Yellow-staining Mushroom 40
Yellow Star Thistle 87-88
Yellow Vetchling 146
Yew 223-226, 240
Yorkshire Fog 125

Zea mays 127-129
Zearalenone 50-51

Printed in the UK for HMSO.736409.1.84.35125